D0571213

CGP

GCSE
Combined Science
Physics

Physics is a big part of GCSE Combined Science... and it's not easy. But CGP are on the case — this brilliant book explains everything you'll need to learn!

We've also included plenty of exam-style practice for every topic *and* a full set of Physics practice papers so that you can put your new-found knowledge to the test.

What's more, there are step-by-step answers at the back, so you can easily check your work and find out how to pick up any marks you missed out on!

How to access your free Online Edition

This book includes a free Online Edition to read on your PC, Mac or tablet.
You'll just need to go to **cgpbooks.co.uk/extras** and enter this code:

2800 0564 2006 2756

By the way, this code only works for one person. If somebody else has used this book before you, they might have already claimed the Online Edition.

Complete
Revision & Practice
Everything you need to pass the exams!

Contents

Working Scientifically

The Scientific Method 1
Models and Communication 2
Issues Created by Science 3
Risk 4
Designing Investigations 5
Processing Data 8
Presenting Data 9
More on Graphs 10
Units 11
Converting Units 12
Drawing Conclusions 13
Correlation and Cause 14
Uncertainty 15
Evaluations 16

Topic 1 — Energy

Energy Stores 17
Work Done 18
Kinetic and Potential Energy Stores 19
Specific Heat Capacity 20
Investigating Specific Heat Capacity 21
Warm-Up & Exam Questions 22
Conservation of Energy and Power 23
Conduction and Convection 24
Reducing Unwanted Energy Transfers 25
Efficiency 26
Warm-Up & Exam Questions 27
Energy Resources and their Uses 28
Wind and Solar Power 29
Geothermal and Hydro-electric Power 30
Wave Power and Tidal Barrages 31
Bio-fuels 32

Non-Renewable Resources 33
Trends in Energy Resource Use 34
Warm-Up & Exam Questions 35
Revision Summary for Topic 1 36

Topic 2 — Electricity

Current and Circuit Symbols 37
Resistance 38
Investigating Resistance 39
I-V Characteristics 40
Warm-Up & Exam Questions 41
Circuit Devices 42
Sensing Circuits 43
Series Circuits 44
Parallel Circuits 46
Circuits and Resistance 47
Warm-Up & Exam Questions 48
Electricity in the Home 49
Power of Electrical Appliances 50
More on Power 51
The National Grid 52
Warm-Up & Exam Questions 54
Revision Summary for Topic 2 55

Topic 3 — Particle Model of Matter

Particle Model 56
Density 57
Internal Energy and Changes of State 58
Specific Latent Heat 59
Particle Motion in Gases 60
Warm-Up & Exam Questions 61
Exam Questions 62
Revision Summary for Topic 3 63

Throughout this book you'll see grade stamps like these:

These grade stamps help to show how difficult the questions are.
Remember — to get a top grade you need to be able to answer **all** the questions, not just the hardest ones.

Grade 4-6   *Grade 6-7*   *Grade 7-9*

In the real exams, some questions test how well you can write (as well as your scientific knowledge).
In this book, we've marked these questions with an asterisk (*).

Topic 4 — Atomic Structure

Developing the Model of the Atom 64
Isotopes 66
Ionising Radiation 67
Nuclear Equations 68
Half-Life 69
Irradiation and Contamination 71
Warm-Up & Exam Questions 73
Exam Questions 74
Revision Summary for Topic 4 75

Topic 5 — Forces

Contact and Non-Contact Forces 76
Weight, Mass and Gravity 77
Resultant Forces 78
More on Forces 80
Warm-Up & Exam Questions 81
Forces and Elasticity 82
Investigating Springs 84
Warm-Up & Exam Questions 86
Distance, Displacement, Speed and Velocity 87
Acceleration 88
Distance-Time Graphs 89
Velocity-Time Graphs 90
Drag 91
Terminal Velocity 92
Warm-Up & Exam Questions 93
Newton's First and Second Laws 94
Inertia and Newton's Third Law 95
Investigating Motion 96
Warm-Up & Exam Questions 98
Stopping Distances 99
Reaction Times 100
Braking Distances 101
Momentum 102
Warm-Up & Exam Questions 103
Revision Summary for Topic 5 104

Topic 6 — Waves

Wave Basics 105
Transverse and Longitudinal Waves 106
Experiments with Waves 107
Refraction 109
Warm-Up & Exam Questions 111
Electromagnetic Waves and Uses of EM Waves 112
Uses of EM Waves 113
Dangers of Electromagnetic Waves 116
Infrared Radiation and Temperature 117
Investigating Emission 118
Warm-Up & Exam Questions 119
Exam Questions 120
Revision Summary for Topic 6 121

Topic 7 — Magnetism and Electromagnetism

Magnets 122
Magnetism 123
Electromagnets 124
Warm-Up & Exam Questions 125
The Motor Effect 126
Electric Motors 128
Warm-Up & Exam Questions 129
Revision Summary for Topic 7 130

Practical Skills

Measuring Lengths and Angles 131
Measuring Volumes 132
More on Measuring 133
Working With Electronics 134
Safety and Experiments 135

Practice Exams

Practice Paper 1 136
Practice Paper 2 151

Answers 164
Index 174

Published by CGP

From original material by Richard Parsons.

Editors: Sharon Keeley-Holden, Duncan Lindsay, Sophie Scott and Charlotte Whiteley.

Contributors: Paddy Gannon and Barbara Mascetti.

With thanks to Emily Garrett and Frances Rooney for the proofreading.

With thanks to Ana Pungartnik for the copyright research.

Renewables data on page 147 contain public sector information licensed under the Open Government Licence v3.0.
http://www.nationalarchives.gov.uk/doc/open-government-licence/version/3/

Data used to construct braking distances data diagram on page 160 From the Highway Code.
Contains public sector information licensed under the Open Government Licence v3.0.
http://www.nationalarchives.gov.uk/doc/open-government-licence/version/3/

Printed by Elanders Ltd, Newcastle upon Tyne.

Clipart from Corel®

The Scientific Method

This section isn't about how to 'do' science — but it does show you the way most scientists work.

Scientists Come Up With **Hypotheses** — Then **Test** Them

1) Scientists try to explain things. They start by observing something they don't understand.

2) They then come up with a hypothesis — a possible explanation for what they've observed.

3) The next step is to test whether the hypothesis might be right or not. This involves making a prediction based on the hypothesis and testing it by gathering evidence (i.e. data) from investigations. If evidence from experiments backs up a prediction, you're a step closer to figuring out if the hypothesis is true.

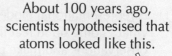

About 100 years ago, scientists hypothesised that atoms looked like this.

Several Scientists Will **Test** a Hypothesis

1) Normally, scientists share their findings in peer-reviewed journals, or at conferences.

2) Peer-review is where other scientists check results and scientific explanations to make sure they're 'scientific' (e.g. that experiments have been done in a sensible way) before they're published. It helps to detect false claims, but it doesn't mean that findings are correct — just that they're not wrong in any obvious way.

3) Once other scientists have found out about a hypothesis, they'll start basing their own predictions on it and carry out their own experiments. They'll also try to reproduce the original experiments to check the results — and if all the experiments in the world back up the hypothesis, then scientists start to think the hypothesis is true.

4) However, if a scientist does an experiment that doesn't fit with the hypothesis (and other scientists can reproduce the results) then the hypothesis may need to be modified or scrapped altogether.

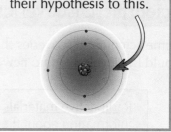
After more evidence was gathered, scientists changed their hypothesis to this.

If **All** the **Evidence** Supports a Hypothesis, It's **Accepted** — For Now

1) Accepted hypotheses are often referred to as theories. Our currently accepted theories are the ones that have survived this 'trial by evidence' — they've been tested many times over the years and survived.

2) However, theories never become totally indisputable fact. If new evidence comes along that can't be explained using the existing theory, then the hypothesising and testing is likely to start all over again.

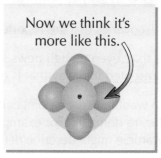
Now we think it's more like this.

Scientific models are constantly being refined...

The scientific method has been developed over time. Aristotle (a Greek philosopher) was the first person to realise that theories need to be based on observations. Muslim scholars then introduced the ideas of creating a hypothesis, testing it, and repeating work to check results.

Models and Communication

Once scientists have made a <u>new discovery</u>, they <u>don't</u> just keep it to themselves. Oh no. Time to learn about how scientific discoveries are <u>communicated</u>, and the <u>models</u> that are used to represent theories.

Theories Can Involve Different Types of Models

1) A <u>representational model</u> is a <u>simplified description</u> or <u>picture</u> of what's going on in real life. Like all models, it can be used to <u>explain observations</u> and <u>make predictions</u>. E.g. the <u>Bohr model</u> of an atom is a simplified way of showing the arrangement of electrons in an atom (see p.65). It can be used to explain electron excitations in atoms.

Scientists test models by carrying out experiments to check that the predictions made by the model happen as expected.

2) <u>Computational models</u> use computers to make <u>simulations</u> of complex real-life processes, such as climate change. They're used when there are a <u>lot</u> of different <u>variables</u> (factors that change) to consider, and because you can easily <u>change their design</u> to take into account <u>new data</u>.

3) All models have <u>limitations</u> on what they can <u>explain</u> or <u>predict</u>. E.g. <u>the Big Bang model</u> (a model used to describe the beginning of the Universe) can be used to explain why everything in the Universe is moving away from us. One of its limitations is that it <u>doesn't explain</u> the moments before the Big Bang.

Scientific Discoveries are Communicated to the General Public

Some scientific discoveries show that people should <u>change their habits</u>, or they might provide ideas that could be <u>developed</u> into new <u>technology</u>. So scientists need to <u>tell the world</u> about their discoveries.

<u>Radioactive materials</u> are used widely in <u>medicine</u> for <u>imaging</u> and <u>treatment</u>. Information about these materials needs to be communicated to <u>doctors</u> so they can <u>make use</u> of them, and to <u>patients</u>, so they can make <u>informed decisions</u> about their <u>treatment</u>.

Scientific Evidence can be Presented in a Biased Way

1) Scientific discoveries that are reported in the <u>media</u> (e.g. newspapers or television) <u>aren't</u> peer-reviewed.

2) This means that, even though news stories are often <u>based</u> on data that has been peer-reviewed, the data might be <u>presented</u> in a way that is <u>over-simplified</u> or <u>inaccurate</u>, making it open to <u>misinterpretation</u>.

3) People who want to make a point can sometimes <u>present data</u> in a <u>biased way</u> (sometimes <u>without knowing</u> they're doing it). For example, a scientist might overemphasise a relationship in the data, or a newspaper article might describe details of data <u>supporting</u> an idea without giving any evidence <u>against</u> it.

Companies can present biased data to help sell products...

Sometimes a company may only want you to see half of the story so they present the data in a <u>biased way</u>. For example, a pharmaceutical company may want to encourage you to buy their drugs by telling you about all the <u>positives</u>, but not report the results of any <u>unfavourable studies</u>.

Issues Created by Science

Science has helped us <u>make progress</u> in loads of areas, from advances in medicine to space travel. But science still has its <u>issues</u>. And it <u>can't answer everything</u>, as you're about to find out.

Scientific Developments are Great, but they can Raise Issues

Scientific <u>knowledge is increased</u> by doing experiments. And this knowledge leads to <u>scientific developments</u>, e.g. new technologies or new advice. These developments can create <u>issues</u> though. For example:

<u>Economic issues:</u> Society <u>can't</u> always <u>afford</u> to do things scientists recommend (e.g. investing in alternative energy sources) without <u>cutting back elsewhere</u>.

<u>Social issues:</u> Decisions based on scientific evidence affect <u>people</u> — e.g. should fossil fuels be taxed more highly? Would the effect on people's lifestyles be <u>acceptable</u>?

<u>Personal issues:</u> Some decisions will affect <u>individuals</u>. For example, someone might support <u>alternative energy</u>, but object if a <u>wind farm</u> was built next to their house.

<u>Environmental issues:</u> <u>Human activity</u> often affects the <u>natural environment</u>. For example, building a <u>dam</u> to produce electricity will change the <u>local habitat</u> so some species might be displaced. But it will also reduce our need for <u>fossil fuels</u>, so will help to reduce <u>climate change</u>.

Science Can't Answer Every Question — Especially Ethical Ones

1) We don't <u>understand everything</u>. We're always finding out <u>more</u>, but we'll never know <u>all</u> the answers.

2) In order to answer scientific questions, scientists need <u>data</u> to provide <u>evidence</u> for their hypotheses.

3) Some questions can't be answered <u>yet</u> because the data <u>can't</u> currently be <u>collected</u>, or because there's <u>not enough</u> data to <u>support</u> a theory.

4) <u>Eventually</u>, as we get <u>more evidence</u>, we'll answer some of the questions that <u>currently</u> can't be answered, e.g. what the impact of global warming on sea levels will be. But there will always be the "<u>Should we be doing this at all?</u>"-type questions that experiments <u>can't</u> help us to answer...

Think about <u>new drugs which can be taken to boost your 'brain power'</u>.

- Some people think they're <u>good</u> as they could improve concentration or memory. New drugs could let people think in ways beyond the powers of normal brains.

- Other people say they're <u>bad</u> — they could give some people an <u>unfair advantage</u> in exams. And people might be <u>pressured</u> into taking them so that they could work more <u>effectively</u>, and for <u>longer hours</u>.

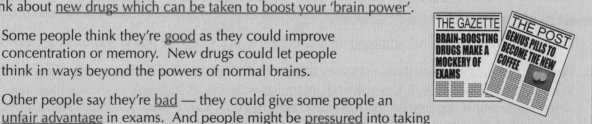

 ## There are often issues with new scientific developments...

The trouble is, there's often <u>no clear right answer</u> where these issues are concerned. Different people have <u>different views</u>, depending on their priorities. These issues are full of <u>grey areas</u>.

Risk

Scientific discoveries are often great, but they can prove risky. With dangers all around, you've got to be aware of hazards — this includes how likely they are to cause harm and how serious the effects may be.

Nothing is Completely Risk-Free

1) A hazard is something that could potentially cause harm.

2) All hazards have a risk attached to them — this is the chance that the hazard will cause harm.

3) The risks of some things seem pretty obvious, or we've known about them for a while, like the risk of causing acid rain by polluting the atmosphere, or of having a car accident when you're travelling in a car.

4) New technology arising from scientific advances can bring new risks, e.g. scientists are unsure whether nanoparticles that are being used in cosmetics and suncream might be harming the cells in our bodies. These risks need to be considered alongside the benefits of the technology, e.g. improved sun protection.

5) You can estimate the size of a risk based on how many times something happens in a big sample (e.g. 100 000 people) over a given period (e.g. a year). For example, you could assess the risk of a driver crashing by recording how many people in a group of 100 000 drivers crashed their cars over a year.

6) To make decisions about activities that involve a risk, we need to take into account the chance of the hazard causing harm, and how serious the consequences would be if it did. If an activity involves a risk that's very likely to cause harm, with serious consequences if it does, that activity is considered high risk.

People Make Their Own Decisions About Risk

1) Not all risks have the same consequences, e.g. if you chop veg with a sharp knife you risk cutting your finger, but if you go scuba-diving you risk death. You're much more likely to cut your finger during half an hour of chopping than to die during half an hour of scuba-diving. But most people are happier to accept a higher probability of an accident if the consequences are short-lived and fairly minor.

2) People tend to be more willing to accept a risk if they choose to do something (e.g. go scuba diving), compared to having the risk imposed on them (e.g. having a nuclear power station built next door).

3) People's perception of risk (how risky they think something is) isn't always accurate. They tend to view familiar activities as low-risk and unfamiliar activities as high-risk — even if that's not the case. For example, cycling on roads is often high-risk, but many people are happy to do it because it's a familiar activity. Air travel is actually pretty safe, but a lot of people perceive it as high-risk.

4) People may underestimate the risk of things with long-term or invisible effects, e.g. using tanning beds.

The pros and cons of new technology must be weighed up...

The world's a dangerous place and it's impossible to rule out the chance of an accident altogether. But if you can recognise hazards and take steps to reduce the risks, you're more likely to stay safe.

Designing Investigations

Dig out your lab coat and dust off your badly-scratched safety goggles... it's <u>investigation time</u>.

Evidence Can Support or Disprove a Hypothesis

1) Scientists <u>observe</u> things and come up with <u>hypotheses</u> to test them (see p.1). You need to be able to do the same. For example:

> <u>Observation</u>: People with big feet have spots. <u>Hypothesis</u>: Having big feet causes spots.

2) To <u>determine</u> whether or not a hypothesis is <u>right</u>, you need to do an <u>investigation</u> to gather evidence. To do this, you need to use your hypothesis to make a <u>prediction</u> — something you think <u>will happen</u> that you can test. E.g. people who have bigger feet will have more spots.

Investigations include experiments and studies.

3) Investigations are used to see if there are <u>patterns</u> or <u>relationships</u> between <u>two variables</u>, e.g. to see if there's a pattern or relationship between the variables 'number of spots' and 'size of feet'.

Evidence Needs to be Repeatable, Reproducible and Valid

1) <u>Repeatable</u> means that if the <u>same person</u> does an experiment again using the <u>same methods</u> and equipment, they'll get <u>similar results</u>.

2) <u>Reproducible</u> means that if <u>someone else</u> does the experiment, or a <u>different</u> method or piece of equipment is used, the results will still be <u>similar</u>.

3) If data is <u>repeatable</u> and <u>reproducible</u>, it's <u>reliable</u> and scientists are more likely to <u>have confidence</u> in it.

4) <u>Valid results</u> are both repeatable and reproducible AND they <u>answer the original question</u>. They come from experiments that were designed to be a <u>FAIR TEST</u>...

Make an Investigation a Fair Test By Controlling the Variables

1) In a lab experiment you usually <u>change one variable</u> and <u>measure</u> how it affects <u>another variable</u>.

2) To make it a fair test, <u>everything else</u> that could affect the results should <u>stay the same</u> — otherwise you can't tell if the thing you're changing is causing the results or not.

3) The variable you <u>CHANGE</u> is called the <u>INDEPENDENT</u> variable.

4) The variable you <u>MEASURE</u> when you change the independent variable is the <u>DEPENDENT</u> variable.

5) The variables that you <u>KEEP THE SAME</u> are called <u>CONTROL</u> variables.

> You could find how <u>current</u> through a circuit component affects the <u>potential difference</u> across the component by measuring the <u>potential difference</u> at different currents. The <u>independent variable</u> is the <u>current</u>. The <u>dependent variable</u> is the <u>potential difference</u>. <u>Control variables</u> include the <u>temperature</u> of the component, the <u>pd</u> of the power supply, etc.

6) Because you can't always control all the variables, you often need to use a <u>control experiment</u>. This is an experiment that's kept under the <u>same conditions</u> as the rest of the investigation, but <u>doesn't</u> have anything <u>done</u> to it. This is so that you can see what happens when you don't change anything at all.

Designing Investigations

The **Bigger** the **Sample Size** the **Better**

1) Data based on small samples isn't as good as data based on large samples. A sample should represent the whole population (i.e. it should share as many of the characteristics in the population as possible) — a small sample can't do that as well. It's also harder to spot anomalies if your sample size is too small.

2) The bigger the sample size the better, but scientists have to be realistic when choosing how big. For example, if you were studying the effects of living near a nuclear power plant, it'd be great to study everyone who lived near a nuclear power plant (a huge sample), but it'd take ages and cost a bomb. It's more realistic to study a thousand people, with a range of ages and races and across both genders.

Your **Equipment** has to be **Right for the Job**

1) The measuring equipment you use has to be sensitive enough to measure the changes you're looking for. For example, if you need to measure changes of 1 cm³ you need to use a measuring cylinder that can measure in 1 cm³ steps — it'd be no good trying with one that only measures 10 cm³ steps.

2) The smallest change a measuring instrument can detect is called its resolution. E.g. some mass balances have a resolution of 1 g, some have a resolution of 0.1 g, and some are even more sensitive.

3) Also, equipment needs to be calibrated by measuring a known value. If there's a difference between the measured and known value, you can use this to adjust your measurements to compensate for the inaccuracy of the equipment.

Data Should be **Repeatable, Reproducible, Accurate** and **Precise**

1) To check repeatability you need to repeat the readings and check that the results are similar. You need to repeat each reading at least three times.

2) To make sure your results are reproducible you can cross check them by taking a second set of readings with another instrument (or a different observer).

3) Your data also needs to be accurate. Really accurate results are those that are really close to the true answer. The accuracy of your results usually depends on your method — you need to make sure you're measuring the right thing and that you don't miss anything that should be included in the measurements. E.g. estimating the volume of an irregularly shaped solid by measuring the sides isn't very accurate because this will not take into account any gaps in the object. It's more accurate to measure the volume using a eureka can (see p.132).

Repeat	Data set 1	Data set 2
1	12	11
2	14	17
3	13	14
Mean	13	14

Data set 1 is more precise than data set 2.

4) Your data also needs to be precise. Precise results are ones where the data is all really close to the mean (average) of your repeated results (i.e. not spread out).

Designing Investigations

You Need to Look out for **Errors** and **Anomalous Results**

1) The results of your experiment will always <u>vary a bit</u> because of <u>random errors</u> — unpredictable differences caused by things like <u>human errors</u> in <u>measuring</u>. The errors when you make a reading from a ruler are random. You have to estimate or round the distance when it's between two marks — so sometimes your figure will be a bit above the real one, and sometimes it will be a bit below.

2) You can <u>reduce</u> the effect of random errors by taking <u>repeat readings</u> and finding the <u>mean</u>. This will make your results <u>more precise</u>.

If there's no systematic error, then doing repeats and calculating a mean could make your results more accurate.

3) If a measurement is wrong by the <u>same amount every time</u>, it's called a <u>systematic error</u>. For example, if you measured from the very end of your ruler instead of from the 0 cm mark every time, all your measurements would be a bit small. Repeating the experiment in the exact same way and calculating a mean <u>won't</u> correct a systematic error.

4) Just to make things more complicated, if a systematic error is caused by using <u>equipment</u> that <u>isn't zeroed properly</u>, it's called a <u>zero error</u>. For example, if a mass balance always reads 1 gram before you put anything on it, all your measurements will be 1 gram too heavy.

5) You can <u>compensate</u> for some systematic errors if you know about them, e.g. if a mass balance always reads 1 gram before you put anything on it, you can subtract 1 gram from all your results.

6) Sometimes you get a result that <u>doesn't fit in</u> with the rest at all. This is called an <u>anomalous result</u>. You should investigate it and try to <u>work out what happened</u>. If you can work out what happened (e.g. you measured something wrong) you can <u>ignore</u> it when processing your results.

Investigations Can be **Hazardous**

1) <u>Hazards</u> from science experiments might include:

- <u>Lasers</u>, e.g. if a laser is directed into the eye, this can cause blindness.
- <u>Gamma radiation</u>, e.g. gamma-emitting radioactive sources can cause cancer.
- <u>Fire</u>, e.g. an unattended Bunsen burner is a fire hazard.
- <u>Electricity</u>, e.g. faulty electrical equipment could give you a shock.

You can find out about potential hazards by looking in textbooks, doing some internet research, or asking your teacher.

2) Part of planning an investigation is making sure that it's <u>safe</u>.

3) You should always make sure that you <u>identify</u> all the hazards that you might encounter. Then you should think of ways of <u>reducing the risks</u> from the hazards you've identified. For example:

- If you're working with <u>springs</u>, always wear safety goggles. This will reduce the risk of the spring hitting your eye if the spring snaps.
- If you're using a <u>Bunsen burner</u>, stand it on a heat proof mat to reduce the risk of starting a fire.

Designing an investigation is an involved process...

<u>Collecting data</u> is what investigations are all about. Designing a good investigation is really important to make sure that any data collected is <u>accurate</u>, <u>precise</u>, <u>repeatable</u> and <u>reproducible</u>.

Processing Data

Processing your data means doing some <u>calculations</u> with it to make it <u>more useful</u>.

Data Needs to be Organised

1) Tables are really useful for <u>organising data</u>.

2) When you draw a table <u>use a ruler</u> and make sure <u>each column</u> has a <u>heading</u> (including the <u>units</u>).

There are Different Ways to Process Your Data

1) When you've done repeats of an experiment you should always calculate the <u>mean</u> (average). To do this <u>add together</u> all the data values and <u>divide</u> by the total number of values in the sample.

2) You can also find the <u>mode</u> of your results — this is the <u>value</u> that <u>occurs</u> the <u>most</u> in your set of results.

3) The <u>median</u> can be found by writing your results in numerical <u>order</u> — the median is the <u>middle number</u>.

Ignore anomalous results when calculating the mean, mode and median.

EXAMPLE: The results of an experiment show the extension of two springs when a force is applied to both of them. Calculate the mean, mode and median of the extension for both springs.

Spring	Repeat (cm)					Mean (cm)	Mode (cm)	Median (cm)
	1	2	3	4	5			
A	18	26	22	26	28	(18 + 26 + 22 + 26 + 28) ÷ 5 = 24	26	26
B	11	14	20	15	20	(11 + 14 + 20 + 15 + 20) ÷ 5 = 16	20	15

Round to the Lowest Number of Significant Figures

The <u>first significant figure</u> of a number is the first digit that's <u>not zero</u>. The second and third significant figures come <u>straight after</u> (even if they're zeros). You should be aware of significant figures in calculations.

1) In <u>any</u> calculation where you need to round, you should round the answer to the <u>lowest number of significant figures</u> (s.f.) given.

2) Remember to write down <u>how many</u> significant figures you've rounded to after your answer.

3) If your calculation has multiple steps, <u>only</u> round the <u>final</u> answer, or it won't be as accurate.

EXAMPLE: The mass of a solid is 0.24 g and its volume is 0.715 cm³. Calculate the density of the solid.

Density = 0.24 g ÷ 0.715 cm³ = 0.33566... = 0.34 g/cm³ (2 s.f.)

2 s.f.   3 s.f.   Final answer should be rounded to 2 s.f.

Don't forget your calculator...

EXAM TIP In the exam you could be given some <u>data</u> and be expected to <u>process it</u> in some way. Make sure you keep an eye on <u>significant figures</u> in your answers and <u>always write down your working</u>.

Presenting Data

Once you've processed your data, e.g. by calculating the mean, you can present your results in a nice <u>chart</u> or <u>graph</u>. This will help you to <u>spot any patterns</u> in your data.

If Your Data Comes in **Categories**, Present It in a **Bar Chart**

1) If the independent variable is <u>categoric</u> (comes in distinct categories, e.g. solid, liquid, gas) you should use a <u>bar chart</u> to display the data.

2) You also use them if the independent variable is <u>discrete</u> (the data can be counted in chunks, where there's no in-between value, e.g. number of protons is discrete because you can't have half a proton).

3) There are some <u>golden rules</u> you need to follow for <u>drawing</u> bar charts:

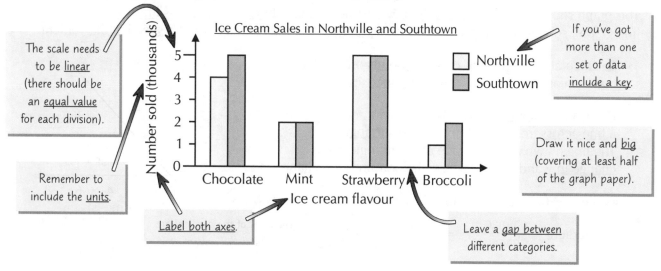

The scale needs to be <u>linear</u> (there should be an <u>equal value</u> for each division).

Remember to include the <u>units</u>.

Label both axes.

If you've got more than one set of data <u>include a key</u>.

Draw it nice and <u>big</u> (covering at least half of the graph paper).

Leave a <u>gap between</u> different categories.

If Your Data is **Continuous**, Plot a **Graph**

1) If both variables are <u>continuous</u> (numerical data that can have any value within a range, e.g. length, volume, temperature) you should use a <u>graph</u> to display the data.

2) Here are the <u>rules</u> for plotting points on a graph:

Use the biggest data values you've got to draw a <u>sensible scale</u> on your axes. Here, the longest distance is <u>8.8 m</u>, so it makes sense to label the y-axis up to <u>10 m</u>.

The <u>dependent</u> variable goes on the <u>y-axis</u> (the <u>vertical</u> one).

The <u>independent</u> variable goes on the <u>x-axis</u> (the <u>horizontal</u> one).

To plot points, use a sharp pencil and make <u>neat little crosses</u> (don't do blobs).

nice clear mark

smudged unclear marks

If you're asked to draw a <u>line</u> (or <u>curve</u>) of <u>best fit</u>, draw a line <u>through</u> or as <u>near</u> to as <u>many points as possible</u>, ignoring any <u>anomalous results</u>. <u>Don't</u> join the crosses up.

anomalous result

Remember to include the <u>units</u>.

Draw it nice and <u>big</u> (covering at least half of the graph paper).

More on Graphs

Graph's aren't just fun to plot, they're also really useful for showing <u>trends</u> in your data.

Graphs Can Give You a Lot of Information About Your Data

1) The <u>gradient</u> (slope) of a graph tells you how quickly the <u>dependent variable</u> changes if you change the <u>independent variable</u>.

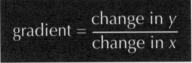

$$\text{gradient} = \frac{\text{change in } y}{\text{change in } x}$$

You can use this method to calculate other rates from a graph, so long as you always make x time.

This <u>graph</u> shows the <u>distance travelled</u> by a vehicle against <u>time</u>. The graph is <u>linear</u> (it's a straight line graph), so you can simply calculate the <u>gradient</u> of the line to find out the <u>speed</u> of the vehicle.

1) To calculate the gradient, pick <u>two points</u> on the line that are easy to read and a <u>good distance</u> apart.

2) <u>Draw a line down</u> from one of the points and a <u>line across</u> from the other to make a <u>triangle</u>. The line drawn down the side of the triangle is the <u>change in y</u> and the line across the bottom is the <u>change in x</u>.

Change in y = 6.8 – 2.0 = 4.8 m Change in x = 5.2 – 1.6 = 3.6 s

Rate = gradient = $\dfrac{\text{change in } y}{\text{change in } x} = \dfrac{4.8\,\text{m}}{3.6\,\text{s}} = \underline{1.3\ \text{m/s}}$ *The units of the gradient are (units of y)/(units of x).*

2) To find the <u>gradient of a curve</u> at a <u>certain point</u>, draw a <u>tangent</u> to the curve at that point. This is a <u>straight line</u> that <u>touches</u> the curve at that <u>point</u>, but doesn't <u>cross</u> it. Then just find the <u>gradient of the tangent</u> in the same way as above.

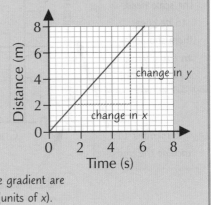

3) The <u>intercept</u> of a graph is where the line of best fit crosses one of the <u>axes</u>. The <u>x-intercept</u> is where the line of best fit crosses the x-axis and the <u>y-intercept</u> is where it crosses the <u>y-axis</u>.

Graphs Show the Relationship Between Two Variables

1) You can get <u>three</u> types of <u>correlation</u> (relationship) between variables:

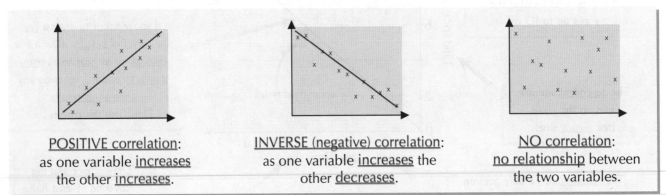

<u>POSITIVE correlation</u>: as one variable <u>increases</u> the other <u>increases</u>.

<u>INVERSE (negative) correlation</u>: as one variable <u>increases</u> the other <u>decreases</u>.

<u>NO correlation</u>: <u>no relationship</u> between the two variables.

2) Just because there's correlation, it doesn't mean the change in one variable is <u>causing</u> the change in the other — there might be <u>other factors</u> involved (see page 14).

Units

Graphs and maths skills are all very well, but the numbers don't mean much if you don't get the units right.

S.I. Units Are Used All Round the World

1) It wouldn't be all that useful if I defined volume in terms of bath tubs, you defined it in terms of egg-cups and my pal Fred defined it in terms of balloons — we'd never be able to compare our data.

2) To stop this happening, scientists have come up with a set of standard units, called S.I. units, that all scientists use to measure their data. Here are some S.I. units you'll see in physics:

Quantity	S.I. Base Unit
mass	kilogram, kg
length	metre, m
time	second, s
temperature	kelvin, K

Always Check The Values Used in Equations Have the Right Units

1) Formulas and equations show relationships between variables.

2) To rearrange an equation, make sure that whatever you do to one side of the equation you also do to the other side.

For example, you can find the speed of a wave using the equation: ⟹ wave speed = frequency × wavelength

You can rearrange this equation to find the frequency by dividing each side by wavelength to give: ⟹ frequency = wave speed ÷ wavelength

3) To use a formula, you need to know the values of all but one of the variables. Substitute the values you do know into the formula, and do the calculation to work out the final variable.

4) Always make sure the values you put into an equation or formula have the right units. For example, you might have done an experiment to find the speed of a trolley. The distance the trolley travels will probably have been measured in cm, but the equation to find speed uses distance in m. So you'll have to convert your distance from cm to m before you put it into the equation.

5) To make sure your units are correct, it can help to write down the units on each line of your calculation.

S.I. units help scientists to compare data...

You can only really compare things if they're in the same units. For example, if you measured the speed of one car in m/s, and one in km/h, it would be hard to know which car was going faster.

Converting Units

You can <u>convert units</u> using <u>scaling prefixes</u>. This can save you from having to write a lot of 0's...

Scaling Prefixes Can Be Used for Large and Small Quantities

1) Quantities come in a huge <u>range</u> of sizes. For example, the volume of a swimming pool might be around 2 000 000 000 cm³, while the volume of a cup is around 250 cm³.

2) To make the size of numbers more <u>manageable</u>, larger or smaller units are used. These are the <u>S.I. base units</u> (e.g. metres) with a <u>prefix</u> in front:

Prefix	tera (T)	giga (G)	mega (M)	kilo (k)	deci (d)	centi (c)	milli (m)	micro (μ)	nano (n)
Multiple of Unit	10^{12}	10^9	1 000 000 (10^6)	1000	0.1	0.01	0.001	0.000001 (10^{-6})	10^{-9}

3) These <u>prefixes</u> tell you <u>how much bigger</u> or <u>smaller</u> a unit is than the base unit. So one <u>kilo</u>metre is <u>one thousand</u> metres.

4) To <u>swap</u> from one unit to another, all you need to know is what number you have to divide or multiply by to get from the original unit to the new unit — this is called the <u>conversion factor</u>.

The conversion factor is the number of times the smaller unit goes into the larger unit.

- To go from a <u>bigger unit</u> (like m) to a <u>smaller unit</u> (like cm), you <u>multiply</u> by the conversion factor.
- To go from a <u>smaller unit</u> (like g) to a <u>bigger unit</u> (like kg), you <u>divide</u> by the conversion factor.

5) Here are some conversions that'll be useful for physics:

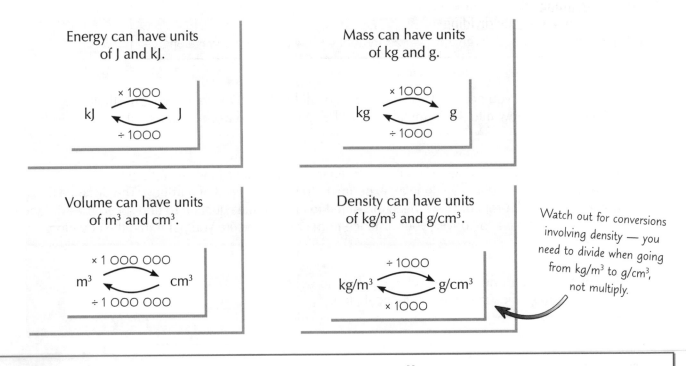

Energy can have units of J and kJ.

kJ ×1000 → ÷1000 ← J

Mass can have units of kg and g.

kg ×1000 → ÷1000 ← g

Volume can have units of m³ and cm³.

m³ ×1 000 000 → ÷1 000 000 ← cm³

Density can have units of kg/m³ and g/cm³.

kg/m³ ÷1000 → ×1000 ← g/cm³

Watch out for conversions involving density — you need to divide when going from kg/m³ to g/cm³, not multiply.

To convert from bigger units to smaller units...

(MATHS TIP)

...multiply by the conversion factor. And to convert from <u>smaller units</u> to <u>bigger units</u>, <u>divide</u> by the <u>conversion factor</u>. Don't go getting this rule muddled up and the wrong way round...

Drawing Conclusions

Once you've designed your experiment, carried it out, processed and presented your data, it's finally time to sit down and work out exactly what your data tells you. Time for some fun with <u>conclusions</u>...

You Can **Only Conclude** What the Data Shows and **No More**

1) Drawing conclusions might seem pretty straightforward — you just <u>look at your data</u> and <u>say what pattern or relationship you see</u> between the dependent and independent variables.

The table on the right shows the potential difference across a light bulb for three <u>different</u> currents through the bulb:

Current (A)	Potential difference (V)
6	4
9	10
12	13

CONCLUSION:
A <u>higher current</u> through the bulb gives a higher <u>potential difference</u> across the bulb.

2) But you've got to be really careful that your conclusion <u>matches the data</u> you've got and <u>doesn't go any further</u>.

> You <u>can't</u> conclude that the potential difference across <u>any circuit component</u> will be higher for a larger current — the results might be completely different.

3) You also need to be able to <u>use your results</u> to <u>justify your conclusion</u> (i.e. back up your conclusion with some specific data).

> The potential difference across the bulb was <u>9 V higher</u> with a current of 12 A compared to a current of 6 A.

4) When writing a conclusion you need to <u>refer back</u> to the original hypothesis and say whether the data <u>supports it</u> or not:

> The hypothesis for this experiment might have been that a higher current through the bulb would <u>increase</u> the potential difference across the bulb. If so, the data <u>supports</u> the hypothesis.

You should be able to justify your conclusion with your data...

You should always be able to explain how your data <u>supports</u> your <u>conclusion</u>. It's easy to go too far with conclusions and start making <u>bold claims</u> that your data simply can't back up. When you're drawing conclusions, it's also important that you refer back to your <u>initial hypothesis</u>, the one you made right back at the start of the investigation, to see whether your data supports it or not.

Correlation and Cause

Don't get carried away when you're <u>drawing conclusions</u> — <u>correlation</u> doesn't always mean <u>cause</u>. There could be a few reasons why two variables appear to be linked, as you're about to find out.

Correlation DOES NOT Mean Cause

If two things are correlated (i.e. there's a relationship between them) it <u>doesn't</u> necessarily mean a change in one variable is <u>causing</u> the change in the other — this is <u>REALLY IMPORTANT</u> — <u>DON'T FORGET IT</u>.

There are **Three** Possible **Reasons** for a **Correlation**

1) <u>CHANCE</u>: It might seem strange, but two things can show a correlation purely due to <u>chance</u>.

> For example, one study might find a correlation between people's hair colour and how good they are at frisbee. But other scientists <u>don't</u> get a correlation when they investigate it — the results of the first study are just a <u>fluke</u>.

2) <u>LINKED BY A 3RD VARIABLE</u>: A lot of the time it may <u>look</u> as if a change in one variable is causing a change in the other, but it <u>isn't</u> — a <u>third variable links</u> the two things.

> For example, there's a correlation between <u>water temperature</u> and <u>shark attacks</u>. This isn't because warmer water makes sharks crazy. Instead, they're linked by a third variable — the <u>number of people swimming</u> (more people swim when the water's hotter, and with more people in the water you get more shark attacks).

3) <u>CAUSE</u>: Sometimes a change in one variable does <u>cause</u> a change in the other. You can only conclude that a correlation is due to cause when you've <u>controlled all the variables</u> that could, just could, be affecting the result.

> For example, there's a correlation between <u>smoking</u> and <u>lung cancer</u>. This is because chemicals in tobacco smoke cause lung cancer. This conclusion was only made once <u>other variables</u> (such as age and exposure to other things that cause cancer) had been <u>controlled</u>.

Two variables could appear to be linked by chance...

<u>Correlation</u> doesn't necessarily mean <u>cause</u> — two variables might appear to be linked but it could just be down to <u>chance</u>, or they could be linked by a <u>third variable</u>. When you draw conclusions, make sure you're not jumping to conclusions about cause, and check that you properly <u>consider</u> all the reasons why two variables might appear to be linked.

Uncertainty

<u>Uncertainty</u> is how sure you can really be about your data. There's a little bit of <u>maths</u> to do, and also a formula to learn. But don't worry too much — it's no more than a simple bit of subtraction and division.

Uncertainty is the Amount of **Error** Your Measurements Might Have

1) When you <u>repeat</u> a measurement, you often get a <u>slightly different</u> figure each time you do it due to <u>random error</u>. This means that <u>each result</u> has some <u>uncertainty</u> to it.

2) The measurements you make will also have some uncertainty in them due to <u>limits</u> in the <u>resolution</u> of the equipment you use (see page 6).

3) This all means that the <u>mean</u> of a set of results will also have some uncertainty to it. You can calculate the uncertainty of a <u>mean result</u> using the equation:

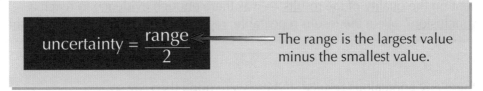

$$\text{uncertainty} = \frac{\text{range}}{2}$$

The range is the largest value minus the smallest value.

4) The <u>larger</u> the range, the <u>less precise</u> your results are and the <u>more uncertainty</u> there will be in your results. Uncertainties are shown using the '±' symbol.

EXAMPLE:

The table below shows the results of an experiment to determine the speed of the trolley as it moves along a horizontal surface. Calculate the uncertainty of the mean.

Repeat	1	2	3	4
Speed (m/s)	2.01	1.98	2.00	2.01

1) First work out the range:

Range = 2.01 − 1.98 = 0.030 m/s

2) Then find the mean:

Mean = (2.01 + 1.98 + 2.00 + 2.01) ÷ 4
= 8.00 ÷ 4 = 2.00

3) Use the range to find the uncertainty:

Uncertainty = range ÷ 2 = 0.030 ÷ 2 = 0.015 m/s

So the uncertainty of the mean = 2.00 ± 0.015 m/s

---

5) Measuring a <u>greater amount</u> of something helps to <u>reduce uncertainty</u>. For example, in an experiment investigating speed, measuring the distance travelled over a <u>longer period</u> compared to a shorter period will <u>reduce</u> the <u>uncertainty</u> in your results.

The smaller the uncertainty, the more precise your results...

Remember that equation for <u>uncertainty</u>. You never know when you might need it — you could be expected to use it in the exams. You need to make sure all the <u>data</u> is in the <u>same units</u> though. For example, if you had some measurements in metres, and some in centimetres, you'd need to convert them all into either metres or centimetres before you set about calculating uncertainty.

Evaluations

Hurrah! The end of another investigation. Well, now you have to work out all the things you did <u>wrong</u>. That's what <u>evaluations</u> are all about I'm afraid. Best get cracking with this page...

Evaluations — Describe **How** Experiments Could be **Improved**

An evaluation is a <u>critical analysis</u> of the whole investigation.

1) You should comment on the <u>method</u> — was it <u>valid</u>?
Did you control all the other variables to make it a <u>fair test</u>?

2) Comment on the <u>quality</u> of the <u>results</u> — was there <u>enough evidence</u> to reach a valid <u>conclusion</u>? Were the results <u>repeatable</u>, <u>reproducible</u>, <u>accurate</u> and <u>precise</u>?

3) Were there any <u>anomalous</u> results? If there were <u>none</u> then <u>say so</u>.
If there were any, try to <u>explain</u> them — were they caused by <u>errors</u> in measurement?
Were there any other <u>variables</u> that could have <u>affected</u> the results?
You should comment on the level of <u>uncertainty</u> in your results too.

4) All this analysis will allow you to say how <u>confident</u> you are that your conclusion is <u>right</u>.

5) Then you can suggest any <u>changes</u> to the <u>method</u> that would <u>improve</u> the quality of the results, so that you could have <u>more confidence</u> in your conclusion. For example, you might suggest <u>changing</u> the way you controlled a variable, or <u>increasing</u> the number of <u>measurements</u> you took. Taking more measurements at <u>narrower intervals</u> could give you a <u>more accurate result</u>. For example:

> <u>Springs</u> have a <u>limit of proportionality</u> (a maximum force before force and extension are no longer proportional). Say you use several <u>identical</u> springs to do an experiment to find the limit of proportionality of the springs. If you apply forces of 1 N, 2 N, 3 N, 4 N and 5 N, and from the results see that it is somewhere <u>between 4 N and 5 N</u>, you could <u>repeat</u> the experiment with one of the other springs, taking <u>more measurements</u> <u>between 4 N and 5 N</u> to get a <u>more accurate</u> value for the limit of proportionality.

6) You could also make more <u>predictions</u> based on your conclusion, then <u>further experiments</u> could be carried out to test them.

When suggesting improvements to the investigation, always make sure that you say why you think this would make the results better.

Always look for ways to improve your investigations...

So there you have it — <u>Working Scientifically</u>. Make sure you know this stuff like the back of your hand. It's not just in the lab, when you're carrying out your groundbreaking <u>investigations</u>, that you'll need to know how to work scientifically. You can be asked about it in the <u>exams</u> as well. So swot up...

Energy Stores

Energy is <u>never used up</u>. Instead it's just <u>transferred</u> between different <u>energy stores</u> and different objects...

Energy is **Transferred** Between **Stores**

When energy is <u>transferred</u> to an object, the energy is <u>stored</u> in one of the object's <u>energy stores</u>. The <u>energy stores</u> you need to know are:

You may also see thermal energy stores called internal energy stores.

1) <u>Thermal</u> energy stores.

2) <u>Kinetic</u> energy stores.

3) <u>Gravitational potential</u> energy stores.

4) <u>Elastic potential</u> energy stores.

5) <u>Chemical</u> energy stores.

6) <u>Magnetic</u> energy stores.

7) <u>Electrostatic</u> energy stores.

8) <u>Nuclear</u> energy stores.

Energy is transferred <u>mechanically</u> (by a <u>force doing work</u>), <u>electrically</u> (work done by a <u>moving charges</u>), by <u>heating</u> (see below) or by <u>radiation</u> (e.g. <u>light</u>, p.112, or <u>sound</u>).

There's more on doing work on the next page.

When a **System Changes**, **Energy** is **Transferred**

1) A <u>system</u> is just a fancy word for a <u>single</u> object (e.g. the air in a piston) or a <u>group</u> of <u>objects</u> (e.g. two colliding vehicles) that you're interested in.

2) When a system <u>changes</u>, <u>energy is transferred</u>. It can be transferred <u>into</u> or <u>away from</u> the system, between <u>different objects</u> in the system or between <u>different types</u> of energy stores (e.g. from the kinetic energy store of an object to its thermal energy store).

3) <u>Closed systems</u> are systems where neither <u>matter nor energy can enter or leave</u>. The <u>net change</u> in the <u>total energy</u> of a <u>closed system</u> is <u>always zero</u>.

Energy can be **Transferred** by **Heating**

1) Take the example of <u>boiling water</u> in a <u>kettle</u> — you can think of the <u>water</u> as <u>the system</u>. Energy is <u>transferred to</u> the water (from the kettle's heating element) <u>by heating</u>, into the water's <u>thermal</u> energy store (causing the <u>temperature</u> of the water to <u>rise</u>).

2) You could also think of the <u>kettle's</u> heating element and the <u>water</u> together as a <u>two-object system</u>. Energy is transferred <u>electrically</u> to the <u>thermal</u> energy store of the kettle's heating element, which transfers energy <u>by heating</u> to the water's <u>thermal</u> energy store.

No matter what store it's in, it's all energy...

EXAM TIP In the exam, make sure you refer to <u>energy</u> in terms of the <u>store</u> it's in. For example, if you're describing energy in a <u>hot object</u>, say it '<u>has energy in its thermal energy store</u>'.

Work Done

On the previous page, you saw how energy can be <u>transferred</u> between <u>energy stores</u> by <u>heating</u>. Well, that was just the start... This page is all about how energy is transferred when <u>work is done</u>.

Energy can be Transferred by Doing Work

1) <u>Work done</u> is just another way of saying <u>energy transferred</u> — they're the <u>same thing</u>.

2) <u>Work</u> can be done when <u>current flows</u> (work is done <u>against resistance</u> in a <u>circuit</u>, see page 38) or by a <u>force</u> moving an object (there's more on this on page 79). Here are a few examples:

The <u>initial force</u> exerted by a person to <u>throw</u> a ball <u>upwards</u> does <u>work</u>. It causes an energy transfer <u>from</u> the <u>chemical energy store</u> of the person's arm to the <u>kinetic</u> energy store of the ball and arm.

an upwards force is exerted on the ball

frictional forces cause a transfer of energy

The <u>friction</u> between a car's <u>brakes</u> and its <u>wheels</u> does work as the car <u>slows down</u>. It causes an energy transfer from the <u>wheels' kinetic energy</u> stores to the <u>thermal</u> energy store of the <u>surroundings</u>.

In a collision between a car and a <u>stationary object</u>, the <u>normal contact force</u> between the car and the object <u>does work</u>. It causes energy to be transferred from the car's <u>kinetic</u> energy store to <u>other energy stores</u>, e.g. the <u>elastic potential</u> and <u>thermal</u> energy stores of the object and the car body. Some energy might also be <u>transferred away</u> by <u>sound waves</u>.

normal contact force causes a transfer of energy to the car

Falling Objects Also Transfer Energy

1) When something, e.g. a ball, is <u>dropped</u> from a height, it's accelerated by <u>gravity</u>. The <u>gravitational force</u> does <u>work</u>.

2) As it <u>falls</u>, energy from the object's <u>gravitational potential energy (g.p.e)</u> store is transferred to its <u>kinetic energy store</u>.

gravitational force

3) For a falling object when there's <u>no air resistance</u>:

Energy <u>lost</u> from the <u>g.p.e. store</u> = Energy <u>gained</u> in the <u>kinetic energy store</u>

4) In real life, <u>air resistance</u> (p.91) acts against all falling objects — it causes some energy to be transferred to <u>other energy stores</u>, e.g. the <u>thermal</u> energy stores of the <u>object</u> and <u>surroundings</u>.

REVISION TIP

Energy is transferred between the different stores of objects...

Energy stores pop up <u>everywhere</u> in physics. You need to be able to describe <u>how energy is transferred</u>, and <u>which stores</u> it gets transferred between, for <u>any scenario</u>. So, it's time to make sure you know all the <u>energy stores</u> and <u>transfer methods</u> like the back of your hand.

Kinetic and Potential Energy Stores

Now you've got your head around <u>energy stores</u>, it's time to see how you can calculate the amount of energy in <u>three</u> of the most common ones — <u>kinetic</u>, <u>gravitational potential</u> and <u>elastic potential</u> energy stores.

Movement Means Energy in an Object's Kinetic Energy Store

1) Anything that is <u>moving</u> has energy in its <u>kinetic energy store</u>. Energy is transferred <u>to</u> this store when an object <u>speeds up</u> and is transferred <u>away</u> from this store when an object <u>slows down</u>.

2) The energy in the <u>kinetic energy store</u> depends on the object's <u>mass</u> and <u>speed</u>.
The <u>greater its mass</u> and the <u>faster</u> it's going, the <u>more energy</u> there will be in its kinetic energy store.

3) There's a <u>slightly tricky</u> formula for it, so you have to concentrate <u>a little bit harder</u> for this one.

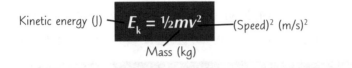

Kinetic energy (J) —— $E_k = \frac{1}{2}mv^2$ ——(Speed)^2 (m/s)^2
Mass (kg)

$\frac{1}{2}mv^2$ means $\frac{1}{2} \times m \times v^2$.

EXAMPLE: **A car of mass 2500 kg is travelling at 20 m/s.**
Calculate the energy in its kinetic energy store.

$E_k = \frac{1}{2}mv^2 = \frac{1}{2} \times 2500 \times 20^2 = 500\ 000$ J

Raised Objects Store Energy in Gravitational Potential Energy Stores

1) <u>Lifting</u> an object in a <u>gravitational field</u> (page 77) requires <u>work</u>. This causes a <u>transfer of energy</u> to the <u>gravitational potential energy</u> (g.p.e.) store of the raised object. The <u>higher</u> the object is lifted, the <u>more</u> energy is transferred to this store.

2) The amount of energy in a gravitational potential energy store depends on the object's <u>mass</u>, its <u>height</u> and the <u>strength</u> of the gravitational field the object is in.

3) You can use this equation to find the <u>change in energy</u> in an object's gravitational potential energy store for a <u>change in height</u>, <u>h</u>.

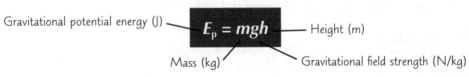

Gravitational potential energy (J) —— $E_p = mgh$ —— Height (m)
Mass (kg) Gravitational field strength (N/kg)

Stretching can Transfer Energy to Elastic Potential Energy Stores

<u>Stretching</u> or <u>squashing</u> an object can transfer energy to its <u>elastic potential energy store</u>.
So long as the <u>limit of proportionality</u> has not been <u>exceeded</u> (page 83) energy in the <u>elastic potential energy store</u> of a stretched spring can be found using:

Spring constant (N/m)
Elastic potential energy (J) —— $E_e = \frac{1}{2}ke^2$ —— Extension (m)

Greater height means more energy in gravitational potential stores...

Wow, that's a lot of equations on a single page... As with all equations you come across, make sure you know what all the <u>variables</u> in them are, as well as what <u>units</u> all the variables in the equations are in.

Specific Heat Capacity

Specific heat capacity is really just a sciencey way of saying how hard it is to heat something up...

Different Materials Have Different Specific Heat Capacities

1) More energy needs to be transferred to the thermal energy store of some materials to increase their temperature than others.

2) For example:

> You need 4200 J to warm 1 kg of water by 1 °C, but only 139 J to warm 1 kg of mercury by 1 °C.

3) Materials that need to gain lots of energy in their thermal energy stores to warm up also transfer loads of energy when they cool down again. They can 'store' a lot of energy.

4) The measure of how much energy a substance can store is called its specific heat capacity.

> Specific heat capacity is the amount of energy needed to raise the temperature of 1 kg of a substance by 1 °C.

There's a Helpful Formula Involving Specific Heat Capacity

Below is the equation that links energy transferred to specific heat capacity (the Δ's just mean "change in").

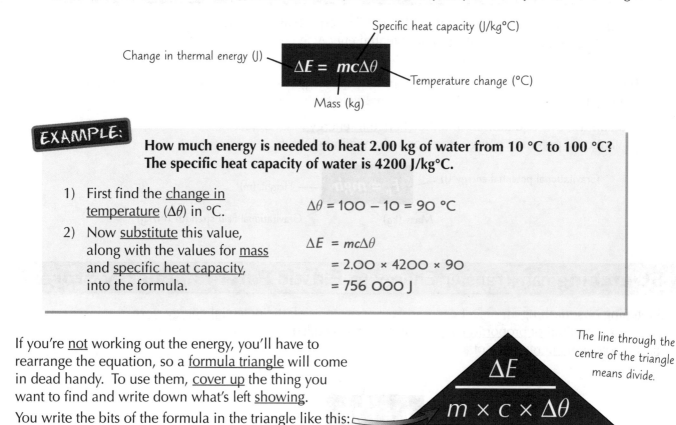

Specific heat capacity (J/kg°C)

Change in thermal energy (J)

$$\Delta E = mc\Delta\theta$$

Temperature change (°C)

Mass (kg)

EXAMPLE:

How much energy is needed to heat 2.00 kg of water from 10 °C to 100 °C? The specific heat capacity of water is 4200 J/kg°C.

1) First find the change in temperature (Δθ) in °C.

$\Delta\theta = 100 - 10 = 90$ °C

2) Now substitute this value, along with the values for mass and specific heat capacity, into the formula.

$\Delta E = mc\Delta\theta$
$= 2.00 \times 4200 \times 90$
$= 756\ 000$ J

If you're not working out the energy, you'll have to rearrange the equation, so a formula triangle will come in dead handy. To use them, cover up the thing you want to find and write down what's left showing.

You write the bits of the formula in the triangle like this:

$$\frac{\Delta E}{m \times c \times \Delta\theta}$$

The line through the centre of the triangle means divide.

Some substances can store more energy than others...

Water is a substance that can store a lot of energy in its thermal stores — it has a high specific heat capacity. This is lucky for us as our bodies are mostly water. It'd be unfortunate if we started boiling on a hot day. Learn the definition of specific heat capacity and make sure you know how to use the formula involving it.

Investigating Specific Heat Capacity [PRACTICAL]

This fun practical can be used to find out the <u>specific heat capacity</u> of a material.

You Can Investigate Specific Heat Capacities

1) To investigate a <u>solid</u> material (e.g. copper), you'll need a <u>block</u> of the material with <u>two holes</u> in it (for the <u>heater</u> and <u>thermometer</u> to go into, see the image on the right).

2) Measure the <u>mass</u> of the <u>block</u>, then wrap it in an insulating layer (e.g. a thick layer of newspaper) to <u>reduce</u> the <u>energy transferred</u> from the block to the <u>surroundings</u>. Insert the <u>thermometer</u> and <u>heater</u> as shown on the right.

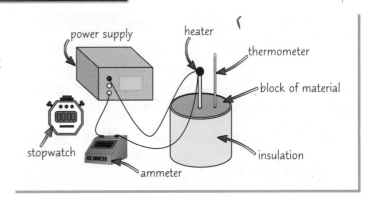

3) Measure the <u>initial temperature</u> of the block and set the potential difference, V, of the power supply to be <u>10 V</u>. <u>Turn on</u> the power supply and <u>start</u> a <u>stopwatch</u>.

4) When you turn on the power, the <u>current</u> in the circuit (i.e. the moving charges) <u>does work</u> on the heater, transferring energy <u>electrically</u> from the power supply to the heater's <u>thermal energy store</u>. This energy is then transferred to the material's <u>thermal</u> energy store <u>by heating</u>, causing the material's <u>temperature</u> to increase.

5) As the block heats up, use the <u>thermometer</u> to measure its temperature e.g. <u>every minute</u>. Keep an eye on the <u>ammeter</u> — the <u>current</u> through the circuit, I, <u>shouldn't change</u>.

6) When you've collected enough readings (10 should do it), <u>turn off</u> the power supply.

7) Now you have to do some <u>calculations</u> to find the material's <u>specific heat capacity</u>:

- Using your measurement of the <u>current</u> and the <u>potential difference</u> of the <u>power supply</u>, you can calculate the <u>power</u> supplied to the heater, using <u>$P = VI$</u> (p.51). You can use this to calculate <u>how much energy</u>, E, has been <u>transferred to the heater</u> at the time of each temperature reading using the formula <u>$E = Pt$</u>, where t is the <u>time in seconds</u> since the experiment began.

- If you assume <u>all the energy</u> supplied to the heater has been <u>transferred to the block</u>, you can plot a <u>graph</u> of <u>energy transferred</u> to the thermal energy store of the block against <u>temperature</u>. It should look something like this: ➡

- Find the <u>gradient</u> of the straight part of the graph. This is $\Delta\theta \div \Delta E$. You know from the equation on the last page that $\underline{\Delta E = mc\Delta\theta}$. So the specific heat capacity of the material of the block is: <u>$1 \div$ (gradient × the mass of the block)</u>.

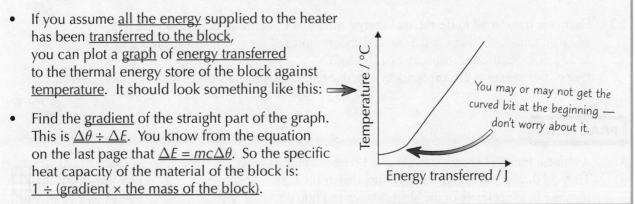

You may or may not get the curved bit at the beginning — don't worry about it.

8) You can <u>repeat</u> this experiment with <u>different materials</u> to see how their specific heat capacities <u>compare</u>.

You can also investigate the specific heat capacity of liquids — just place the heater and thermometer in an insulated beaker filled with a known mass of the liquid.

Think about how you could improve your experiments...

If the hole in your material is <u>bigger</u> than your <u>thermometer</u>, you could put a small amount of water in the hole with the thermometer. This helps the thermometer to measure the temperature of the block more accurately, as water is a better thermal conductor than <u>air</u> (see page 24).

Warm-Up & Exam Questions

These questions give you chance to use your knowledge about energy transfers and specific heat capacity.

Warm-Up Questions

1) Give two methods of energy transfer.
2) How does the way energy is stored change when someone throws a ball upwards?
3) State the equation that links energy in an object's kinetic energy store with mass and speed.
4) Which has more energy in its kinetic energy store: a person walking at 3 miles per hour, or a lorry travelling at 60 miles per hour?

Exam Questions

1 A motor lifts a load of mass 20 kg.
The load gains 137.2 J of energy in its gravitational potential energy store.

1.1 State the equation that links gravitational potential energy, mass, gravitational field strength and height.
Use this equation to calculate the height through which the motor lifts the load.
Assume the gravitational field strength = 9.8 N/kg

[4 marks]

1.2 The motor releases the load and the load falls.
Ignoring air resistance, describe the changes in the way energy is stored that take place as the load falls.

[2 marks]

1.3 Describe how your answer to **1.2** would differ if air resistance was not ignored.

[1 mark]

2 36 000 J of energy to be transferred to heat a 0.5 kg concrete block is from 20 °C to 100 °C.

2.1 Calculate the specific heat capacity of the concrete block.
Use the correct equation from the Physics Equation Sheet on the inside back cover.

[4 marks]

2.2 Energy is transferred to the thermal energy store of an electric storage heater at night, and then transferred away to the thermal energy stores of the surroundings during the day.
Lead has a specific heat capacity of 126 J/kg°C.
Using your answer to **2.1**, explain why concrete blocks are used in storage heaters rather than lead blocks.

[2 marks]

PRACTICAL

3 A student transfers energy steadily to a 1.0 kg aluminium block.
They produce a graph of the energy supplied against the
increase in temperature of the block, shown in **Figure 1**.

3.1 Use **Figure 1** to find a value for the specific heat capacity
of aluminium in J/kg°C. Use the correct equation from the
Physics Equation Sheet on the inside back cover.

[4 marks]

3.2 Would you expect the true value for the specific heat capacity of
aluminium to be higher or lower than the value found in this experiment? Explain your answer.

[3 marks]

Figure 1

Conservation of Energy and Power

Repeat after me: <u>energy</u> is <u>NEVER</u> destroyed. Make sure you learn that fact, it's really important.

You **Need to Know the Conservation of Energy Principle**

1) The <u>conservation of energy principle</u> is that energy is <u>always</u> conserved:

> Energy can be <u>transferred</u> usefully, stored or dissipated, but can <u>never</u> be <u>created</u> or <u>destroyed</u>.

2) When energy is <u>transferred</u> between stores, not <u>all</u> of the energy is transferred <u>usefully</u> into the store that you want it to go to. Some energy is always <u>dissipated</u> when an energy transfer takes place.

3) Dissipated energy is sometimes called 'wasted energy' because the energy is being <u>stored</u> in a way that is <u>not useful</u> (usually energy has been transferred into thermal energy stores).

A mobile phone is a <u>system</u>. When you use the phone, energy is <u>usefully</u> transferred from the <u>chemical</u> energy store of the <u>battery</u> in the phone. But some of this energy is <u>dissipated</u> in this transfer to the <u>thermal</u> energy store of the <u>phone</u> (you may have noticed your phone feels warm if you've been using it for a while).

4) You also need to be able to describe energy transfers for <u>closed systems</u>:

A <u>cold spoon</u> is dropped into an insulated flask of <u>hot soup</u>, which is then sealed. You can assume that the flask is a <u>perfect thermal insulator</u> so the <u>spoon</u> and the <u>soup</u> form a <u>closed system</u>. Energy is transferred from the <u>thermal</u> energy store of the <u>soup</u> to the <u>useless</u> thermal energy store of the <u>spoon</u> (causing the soup to cool down slightly). Energy transfers have occurred <u>within</u> the system, but no energy has <u>left</u> the system — so the net change in energy is <u>zero</u>.

Power is the 'Rate of Doing Work' — i.e. How Much per Second

1) Power is the <u>rate of energy transfer</u>, or the <u>rate of doing work</u>.

2) <u>Power</u> is measured in <u>watts</u>. <u>One watt = 1 joule of energy transferred per second</u>.

3) You can calculate power using these equations:

Power (W) — $P = \dfrac{E}{t}$ — Energy transferred (J) / Time (s)

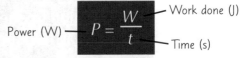

Power (W) — $P = \dfrac{W}{t}$ — Work done (J) / Time (s)

4) A <u>powerful</u> machine is not necessarily one which can exert a strong <u>force</u> (although it usually ends up that way). A <u>powerful</u> machine is one which transfers <u>a lot of energy</u> in a <u>short space of time</u>.

Take two cars that are <u>identical</u> in every way apart from the <u>power</u> of their <u>engines</u>. Both cars race the <u>same distance</u> along a straight track to a finish line. The car with the <u>more powerful</u> engine will reach the finish line <u>faster</u> than the other car (it will transfer the <u>same amount of energy</u> but over <u>less time</u>).

EXAMPLE:

It takes 8000 J of work to lift a stunt performer to the top of a building. Motor A can lift the stunt performer to the correct height in 50 s. Motor B would take 300 s to lift the performer to the same height. Which motor is most powerful? Calculate the power of this motor.

1) <u>Both</u> motors transfer the <u>same amount</u> of energy, but motor A would do it <u>quicker</u> than motor B.

   So motor A is the most powerful motor.

2) Plug the <u>time taken</u> and <u>work done</u> for motor A into the equation $P = W \div t$ and find the <u>power</u>.

   $P = W \div t$
   $= 8000 \div 50 = 160 \text{ W}$

Conduction and Convection

It's time to meet two methods of energy transfer by <u>heating</u> — <u>conduction</u> and <u>convection</u>.
Read on to find out how they <u>actually happen</u> and about the <u>energy transfers</u> that take place.

Conduction Occurs Mainly in Solids

> <u>Conduction</u> is the process where <u>vibrating particles</u>
> <u>transfer energy</u> to <u>neighbouring particles</u>.

1) Energy transferred to an object <u>by heating</u> is transferred to the <u>thermal store</u> of the object.
   This energy is shared across the <u>kinetic</u> energy stores of the <u>particles</u> in the object.

2) The particles in the part of the object being heated <u>vibrate</u> more and
   <u>collide</u> with each other. These <u>collisions</u> cause energy to be transferred
   between particles' <u>kinetic</u> energy stores. This is <u>conduction</u>.

3) This process <u>continues throughout</u> the object until the
   energy is transferred to the <u>other side</u> of the object.
   It's then usually transferred to the <u>thermal</u> energy store of
   the <u>surroundings</u> (or anything else <u>touching</u> the object).

   *Particles in liquids and gases are much more free
   to move around, which is why they usually transfer
   energy by convection instead of conduction.*

4) <u>Thermal conductivity</u> is a measure of how <u>quickly</u> energy is transferred through a material in this way.
   Materials with a <u>high thermal conductivity</u> transfer energy between their particles <u>quickly</u>.

Convection Occurs Only in Liquids and Gases

> <u>Convection</u> is where energetic particles
> <u>move away</u> from <u>hotter</u> to <u>cooler regions</u>.

1) <u>Convection</u> can happen in <u>gases</u> and <u>liquids</u>. Energy is transferred <u>by heating</u>
   to the <u>thermal store</u> of the liquid or gas. As with conduction, this energy is
   shared across the <u>kinetic</u> energy stores of the gas or liquid's particles.

2) Unlike in solids, the particles in liquids and gases are <u>able to move</u>. When you heat a region
   of a gas or liquid, the particles <u>move faster</u> and the <u>space</u> between individual particles <u>increases</u>.
   This causes the <u>density</u> (p.57) of the <u>region</u> being heated to <u>decrease</u>.

3) Because liquids and gases can <u>flow</u>, the warmer and less dense region will <u>rise</u> above <u>denser, cooler</u>
   regions. So energetic particles <u>move away</u> from <u>hotter</u> to <u>cooler</u> regions — this is <u>convection</u>.

Some substances are better thermal conductors than others...

<u>Denser</u> materials (see page 57) are usually <u>better conductors</u> than less dense materials. It's easy to see why
— particles that are <u>right next to</u> each other will pass energy between their <u>kinetic energy stores</u> far more
effectively than particles that are far apart. For example, water is a much better thermal conductor than air.

Reducing Unwanted Energy Transfers

There are a few ways you can <u>reduce</u> the amount of energy scampering off to a <u>completely useless</u> store — <u>lubrication</u> and <u>thermal insulation</u> are the ones you need to know about. Read on to find out more...

Lubrication Reduces **Frictional Forces**

1) Whenever something <u>moves</u>, there's usually at least one <u>frictional force</u> acting against it (p.91). This causes some energy in the system to be <u>dissipated</u> (p.23), e.g. <u>air resistance</u> can transfer energy from a falling object's <u>kinetic energy store</u> to its <u>thermal energy store</u>.

Streamlining reduces air resistance too, see p.91.

2) For objects that are being rubbed together, <u>lubricants</u> can be used to reduce the friction between the objects' surfaces when they move. Lubricants are usually <u>liquids</u> (like <u>oil</u>), so they can <u>flow</u> easily between objects and <u>coat</u> them.

Insulation Reduces the Rate of **Energy Transfer** by **Heating**

The last thing you want when you've made your house nice and toasty is for that energy to <u>escape</u> outside. There are a few things you can do to <u>prevent energy losses</u> through <u>heating</u>:

- Have <u>thick walls</u> that are made from a material with a <u>low thermal conductivity</u>. The <u>thicker</u> the walls and the <u>lower</u> their <u>thermal conductivity</u>, the <u>slower</u> the rate of energy transfer will be (so the building will <u>cool more slowly</u>).
- Use <u>thermal insulation</u>. Here are some examples:

1) Some houses have <u>cavity walls</u>, made up of an <u>inner</u> and an <u>outer</u> wall with an air gap in the middle. The <u>air gap</u> reduces the amount of energy transferred by conduction through the walls. <u>Cavity wall insulation</u>, where the cavity wall air gap is filled with a <u>foam</u>, can also reduce energy transfer by <u>convection</u> in the wall cavity.

2) <u>Loft insulation</u> can be laid out across the loft floor and ceiling. Fibreglass wool is often used which is a <u>good insulator</u> as it has pockets of trapped air. Loft insulation reduces energy loss by <u>conduction</u> and also helps prevent <u>convection</u> currents (a <u>cycle</u> where air particles are constantly being <u>heated</u>, <u>rising</u>, <u>cooling</u> and then <u>sinking</u>) from being created.

3) <u>Double-glazed windows</u> work in the same way as cavity walls — they have an air gap between two sheets of glass to prevent energy transfer by <u>conduction</u> through the windows.

4) <u>Draught excluders</u> around doors and windows reduce energy transfers by <u>convection</u>.

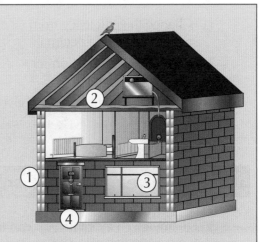

Reducing the difference between the temperature inside and outside the house will also reduce the rate of energy transfer.

Having a well-insulated house can reduce your heating bills...

When people talk of <u>energy loss</u>, it's <u>not</u> that the energy has disappeared. It still exists (see page 23), just not necessarily in the <u>store</u> we want. For example, in a car, you want the energy to transfer to the <u>kinetic energy store</u> of the wheels, and not to the <u>thermal energy stores</u> of the moving components.

Efficiency

Devices have <u>energy transferred</u> to them, but only transfer <u>some</u> of that energy to <u>useful energy stores</u>. Wouldn't it be great if we could tell <u>how much</u> it <u>usefully transfers</u>? That's where <u>efficiency</u> comes in.

Most **Energy Transfers** Involve Some **Waste Energy**

1) <u>Useful devices</u> are only <u>useful</u> because they can <u>transfer energy</u> from one store to another.

2) As you'll probably have gathered by now, some of the <u>input energy</u> is usually wasted by being transferred to a useless energy store — usually a <u>thermal energy store</u>.

3) The <u>less energy</u> that is '<u>wasted</u>' in this energy store, the <u>more efficient</u> the device is said to be.

4) You can <u>improve</u> the efficiency of energy transfers by <u>insulating</u> objects, <u>lubricating</u> them or making them more <u>streamlined</u> (see pages 25 and 91).

5) The efficiency for any energy transfer can be <u>worked out</u> using this equation:

$$\text{Efficiency} = \frac{\text{Useful output energy transfer}}{\text{Total input energy transfer}}$$

You can give efficiency as a <u>decimal</u> or you can <u>multiply</u> your answer by 100 to get a <u>percentage</u>, i.e. <u>0.75</u> or <u>75%</u>.

6) You might not know the <u>energy</u> inputs and outputs of a device, but you can still calculate its efficiency as long as you know the <u>power input</u> and <u>output</u>:

$$\text{Efficiency} = \frac{\text{Useful power output}}{\text{Total power input}}$$

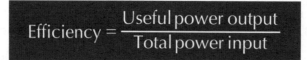 **EXAMPLE:** **A blender is 70% efficient. It has a total input power of 600 W. Calculate the useful output power.**

1) Change the <u>efficiency</u> from a <u>percentage</u> to a <u>decimal</u>.

2) <u>Rearrange</u> the equation for <u>useful power output</u>.

3) <u>Stick in</u> the numbers you're given.

efficiency = 70% = 0.70

useful power output = efficiency × total power input
= 0.70 × 600
= 420 W

Useful Energy Input Isn't Usually Equal to **Total Energy Output**

1) For any given example you can talk about the types of energy being input and output, but remember — <u>NO</u> device is <u>100% efficient</u> and the wasted energy is usually transferred to useless <u>thermal energy stores</u>.

2) <u>Electric heaters</u> are the <u>exception</u> to this. They're usually <u>100% efficient</u> because <u>all</u> the energy in the electrostatic energy store is transferred to "useful" thermal energy stores.

3) Ultimately, <u>all</u> energy ends up transferred to <u>thermal energy stores</u>. For example, if you use an <u>electric drill</u>, its energy is transferred to lots of different energy stores, but quickly ends up all in thermal energy stores.

Warm-Up & Exam Questions

Don't let your energy dissipate. These questions will let you see how efficient your revision has been.

Warm-Up Questions

1) State the principle of the conservation of energy.
2) What is power? State the units it is measured in.
3) Name two mechanisms in which energy is transferred by heating.
4) Give one way you could reduce the frictional forces in the hinge of an automatic door?
5) For a given material, how does its thermal conductivity affect the rate of energy transfer through it?
6) Why is the efficiency of an appliance always less than 100%?

Exam Questions

1 The motor of an electric scooter moves the scooter 10 metres along a flat, horizontal course in 20 seconds. During this time the motor does 1000 J of work. *(Grade 4-6)*

1.1 Write down the equation that links power, work done and time.
Use this equation to calculate the power of the motor.

[3 marks]

1.2 The moving parts of the scooter are lubricated. The scooter then completes the course in 18 seconds.
Explain, in terms of energy transfer, why the scooter completes the course in a faster time.

[2 marks]

1.3 The scooter's motor is replaced with a more powerful, but otherwise identical, motor.
It moves along the same 10 m course.
Describe how its performance will differ from before. Explain your answer.

[2 marks]

2 Torch A transfers 1200 J of energy per minute.
480 J of this is transferred away usefully as light, 690 J is transferred
to useless thermal energy stores and 30 J is transferred away as sound. *(Grade 6-7)*

2.1 Write down the equation linking efficiency, useful output energy transfer and total input energy transfer.

[1 mark]

2.2 Calculate the efficiency of torch A.

[2 marks]

2.3 Torch B transfers 600 J of energy away usefully by light each minute.
Calculate the output power of torch B.

[2 marks]

2.4 Torch B has an efficiency of 0.55. Calculate input power of torch B.

[3 marks]

2.5 Each torch is powered by an identical battery. A student claims that the battery in torch B will
go 'flat' quicker than in torch A because it transfers more energy away as light each minute.
Explain whether or not you agree with the student.

[2 marks]

Energy Resources and their Uses

There are lots of <u>energy resources</u> available on Earth. They are either <u>renewable</u> or <u>non-renewable</u> resources.

Non-Renewable Energy Resources Will **Run Out** One Day

<u>Non-renewable</u> energy resources are <u>fossil fuels</u> and <u>nuclear fuel</u> (uranium and plutonium). <u>Fossil fuels</u> are natural resources that form <u>underground</u> over <u>millions</u> of years. They are typically <u>burnt</u> to provide energy. The <u>three main</u> fossil fuels are:

1) Coal
2) Oil
3) (Natural) Gas

- These will <u>all</u> 'run out' one day.
- They all do <u>damage</u> to the environment.
- But they provide <u>most of our energy</u>.

Renewable Energy Resources Will **Never** Run Out

<u>Renewable</u> energy resources are:

1) The Sun (Solar)
2) Wind
3) Water waves
4) Hydro-electricity
5) Bio-fuel
6) Tides
7) Geothermal

- These will <u>never run out</u> — the energy can be '<u>renewed</u>' as it is used.
- Most of them do <u>damage</u> the environment, but in <u>less nasty</u> ways than non-renewables.
- The trouble is they <u>don't</u> provide much <u>energy</u> and some of them are <u>unreliable</u> because they depend on the weather.

Energy Resources can be Used for **Transport**...

Electricity can also be used to power vehicles, (e.g. trains and some cars). It can be generated using renewable or non-renewable energy resources (p.29-33).

<u>Transport</u> is one of the most obvious places where <u>fuel</u> is used. Here are a few transportation methods that use either <u>renewable</u> or <u>non-renewable</u> energy resources:

NON-RENEWABLE ENERGY RESOURCES
- <u>Petrol</u> and <u>diesel</u> powered vehicles (including most cars) use fuel created from <u>oil</u>.
- <u>Coal</u> is used in some old-fashioned <u>steam trains</u> to boil water to produce steam.

RENEWABLE ENERGY RESOURCES
Vehicles that run on pure <u>bio-fuels</u> (p.32) or a <u>mix</u> of a bio-fuel and petrol or diesel (only the bio-fuel bit is renewable, though).

...And for **Heating**

<u>Energy resources</u> are also needed for <u>heating</u> things like your home.

NON-RENEWABLE ENERGY RESOURCES
- <u>Natural gas</u> is the most widely used fuel for heating homes in the UK. The gas is used to heat <u>water</u>, which is then pumped into <u>radiators</u> throughout the home.
- <u>Coal</u> is commonly burnt in fireplaces.
- <u>Electric heaters</u> (sometimes called storage heaters) which use electricity generated from <u>non-renewable</u> energy resources.

RENEWABLE ENERGY RESOURCES
- A <u>geothermal</u> (or ground source) <u>heat pump</u> uses geothermal energy resources (p.30) to heat buildings.
- <u>Solar water heaters</u> work by using the sun to heat <u>water</u> which is then pumped into radiators in the building.
- Burning <u>bio-fuel</u> or using <u>electricity</u> generated from renewable resources can also be used for heating.

Wind and Solar Power

Renewable energy resources, like wind and solar resources, will not run out. They don't generate as much electricity as non-renewables though — if they did we'd all be using solar-powered toasters by now.

Wind Power — Lots of Little Wind Turbines

This involves putting lots of wind turbines (windmills) up in exposed places like on moors or round coasts.

1) Each turbine has a generator inside it — the rotating blades turn the generator and produce electricity.

2) There's no pollution (except for a bit when they're manufactured).

3) But they do spoil the view. You need about 1500 wind turbines to replace one coal-fired power station and 1500 of them cover a lot of ground — which would have a big effect on the scenery.

4) And they can be very noisy, which can be annoying for people living nearby.

5) There's also the problem of the turbines stopping when the wind stops or if the wind is too strong, and it's impossible to increase supply when there's extra demand (p.52). On average, wind turbines produce electricity 70-85% of the time.

6) The initial costs are quite high, but there are no fuel costs and minimal running costs.

7) There's no permanent damage to the landscape — if you remove the turbines, you remove the noise and the view returns to normal.

Solar Cells — Expensive but Not Much Environmental Damage

Solar cells generate electric currents directly from sunlight.

1) Solar cells are often the best source of energy to charge batteries in calculators and watches which don't use much electricity.

2) Solar power is often used in remote places where there's not much choice (e.g. the Australian outback) and to power electric road signs and satellites.

3) There's no pollution. (Although the factories do use quite a lot of energy and produce some pollution when they manufacture the cells.)

4) In sunny countries solar power is a very reliable source of energy — but only in the daytime. Solar power can still be cost-effective in cloudy countries like Britain though.

5) Like wind, you can't increase the power output when there is extra demand.

6) Initial costs are high but after that the energy is free and running costs almost nil.

7) Solar cells are usually used to generate electricity on a relatively small scale.

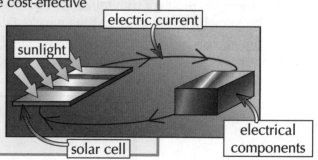

People love the idea of wind power — just not in their back yard...

It's easy to think that non-renewables are the answer to the world's energy problems. However, they have their downsides, and we definitely couldn't rely on them totally at present. Make sure you know the pros and cons for wind and solar power because there are more renewables coming up on the next page.

Geothermal and Hydro-electric Power

Here are some more examples of <u>renewable energy resources</u> — <u>geothermal</u> and <u>hydro-electric</u>.
These ones are a bit more <u>reliable</u> than wind and solar — read on to find out why.

Geothermal Power — Energy from **Underground**

Geothermal power uses energy from
<u>underground thermal energy</u> stores.

1) This is <u>only possible</u> in <u>volcanic areas</u> where
<u>hot rocks</u> lie quite near to the <u>surface</u>.
The source of much of the energy is the
<u>slow decay</u> of various <u>radioactive elements</u>,
including <u>uranium</u>, deep inside the Earth.

2) This is actually <u>brilliant free energy</u> that's
<u>reliable</u> with very few environmental problems.

3) Geothermal energy can be used to <u>generate</u>
<u>electricity</u>, or to <u>heat buildings directly</u>.

4) The <u>main drawbacks</u> with geothermal
energy are that there <u>aren't</u> very many
<u>suitable locations</u> for power plants,
and that the <u>cost</u> of building a power
plant is often <u>high</u> compared to the
<u>amount</u> of energy it produces.

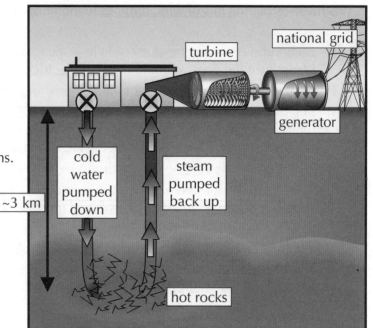

Hydro-electric Power Uses **Falling Water**

Hydro-electric power transfers energy from the <u>kinetic store</u> of <u>falling water</u>.

1) <u>Hydro-electric power</u> usually requires the <u>flooding</u> of a valley by building a big <u>dam</u>.
<u>Rainwater</u> is caught and allowed out <u>through turbines</u>. There is <u>no pollution</u> (as such).

2) But there is a <u>big impact</u> on the <u>environment</u> due to the flooding of the valley (rotting vegetation
releases methane and carbon dioxide) and possible <u>loss of habitat</u> for some species (sometimes
the loss of whole villages). The reservoirs can also look very <u>unsightly</u> when they <u>dry up</u>.
Putting hydroelectric power stations in <u>remote valleys</u> tends to reduce their impact on <u>humans</u>.

3) A <u>big advantage</u> is it can provide an <u>immediate response</u> to an increased demand for electricity.

4) There's no problem with <u>reliability</u> except in times of <u>drought</u> —
but remember this is Great Britain we're talking about.

5) <u>Initial costs</u> are <u>high</u>, but there are <u>no fuel costs</u> and <u>minimal running costs</u>.

6) It can be a useful way to generate electricity on a <u>small scale</u> in <u>remote areas</u>.

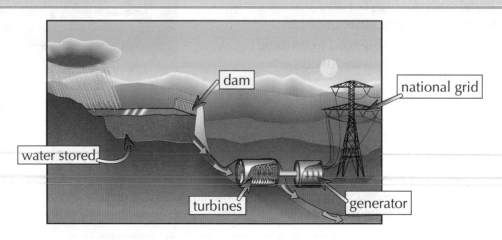

Wave Power and Tidal Barrages

Good ol' <u>water</u>. Not only can we drink it, we can also use it to <u>generate electricity</u>. It's easy to get confused between <u>wave</u> and <u>tidal</u> power as they both involve the seaside — but don't. They are completely different.

Wave Power — Lots of Little **Wave-Powered Turbines**

1) You need <u>lots</u> of small <u>wave-powered turbines</u> located <u>around the coast</u>. Like with wind power (p.29) the moving turbines are connected to a generator.

2) There is <u>no pollution</u>. The main problems are <u>disturbing the seabed</u> and the <u>habitats</u> of marine animals, <u>spoiling the view</u> and being a <u>hazard to boats</u>.

3) They are <u>fairly unreliable</u>, since waves tend to die out when the <u>wind drops</u>.

4) <u>Initial costs are high</u>, but there are <u>no fuel costs</u> and <u>minimal running costs</u>. Wave power is never likely to provide energy on a <u>large scale</u>, but it can be <u>very useful</u> on <u>small islands</u>.

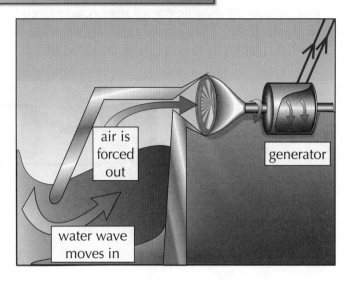

air is forced out

generator

water wave moves in

Tidal Barrages — Using the **Sun and Moon's Gravity**

1) <u>Tides</u> are used in lots of ways to generate <u>electricity</u>. The most <u>common</u> method is building a <u>tidal barrage</u>.

2) <u>Tidal barrages</u> are <u>big dams</u> built across <u>river estuaries</u>, with turbines in them. As the <u>tide comes in</u> it fills up the estuary. The water is then allowed out through turbines at a <u>controlled speed</u>.

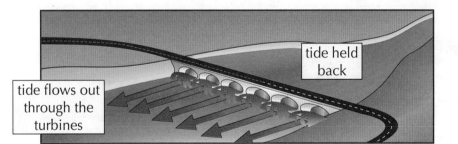

tide held back

tide flows out through the turbines

3) Tides are produced by the <u>gravitational pull</u> of the <u>Sun</u> and <u>Moon</u>.

4) There is <u>no pollution</u>. The main problems are <u>preventing free access by boats</u>, <u>spoiling the view</u> and <u>altering the habitat</u> of the wildlife, e.g. wading birds and sea creatures who live in the sand.

5) Tides are pretty <u>reliable</u> in the sense that they happen twice a day <u>without fail</u>, and always near to the predicted height. The only drawback is that the <u>height</u> of the tide is <u>variable</u> so lower (neap) tides will provide significantly <u>less energy</u> than the bigger (spring) tides. They also don't work when the water level is the same either side of the barrage — this happens four times a day because of the tides.

6) <u>Initial costs</u> are <u>moderately high</u>, but there are <u>no fuel costs</u> and <u>minimal running costs</u>. Even though it can only be used in <u>some</u> of the most <u>suitable estuaries</u> tidal power has the potential for generating a <u>significant amount</u> of energy.

Wave and tidal — power from the motion of the ocean...

The first <u>large-scale tidal barrages</u> started being built in the <u>1960s</u>, so tidal power isn't a new thing. <u>Wave power</u> is still pretty experimental though. Make sure you know the differences in how they work.

Bio-fuels

And the <u>energy resources</u> just keep on coming. It's over soon, I promise. Just a few more to go.

Bio-fuels are Made from **Plants** and **Waste**

<u>Bio-fuels</u> are <u>renewable energy resources</u> created from either plant products
or animal dung. They can be <u>solid</u>, <u>liquid</u> or <u>gas</u> and can be burnt to
produce <u>electricity</u> or run <u>cars</u> in the same way as <u>fossil fuels</u>.

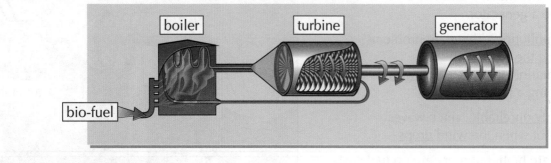

They have **Pros**...

1) They are supposedly <u>carbon neutral</u>, although there is some <u>debate</u> about this as it's
   only really true if you keep growing plants <u>at the rate</u> that you're burning things.

2) Bio-fuels are fairly <u>reliable</u>, as crops take a relatively <u>short time</u> to grow
   and different crops can be grown all year round. However, they cannot
   respond to <u>immediate energy demands</u>. To combat this, bio-fuels are
   continuously produced and <u>stored</u> for when they are needed.

... and **Cons**

1) The <u>cost</u> to refine <u>bio-fuels</u> so they are suitable for use is <u>very high</u>.

2) Some people worry that growing crops specifically for bio-fuels will mean there
   isn't enough <u>space</u> or <u>water</u> to meet the demands for crops that are grown for <u>food</u>.

3) In some regions, large areas of <u>forest</u> have been <u>cleared</u> to make room to grow
   <u>bio-fuels</u>, resulting in lots of species losing their <u>natural habitats</u>. The <u>decay</u> and
   <u>burning</u> of this vegetation also increases <u>carbon dioxide</u> (<u>CO_2</u>) and <u>methane</u> emissions.

In theory, bio-fuels are carbon neutral...

Stuff you've learnt in <u>biology</u> may help you get your head around this one.   When plants grow,
they <u>absorb</u> CO_2 from the atmosphere for <u>photosynthesis</u>, but when you <u>burn bio-fuels</u>, you
<u>release</u> CO_2 into the atmosphere. A bio-fuel is '<u>carbon neutral</u>' if the amount of CO_2 released by
burning it is <u>equal</u> to the amount absorbed by the plants you grow to make the bio-fuel.

Non-Renewable Resources

Renewable resources may sound like great news for the environment. But when it comes down to it, they don't currently meet all our needs so we still need those nasty, polluting non-renewables.

Non-Renewables are Reliable...

1) Fossil fuels and nuclear energy are reliable. There's enough fossil and nuclear fuels to meet current demand, and they are extracted from the Earth at a fast enough rate that power plants always have fuel in stock. This means that the power plants can respond quickly to changes in demand (p.52).

Nuclear power plants use nuclear fission to produce electricity.

2) However, these fuels are slowly running out. If no new resources are found, some fossil fuel stocks may run out within a hundred years.

3) While the set-up costs of power plants can be quite high compared to some other energy resources, the running costs aren't that expensive. Combined with fairly low fuel extraction costs, using fossil fuels is a cost effective way to produce energy (which is why it's so popular).

...But Create Environmental Problems

1) Coal, oil and gas release carbon dioxide (CO_2) into the atmosphere when they're burned. All this CO_2 adds to the greenhouse effect, and contributes to global warming.

2) Burning coal and oil also releases sulfur dioxide, which causes acid rain — which can be harmful to trees and soils and can have far-reaching effects in ecosystems.

3) Acid rain can be reduced by taking the sulfur out before the fuel is burned, or cleaning up the emissions.

4) Views can be spoilt by fossil fuel power plants, and coal mining makes a mess of the landscape, especially "open-cast mining".

5) Oil spillages cause serious environmental problems, affecting mammals and birds that live in and around the sea. We try to avoid them, but they'll always happen.

6) Nuclear power is clean but the nuclear waste is very dangerous and difficult to dispose of.

7) Nuclear fuel (e.g. uranium or plutonium) is relatively cheap but the overall cost of nuclear power is high due to the cost of the power plant and final decommissioning.

8) Nuclear power always carries the risk of a major catastrophe like the Fukushima disaster in Japan.

Currently we Depend on Fossil Fuels

1) Over the 20th century, the electricity use of the UK hugely increased as the population grew and people began to use electricity for more and more things.

2) Since the beginning of the 21st century, electricity use in the UK has been decreasing (slowly), as we get better at making appliances more efficient (p.26) and become more careful with energy use in our homes.

3) Most of our electricity is produced using fossil fuels (mostly coal and gas) and from nuclear power.

4) Generating electricity isn't the only reason we burn fossil fuels — oil (diesel and petrol) is used to fuel cars, and gas is used to heat homes and cook food.

Trends in Energy Resource Use

Non-renewables may be what we rely on for the vast majority of our energy needs at the moment.
But the balance may soon start shifting...

The Aim is to **Increase Renewable Energy** Use

We are trying to increase our use of renewable energy resources (the UK aims to
use renewable resources to provide 15% of its total yearly energy by 2020).
This move towards renewable energy resources has been triggered by many things:

1) We now know that burning fossil fuels is very damaging to the environment (see last page). This
   makes many people want to use more renewable energy resources that affect the environment less.

2) People and governments are also becoming increasingly aware that
   non-renewables will run out one day. Many people think it's better
   to learn to get by without non-renewables before this happens.

3) Pressure from other countries and the public has meant that governments have begun to introduce
   targets for using renewable resources. This in turn puts pressure on energy providers to build new
   power plants that use renewable resources to make sure they do not lose business and money.

4) Car companies have also been affected by this change in attitude towards the
   environment. Electric cars and hybrids (cars powered by two fuels, e.g. petrol
   and electricity) are already on the market and their popularity is increasing.

It's **Not** That **Straightforward** Though

The use of renewables is limited by reliability, money and politics.

1) There's lots of scientific evidence supporting renewables, but although scientists can give advice,
   they don't have the power to make people, companies or governments change their behaviour.

2) Building new renewable power plants costs money, so some energy providers are reluctant to do this,
   especially when fossil fuels are so cost effective. The cost of switching to renewable power will have
   to be paid, either by customers in their bills, or through government and taxes. Some people don't
   want to or can't afford to pay, and there are arguments about whether it's ethical to make them.

3) Even if new power plants are built, there are arguments over where to put them. E.g. many people
   don't want to live next to a wind farm, causing protests. There are arguments over whether it's ethical
   to make people put up with wind farms built next to them when they may not agree with them.

4) Some energy resources like wind power are not as reliable as traditional fossil fuels, whilst others
   cannot increase their power output on demand. This would mean either having to use a combination
   of different power plants (which would be expensive) or researching ways to improve reliability.

5) Research on improving the reliability and cost of renewables takes time and money — it may be years
   before improvements are made, even with funding. Until then, we need non-renewable power.

6) Making personal changes can also be quite expensive. Hybrid cars are generally more expensive
   than equivalent petrol cars and things like solar panels for your home are still quite pricey.
   The cost of these things is slowly going down, but they are still not an option for many people.

Warm-Up & Exam Questions

This is the last set of warm-up and exam questions on Topic 1. They're not *too* horrendous, I promise.

Warm-Up Questions

1) Name three non-renewable energy resources.
2) Give one advantage and one disadvantage associated with the reliability of renewable resources.
3) Describe one way that renewable energy resources can be used to power vehicles.
4) Give two ways in which using coal as an energy resource causes environmental problems.
5) Suggest two reasons why we can't just stop using fossil fuels immediately.

Exam Questions

1 The inhabitants of a remote island do not have the resources or expertise to build a nuclear power plant. They have no access to fossil fuels. **(Grade 4-6)**

1.1 The islanders have considered using wind, solar and hydro-electric power to generate electricity. Suggest **two** other renewable energy resources they could use.

[2 marks]

1.2 The islanders decide that hydro-electric power could reliably generate enough electricity for all their needs, but they are concerned about the environmental impact. Give **one** environmental impact of using hydro-electric power to generate electricity.

[1 mark]

2 In the hydro-electric power station in **Figure 1**, water is held back behind a dam before being allowed to flow out through turbines. **(Grade 4-6)**

Figure 1

2.1 Describe the transfer between energy stores of the water which occurs during this process.

[2 marks]

2.2 The tides can also be used to generate electricity using tidal barrages. Give **two** environmental advantages of generating electricity using tidal barrages.

[2 marks]

3 A family want to install solar panels on their roof. They have 10 m² of space on their roof for the solar panels. They use 32 500 000 J of energy per day. A 1 m² solar panel has an output of 200 W in good sunlight. **(Grade 6-7)**

3.1 Calculate the minimum number of 1 m² solar panels required to cover the family's daily energy use, assuming there are 5 hours of good sunlight in a day.

[5 marks]

3.2 Determine, using your answer from **3.1**, whether the family can install enough solar panels to provide all of the energy they use, assuming there are 5 hours of good sunlight every day.

[1 mark]

3.3 In reality, the number of hours of good sunlight in a day varies based on the weather and time of year. Discuss the reliability of energy from solar panels compared to from a local coal-fired power station.

[3 marks]

Revision Summary for Topic 1

Well, that's that for <u>Topic 1</u> — this is when you find out <u>how much of it went in</u>.
*   Try these questions and <u>tick off each one</u> when you <u>get it right</u>.
*   When you've done <u>all the questions</u> under a heading and are <u>completely happy</u> with it, tick it off.

Energy Stores and Systems (p.17-19) ☑
1) Write down four energy stores. ☑
2) What is a system? ☑
3) Describe the energy transfers that occur when a car collides with a stationary object. ☑
4) If energy is transferred to an object's kinetic energy store, what happens to its speed? ☑
5) Give the equation for finding the energy in an object's gravitational potential energy store. ☑
6) What kind of energy store is energy transferred to when you compress a spring? ☑
7) Which does the variable 'e' stand for in the equation for energy in an elastic potential energy store? ☑

Specific Heat Capacity (p.20-21) ☑
8) What is the definition of the specific heat capacity of a material? ☑
9) Suggest why a material with a high specific heat capacity is better suited
    for use in a heating system than a material with a low specific heat capacity. ☑
10) Describe an experiment to find the specific heat capacity of a material. ☑

Conservation of Energy and Power (p.23) ☑
11) True of false? Energy can be destroyed. ☑
12) Give two equations to calculate power. ☑
13) How much energy is transferred each second to a 50 W device? ☑

Reducing Unwanted Energy Transfers and Improving Efficiency (p.24-26) ☑
14) True or false? A high thermal conductivity means there is a high rate of energy transfer. ☑
15) How can you reduce unwanted energy transfers in a machine with moving components? ☑
16) Give four ways to prevent unwanted energy transfers in a home. ☑
17) True or false? Thicker walls make a house cool down quicker. ☑
18) What is the efficiency of an energy transfer? Give the equation that relates efficiency to power. ☑

Energy Resources and Trends in their Use (p.28-34) ☑
19) Name four renewable energy resources. ☑
20) What is the difference between renewable and non-renewable energy resources? ☑
21) Give an example of how a renewable energy resource is used in everyday life. ☑
22) Explain why solar power is considered to be a fairly reliable energy resource. ☑
23) Give one environmental impact of using wave power to generate electricity. ☑
24) Describe how you can reduce the acid rain caused by burning coal and oil. ☑
25) Give one environmental benefit of using nuclear power. ☑
26) Explain why the UK plans to use more renewable energy resources in the future. ☑

Current and Circuit Symbols

Isn't <u>electricity</u> great? Mind you it's pretty bad news if the <u>words</u> don't mean anything to you...

Current is the flow of Electric Charge

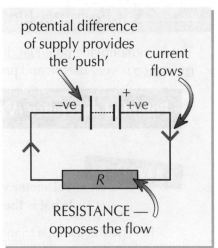

potential difference
of supply provides
the 'push'   current
flows

−ve   +ve

R

RESISTANCE —
opposes the flow

1) <u>Electric current</u> is the <u>flow</u> of electric charge round the circuit.
   Current will <u>only flow</u> around a complete (closed) circuit if there's
   a <u>potential difference</u>. So a current can only flow if there's a
   source of potential difference. Unit of current: <u>ampere, A</u>.

2) In a <u>single</u>, closed <u>loop</u> (like the one on the right) the current
   has the same value <u>everywhere</u> in the circuit (see p.45).

3) <u>Potential difference</u> (or voltage) is the <u>driving force</u> that <u>pushes</u>
   the charge round. Unit of potential difference: <u>volt, V</u>.

4) <u>Resistance</u> is anything in the circuit which
   <u>slows the flow down</u>. Unit of resistance: <u>ohm, Ω</u>.

5) The current flowing <u>through a component</u> depends on the <u>potential</u>
   <u>difference</u> across it and the <u>resistance</u> of the component (see next page).

> The <u>greater the resistance</u> across a component, the <u>smaller the current</u> that
> flows through it (for a given potential difference across the component).

Total Charge Through a Circuit Depends on Current and Time

1) The <u>size</u> of the <u>current</u> is the <u>rate of flow</u> of charge. When <u>current</u> (I) flows past a point in a circuit
   for a length of <u>time</u> (t) then the <u>charge</u> (Q) that has passed is given by this formula:

Charge (C) = Current (A) × Time (s)

$$Q = It$$

2) <u>Current</u> is measured in <u>amperes</u> (A),
   <u>charge</u> is measured in <u>coulombs</u> (C),
   <u>time</u> is measured in <u>seconds</u> (s).

3) <u>More charge</u> passes around the
   circuit when a <u>bigger current</u> flows.

 EXAMPLE:

**A battery charger passes a current of 2.0 A
through a cell over a period of 2.5 hours.
How much charge is transferred to the cell?**

$Q = It = 2.0 × (2.5 × 60 × 60) = 18\ 000$ C

Learn these Circuit Diagram Symbols

You need to be able to <u>understand circuit diagrams</u> and draw them using the <u>correct symbols</u>. Make sure all
the <u>wires</u> in your circuit are <u>straight lines</u> and that the circuit is <u>closed</u>, i.e. you can follow a wire from one
end of the power supply, through any components, to the other end of the supply (ignoring any <u>switches</u>).

Cell	Battery	Switch open	Switch closed	Filament lamp (or bulb)	Fuse	LED
+	+					
Resistor	Variable resistor	Ammeter	Voltmeter	Diode	LDR	Thermistor
		A	V			

Resistance

Prepare yourself to meet one of the most <u>important equations</u> in electronics. It's all about <u>resistance</u>, <u>current</u> and <u>potential difference</u>... Now if that doesn't tempt you on to read this page, I don't know what will.

There's a Formula Linking **Potential Difference** and **Resistance**

The formula linking <u>potential difference</u>, <u>current</u> and <u>resistance</u> is very useful (and pretty common):

You may see potential difference called voltage.

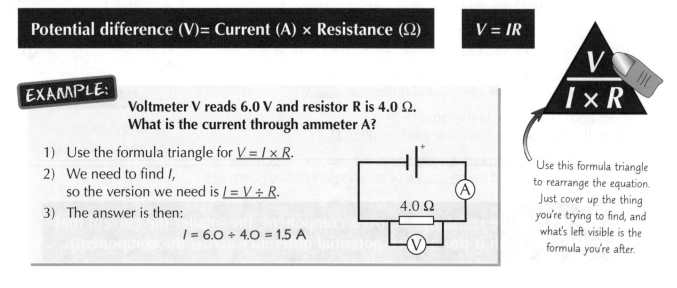

| Potential difference (V)= Current (A) × Resistance (Ω) | $V = IR$ |

EXAMPLE:

Voltmeter V reads 6.0 V and resistor R is 4.0 Ω. What is the current through ammeter A?

1) Use the formula triangle for $\underline{V = I \times R}$.

2) We need to find I, so the version we need is $\underline{I = V \div R}$.

3) The answer is then:

$$I = 6.0 \div 4.0 = 1.5 \text{ A}$$

4.0 Ω

Use this formula triangle to rearrange the equation. Just cover up the thing you're trying to find, and what's left visible is the formula you're after.

Ohmic Conductors Have a Constant Resistance

For some components, as the <u>current</u> through them is changed, the <u>resistance</u> of the component changes as well.

1) The <u>resistance</u> of <u>ohmic conductors</u> (e.g. a <u>wire</u> or a <u>resistor</u>) doesn't change with the <u>current</u>. At a <u>constant temperature</u>, the current flowing through an ohmic conductor is <u>directly proportional</u> to the potential difference across it. (R is constant in $V = IR$.)

2) The resistance of some resistors and components does change, e.g. a <u>filament lamp</u> or a <u>diode</u>.

3) When an <u>electrical charge</u> flows through a filament lamp, it <u>transfers</u> some energy to the <u>thermal energy store</u> of the filament (p.17), which is designed to <u>heat up</u>. Resistance increases with <u>temperature</u>, so as the <u>current</u> increases, the filament lamp heats up more and the resistance increases.

4) For <u>diodes</u>, the resistance depends on the <u>direction</u> of the current. They will happily let current flow in one direction, but have a <u>very high resistance</u> if it is <u>reversed</u>.

Resistance can be temperamental when it comes to temperature...

Remember that <u>ohmic conductors</u> will only have a <u>constant resistance</u> at a <u>constant temperature</u>. In general, <u>resistance increases with temperature</u> (though there are some exceptions, like thermistors — see p.42). So if the temperature is changing, the resistance of your component will be changing too.

Investigating Resistance PRACTICAL

Resistance can depend on a number of factors. Here's an experiment you can do to investigate one of them — how the resistance varies with the length of the conductor.

You Can Investigate the Factors Affecting Resistance

The resistance of a circuit can depend on a number of factors, like whether components are in series or parallel, p.47, or the length of wire used in the circuit. You can investigate the effect of wire length using the circuit below.

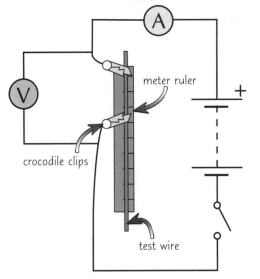

The Ammeter

1) Measures the current (in amps) flowing through the test wire.

2) The ammeter must always be placed in series with whatever you're investigating.

The Voltmeter

1) Measures the potential difference (or pd) across the test wire (in volts).

2) The voltmeter must always be placed in parallel around whatever you're investigating (p.46) — NOT around any other bit of the circuit, e.g. the battery.

See pages 44-46 for more on series and parallel circuits.

Method

1) Attach a crocodile clip to the wire level with 0 cm on the ruler.

2) Attach the second crocodile clip to the wire, e.g. 10 cm away from the first clip. Write down the length of the wire between the clips.

A thin wire will give you the best results. Make sure it's as straight as possible so your length measurements are accurate.

3) Close the switch, then record the current through the wire and the pd across it.

4) Open the switch, then move the second crocodile clip, e.g. another 10 cm, along the wire. Close the switch again, then record the new length, current and pd.

The wire may heat up during the experiment, which will affect its resistance (p.38). Leave the switch open for a bit between readings to let the circuit cool down.

5) Repeat this for a number of different lengths of the test wire.

6) Use your measurements of current and pd to calculate the resistance for each length of wire, using $R = V \div I$ (from $V = IR$).

7) Plot a graph of resistance against wire length and draw a line of best fit.

8) Your graph should be a straight line through the origin, meaning resistance is directly proportional to length — the longer the wire, the greater the resistance.

9) If your graph doesn't go through the origin, it could be because the first clip isn't attached exactly at 0 cm, so all of your length readings are a bit out. This is a systematic error (p.7).

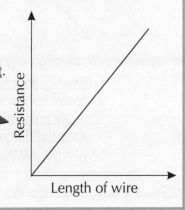

Be careful with the temperature of the wire...

If a large current flows through a wire, it can cause it to heat up (there's more on this on page 38). So use a low pd to stop it getting too hot and turn off the circuit between readings to let it cool.

PRACTICAL
I-V Characteristics

You've met <u>ohmic conductors</u> already on page 38, but most circuit components <u>aren't</u> ohmic.
You can see how circuit components behave by plotting an <u>*I-V* characteristic</u>.

Three Very Important *I-V* Characteristics

1) The term '<u>*I-V* characteristic</u>' refers to a <u>graph</u> which shows how the <u>current</u> (*I*) flowing through a component changes as the <u>potential difference</u> (*V*) across it is increased.

2) <u>Linear</u> components (e.g. an ohmic conductor) have an *I-V* characteristic that's a <u>straight line</u>.

3) <u>Non-linear</u> components (e.g. a filament lamp or a diode) have a <u>curved</u> *I-V* characteristic.

You can do this <u>experiment</u> to find a component's *I-V* characteristic:

Method

1) Set up the <u>test circuit</u> shown on the right.

2) Begin to vary the variable resistor. This alters the <u>current</u> flowing through the circuit and the <u>potential difference</u> across the <u>component</u>.

3) Take several <u>pairs of readings</u> from the <u>ammeter</u> and <u>voltmeter</u> to see how the <u>potential difference</u> across the component <u>varies</u> as the <u>current changes</u>. Repeat each reading twice more to get an <u>average</u> pd at each current.

4) <u>Swap</u> over the wires connected to the cell, so the <u>direction of the current</u> is reversed.

5) <u>Plot a graph</u> of <u>current against voltage</u> for the component.

This type of circuit uses direct current (dc) (p.49) and is a series circuit (p.44).

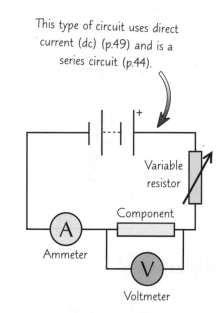

Variable resistor

Component

A
Ammeter

V
Voltmeter

The *I-V* characteristics you get for an <u>ohmic conductor</u>, <u>filament lamp</u> and <u>diode</u> should look like this:

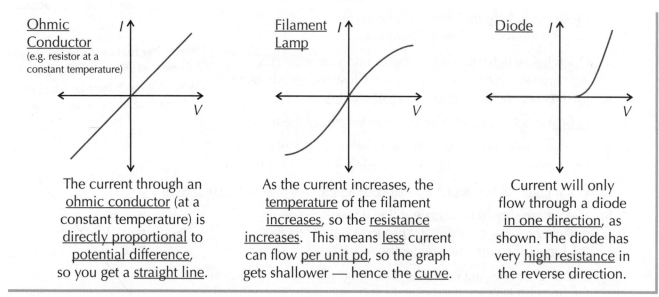

Ohmic Conductor
(e.g. resistor at a constant temperature)

Filament Lamp

Diode

The current through an <u>ohmic conductor</u> (at a constant temperature) is <u>directly proportional</u> to <u>potential difference</u>, so you get a <u>straight line</u>.

As the current increases, the <u>temperature</u> of the filament <u>increases</u>, so the <u>resistance</u> <u>increases</u>. This means <u>less</u> current can flow <u>per unit pd</u>, so the graph gets shallower — hence the <u>curve</u>.

Current will only flow through a diode <u>in one direction</u>, as shown. The diode has very <u>high resistance</u> in the reverse direction.

Since *V = IR*, you can calculate the <u>resistance</u> at any <u>point</u> on the *I-V* characteristic by calculating <u>*R = V ÷ I*</u>.

EXAM TIP
You may be asked to interpret an *I-V* characteristic...
Make sure you take care when reading values off the graph. Pay close attention to the <u>axes</u>, and make sure you've converted all values to the <u>correct units</u> before you do any calculations.

Warm-Up & Exam Questions

Phew — circuits aren't the easiest thing in the world, are they? Make sure you've understood the last few pages by trying these questions. If you get stuck, just go back and re-read the relevant page.

Warm-Up Questions

1) What are the units of resistance?
2) How does current through a component vary with resistance for a fixed potential difference?
3) Draw the symbol for a light-emitting diode (LED).
4) Give an example of an ohmic conductor.
5) How should a voltmeter be connected in a circuit to measure the pd across a component?
6) What is an *I-V* characteristic?

Exam Questions

1   **Figure 1** shows is a circuit diagram for a standard test circuit. When the switch is closed, the ammeter reads 0.30 A and the voltmeter reads 1.5 V. *(Grade 6-7)*

Figure 1

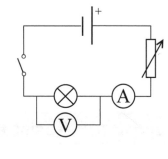

1.1   Calculate the resistance of the filament lamp.

[3 marks]

1.2   The switch is closed for 35 seconds.
      Calculate the total charge that flows through the filament lamp.

[2 marks]

1.3   The variable resistor is used to increase the resistance in the circuit.
      Describe how this will affect the current flowing through the circuit.

[1 mark]

Figure 2

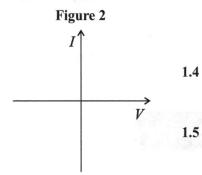

The resistance of a filament lamp changes with temperature.

1.4   On **Figure 2**, sketch the potential difference-current graph for a filament lamp.

[1 mark]

1.5   State what happens to the resistance of the filament lamp as the temperature of the filament increases.

[1 mark]

PRACTICAL

2   A student carried out an experiment using a standard test circuit where she varied the current and monitored what happened to the potential difference across a diode. **Figure 3** shows a graph of her results. *(Grade 6-7)*

Figure 3

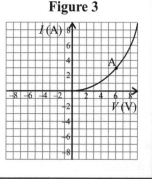

2.1   State the dependent variable in this experiment.

[1 mark]

2.2   Explain why the graph in **Figure 3** shows zero current for negative pds.

[1 mark]

2.3   Calculate the resistance of the diode at the point marked A.

[4 marks]

Circuit Devices

You might consider yourself a bit of an expert in <u>circuit components</u> — you're enlightened about bulbs, you're switched on to switches... Just make sure you know these ones as well — they're a bit trickier.

A **Light-Dependent Resistor** or **"LDR"**

This is the circuit symbol for a light-dependent resistor.

1) An LDR is a resistor that is <u>dependent</u> on the <u>intensity</u> of <u>light</u>. In <u>bright light</u>, the resistance <u>falls</u>.

2) In <u>darkness</u>, the resistance is <u>highest</u>.

3) They have lots of applications including <u>automatic night lights</u>, outdoor lighting and <u>burglar detectors</u>.

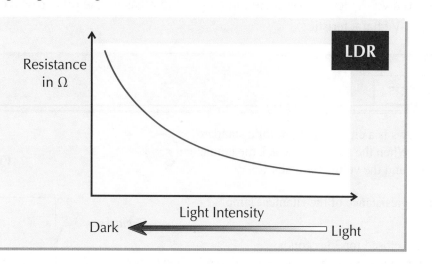

Thermistor Resistance **Decreases** as **Temperature Increases**

1) A <u>thermistor</u> is a <u>temperature dependent</u> resistor.

2) In <u>hot</u> conditions, the resistance <u>drops</u>.

3) In <u>cool</u> conditions, the resistance goes <u>up</u>.

4) Thermistors make useful <u>temperature detectors</u>, e.g. <u>car engine</u> temperature sensors and electronic <u>thermostats</u>.

This is the circuit symbol for a thermistor.

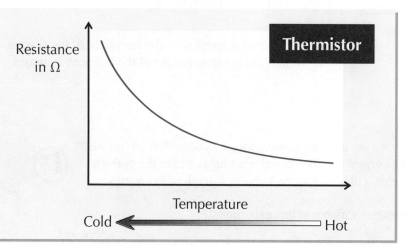

Thermistors and LDRs have many applications...

And they're not just limited to the examples on this page. Oh no. For example, LDRs are used in <u>digital cameras</u> to control how long the <u>shutter</u> should stay open for. If the <u>light level</u> is <u>low</u>, changes in the <u>resistance</u> cause the shutter to <u>stay open for longer</u> than if the light level was higher. How interesting.

Sensing Circuits

Now you've learnt about what <u>LDRs</u> and <u>thermistors</u> do, it's time to take a look at how they're put to use.

You Can Use LDRs and Thermistors in **Sensing Circuits**

<u>Sensing circuits</u> can be used to turn on or <u>increase the power</u> to components depending on the conditions that they are in.

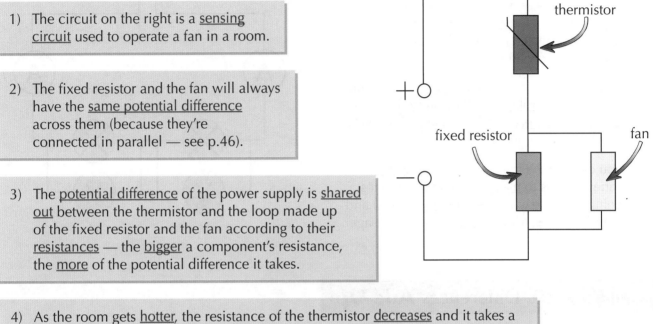

1) The circuit on the right is a <u>sensing circuit</u> used to operate a fan in a room.

2) The fixed resistor and the fan will always have the <u>same potential difference</u> across them (because they're connected in parallel — see p.46).

3) The <u>potential difference</u> of the power supply is <u>shared out</u> between the thermistor and the loop made up of the fixed resistor and the fan according to their <u>resistances</u> — the <u>bigger</u> a component's resistance, the <u>more</u> of the potential difference it takes.

4) As the room gets <u>hotter</u>, the resistance of the thermistor <u>decreases</u> and it takes a <u>smaller share</u> of the potential difference from the power supply. So the potential difference across the fixed resistor and the fan <u>rises</u>, making the fan go faster.

You can Connect the **Component Across** the **Variable Resistor**

1) You can connect the component <u>across</u> the <u>variable resistor</u> instead of across the fixed resistor.

2) For example, if you connect a <u>bulb</u> in parallel to an <u>LDR</u>, the <u>potential difference</u> across both the LDR and the bulb will be <u>high</u> when it's <u>dark</u> and the LDR's resistance is <u>high</u>.

3) The <u>greater the potential difference</u> across a component, the <u>more energy</u> it gets.

4) So a <u>bulb</u> connected <u>across an LDR</u> would get <u>brighter</u> as the room got <u>darker</u>.

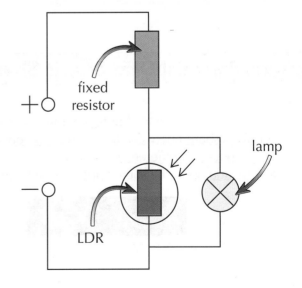

Sensing circuits react to changes in the surroundings...

<u>Sensing circuits</u> are a useful <u>application</u> of <u>thermistors</u> and <u>LDRs</u>, but they can be tricky to make sense of. They rely on the properties of <u>series</u> and <u>parallel circuits</u> — <u>read on</u> to learn all about them.

Series Circuits

You need to be able to tell the if components are connected in series or parallel <u>just by looking at circuit diagrams</u>. You also need to know the <u>rules</u> about what happens with both types. Read on to find out more.

Series Circuits — **All** or **Nothing**

1) In <u>series circuits</u>, the different components are connected <u>in a line</u>, <u>end to end</u>, between the +ve and –ve of the power supply (except for <u>voltmeters</u>, which are always connected <u>in parallel</u>, but they don't count as part of the circuit).

2) If you remove or disconnect <u>one</u> component, the circuit is <u>broken</u> and they all <u>stop</u>. This is generally <u>not very handy</u>, and in practice <u>very few things</u> are connected in series.

3) You can use the following rules to <u>design</u> series circuits to <u>measure quantities</u> and test components (e.g. the <u>test circuits</u> on p.40 and p.47 and the <u>sensing circuits</u> on the last page).

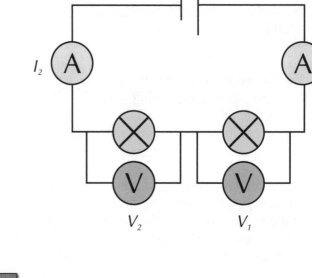

Cell Potential Differences **Add Up**

1) There is a bigger potential difference when more cells are in series, provided the cells are all <u>connected</u> the <u>same way</u>.

2) For example when two batteries of voltage 1.5 V are <u>connected in series</u> they supply a <u>total</u> of 3 V.

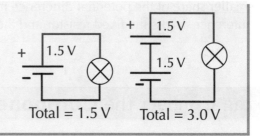

Total Potential Difference is **Shared**

In series circuits the <u>total potential difference</u> of the <u>supply</u> is <u>shared</u> between the various <u>components</u>. So the <u>potential differences</u> round a series circuit <u>always add up</u> to the <u>source potential difference</u>:

$$V_{total} = V_1 + V_2 + ...$$

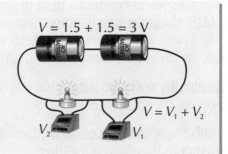

$V = 1.5 + 1.5 = 3\ V$

$V = V_1 + V_2$

There are two main types of circuit — series and parallel...

Remember, <u>ammeters</u> should always be <u>connected in series</u>, and <u>voltmeters</u> should always be <u>connected in parallel</u>. These components don't count towards how you define a circuit — you can have a <u>parallel circuit</u> (p.46) with <u>ammeters</u> connected in <u>series</u>, or a <u>series circuit</u> with <u>voltmeters</u> connected <u>across</u> components.

Series Circuits

We're not done with <u>series circuits</u> yet. Here's the low-down on <u>current</u> and <u>resistance</u>...

Current is the **Same Everywhere**

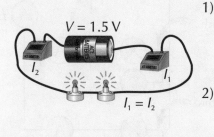

1) In series circuits the <u>same current</u> flows through <u>all components</u>, i.e:

$$I_1 = I_2 = \dots$$

2) The <u>size</u> of the current is determined by the <u>total potential difference</u> of the cells and the <u>total resistance</u> of the circuit: i.e. <u>$I = V \div R$</u>.

Resistance **Adds Up**

1) In series circuits the <u>total resistance</u> of two components is just the <u>sum</u> of their resistances:

$$R_{total} = R_1 + R_2$$

2) This is because by <u>adding a resistor</u> in series, the two resistors have to <u>share</u> the total potential difference.

6 V

A

6 Ω   3 Ω

A

Total resistance = 6 + 3 = 9 Ω

3) The potential difference across each resistor is <u>lower</u>, so the <u>current</u> through each resistor is also lower. In a series circuit, the current is the <u>same everywhere</u> so the total current in the circuit is <u>reduced</u> when a resistor is added. This means the total <u>resistance</u> of the circuit <u>increases</u>.

4) The <u>bigger</u> a component's <u>resistance</u>, the bigger its <u>share</u> of the <u>total potential difference</u>.

EXAMPLE:

For the circuit diagram on the right, calculate the current passing through the circuit.

2 Ω   3 Ω

20 V

1) First find the <u>total resistance</u> by <u>adding together</u> the resistance of the two resistors.

$R_{total} = 2 + 3 = 5\ \Omega$

2) Then <u>rearrange</u> $V = IR$ and <u>substitute</u> in the values you have.

$I = V \div R$
$= 20 \div 5$
$= 4\ A$

Series circuits aren't used very much in the real world...

Since series circuits put <u>all</u> components on the <u>same loop of wire</u>, and the current is the same through each component, if one <u>component breaks</u>, it'll <u>break the circuit</u>, and all other components will <u>stop working</u> too. Parallel circuits are much more useful and can avoid this problem — as you're about to find out...

Parallel Circuits

Parallel circuits can be a little bit trickier to wrap your head around, but they're much more <u>useful</u> than series circuits. Most electronics use a combination of series and parallel circuitry.

Parallel Circuits — Independence and Isolation

1) In <u>parallel circuits</u>, each component is <u>separately</u> connected to the +ve and –ve of the <u>supply</u> (except ammeters, which are <u>always</u> connected in <u>series</u>).

2) If you remove or disconnect <u>one</u> of them, it will <u>hardly affect</u> the others at all.

3) This is <u>obviously</u> how <u>most</u> things must be connected, for example in <u>cars</u> and in <u>household electrics</u>. You have to be able to switch everything on and off <u>separately</u>.

4) Everyday circuits often include a <u>mixture</u> of series and parallel parts.

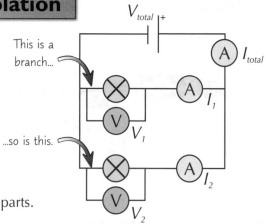

This is a branch...

...so is this.

Potential Difference is the **Same** Across All **Components**

1) In parallel circuits <u>all</u> components get the <u>full source pd</u>, so the voltage is the <u>same</u> across all components:

$$V_1 = V_2 = V_3 = \ldots$$

2) This means that <u>identical bulbs</u> connected in parallel will all be at the <u>same brightness</u>.

Current is **Shared** Between Branches

1) In parallel circuits the <u>total current</u> flowing around the circuit is equal to the <u>total</u> of all the currents through the <u>separate components</u>:

$$I_{total} = I_1 + I_2 + \ldots$$

2) In a parallel circuit, there are <u>junctions</u> where the current either <u>splits</u> or <u>rejoins</u>. The total current going <u>into</u> a junction has to equal the total current <u>leaving it</u>.

3) If two <u>identical components</u> are connected in parallel then the <u>same current</u> will flow through each component.

Adding a Resistor in Parallel **Reduces** the **Total Resistance**

1) If you have <u>two resistors in parallel</u>, their <u>total resistance</u> is <u>less than</u> the resistance of the <u>smallest</u> of the two resistors.

2) This can be tough to get your head around, but think about it like this:

- In <u>parallel</u>, both resistors have the <u>same potential difference</u> across them as the source.
- This means the 'pushing force' making the current flow is the <u>same</u> as the <u>source potential difference</u> for each resistor that you add.
- But by adding another loop, the <u>current</u> has <u>more</u> than one direction to go in.
- This increases the <u>total current</u> that can flow around the circuit. Using $V = IR$, an <u>increase in current</u> means a <u>decrease</u> in the <u>total resistance</u> of the circuit.

Circuits and Resistance

You saw on page 39 how the length of the wire used in a circuit affects its resistance. Now it's time to do an experiment to see how placing resistors in series or in parallel can affect the resistance of the whole circuit.

You Can **Investigate** Adding **Resistors** in **Series...**

1) First, you'll need to find at least four identical resistors.

2) Then build the circuit shown on the right using one of the resistors. Make a note of the potential difference of the battery (V).

3) Measure the current through the circuit using the ammeter. Use this to calculate the resistance of the circuit using $R = V \div I$.

4) Add another resistor, in series with the first.

5) Again, measure the current through the circuit and use this and the potential difference of the battery to calculate the overall resistance of the circuit.

6) Repeat steps 4 and 5 until you've added all of your resistors.

7) Plot a graph of the number of resistors against the total resistance of the circuit (see below).

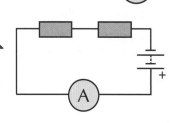

... or in **Parallel**

1) Using the same equipment as before (so the experiment is a fair test), build the same initial circuit.

2) Measure the total current through the circuit and calculate the resistance of the circuit using $R = V \div I$ (again, V is the potential difference of the battery).

3) Next, add another resistor, in parallel with the first.

4) Measure the total current through the circuit and use this and the potential difference of the battery to calculate the overall resistance of the circuit.

5) Repeat steps 3 and 4 until you've added all of your resistors.

6) Plot a graph of the number of resistors in the circuit against the total resistance.

Your Results Should **Match** the **Resistance Rules**

1) You should find that adding resistors in series increases the total resistance of the circuit (adding a resistor decreases the total current through the circuit).

2) The more resistors you add, the larger the resistance of the whole circuit.

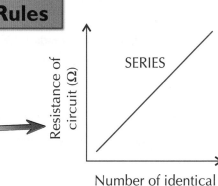

3) When you add resistors in parallel, the total current through the circuit increases — so the total resistance of the circuit has decreased.

4) The more resistors you add, the smaller the overall resistance becomes — as shown by the graph on the left.

5) These results agree with what you learnt about resistance in series and parallel circuits on pages 45 and 46.

Warm-Up & Exam Questions

Time to check and see what you can remember about those circuit devices, parallel and series circuits.

Warm-Up Questions

1) Give one use of a light-dependent resistor (LDR).
2) What happens to the resistance of a thermistor as its temperature increases?
3) Draw a circuit diagram of a sensing circuit where a bulb gets brighter with decreasing temperature.
4) Give one practical disadvantage of series circuits.
5) How do you work out the total resistance in a series circuit?
6) Which has the higher total resistance: two resistors in series, or the same two resistors in parallel?
7) Sketch a graph to show how the number of identical resistors connected together in parallel affects the total resistance in a circuit.

Exam Questions

1   **Figure 1** shows a series circuit.   Grade 4-6

Figure 1

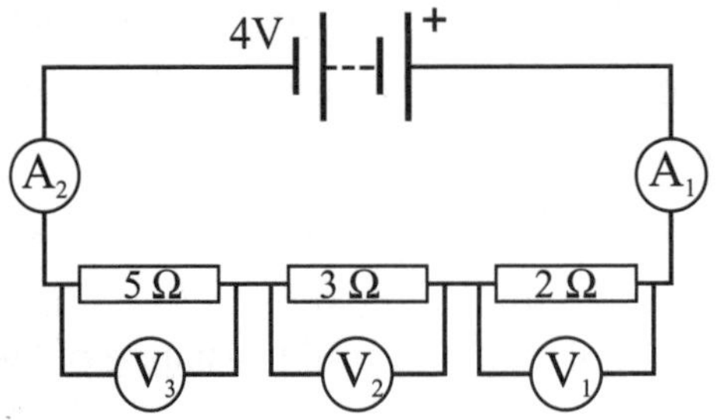

1.1   Calculate the total resistance in the circuit.

[2 marks]

1.2   The current through A_1 is 0.4 A.
What is the current through A_2? Explain your answer.

[2 marks]

1.3 V_1 reads 0.8 V and V_2 reads 1.2 V.
Calculate the reading on V_3.

[2 marks]

2   A parallel circuit is connected as shown in **Figure 2**.   Grade 7-9

Figure 2

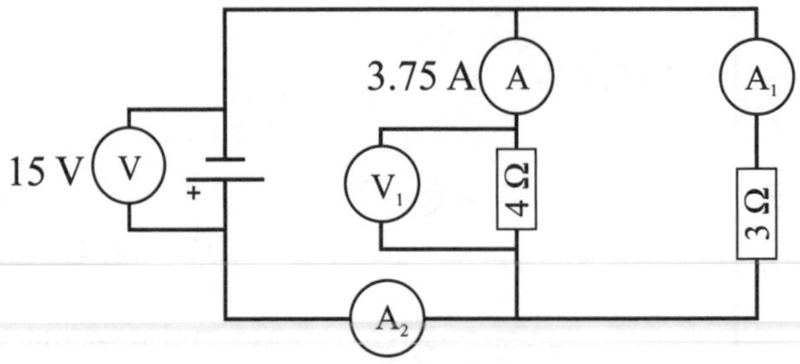

2.1   Give the reading on voltmeter V_1.

[1 mark]

2.2   Calculate the reading on ammeter A_1.

[3 marks]

2.3   Calculate the reading on ammeter A_2.

[2 marks]

Electricity in the Home

Now you've learnt the basics of <u>electrical circuits</u>, it's time to see how <u>electricity</u> is used in <u>everyday life</u>.

Mains Supply is ac, Battery Supply is dc

1) There are two types of electricity supplies — <u>alternating current</u> (ac) and <u>direct current</u> (dc).

2) In <u>ac supplies</u> the current is <u>constantly</u> changing direction. <u>Alternating currents</u> are produced by <u>alternating potential difference</u> in which the <u>positive</u> and <u>negative</u> ends keep <u>alternating</u>.

3) The <u>UK mains supply</u> (the electricity in your home) is an ac supply at around <u>230 V</u>.

4) The frequency of the ac mains supply is <u>50 cycles per second</u> or <u>50 Hz</u> (hertz).

5) By contrast, cells and batteries supply <u>direct current</u> (dc).

6) <u>Direct current</u> is a current that is always flowing in the <u>same direction</u>. It's created by a <u>direct potential difference</u>.

Most Cables Have Three Separate Wires

1) Most electrical appliances are connected to the mains supply by <u>three-core</u> cables. This means that they have <u>three wires</u> inside them, each with a <u>core of copper</u> and a <u>coloured plastic coating</u>.

2) The <u>colour</u> of the insulation on each cable shows its <u>purpose</u>.

3) The colours are <u>always</u> the <u>same</u> for <u>every</u> appliance. This is so that it is easy to tell the different wires <u>apart</u>.

4) You need to know the <u>colour</u> of each wire, what each of them is <u>for</u> and what their <u>pd</u> is.

<u>LIVE WIRE</u> — <u>brown</u>.
The live wire provides the <u>alternating potential difference</u> (at about <u>230 V</u>) from the mains supply

<u>NEUTRAL WIRE</u> — <u>blue</u>.
The neutral wire <u>completes</u> the circuit and carries away current — electricity normally flows <u>in</u> through the <u>live</u> wire and <u>out</u> through the <u>neutral</u> wire. It is around <u>0 V</u>.

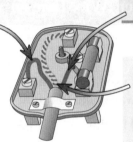

<u>EARTH WIRE</u> — <u>green</u> and <u>yellow</u>.
It is for protecting the wiring, and for safety — it stops the appliance casing from <u>becoming live</u>. It doesn't usually carry a current — only when there's a <u>fault</u>. It's <u>also</u> at 0 V.

Touching the Live Wire Gives You an Electric Shock

1) Your <u>body</u> (just like the earth) is at <u>0 V</u>.

2) This means that if you touch the <u>live wire</u>, a <u>large potential difference</u> is produced across your body and a <u>current</u> flows through you.

3) This causes a large <u>electric shock</u> which could injure or even kill you.

4) Even if a plug socket or a light switch is turned <u>off</u> (i.e. the switch is <u>open</u>) there is still a <u>danger</u> of an electric shock. A current <u>isn't flowing</u>, but there is still a pd in the live wire. If you made <u>contact</u> with the live wire, your body would provide a <u>link</u> between the supply and the earth, so a <u>current</u> would flow <u>through you</u>.

5) <u>Any</u> connection between <u>live</u> and <u>earth</u> can be <u>dangerous</u>. If the link creates a <u>low resistance</u> path to earth, a huge current will flow, which could result in a fire.

Power of Electrical Appliances

You can think about <u>electrical circuits</u> in terms of <u>energy transfer</u> — the charge carriers take energy around the circuit. When they go through an electrical component energy is transferred to make the component work.

Energy is Transferred from Cells and Other Sources

1) You know from page 17 that a moving charge <u>transfers energy</u>. This is because the charge <u>does work against</u> the <u>resistance</u> of the circuit. (Work done is the <u>same</u> as energy transferred, p.18.)

2) Electrical appliances are designed to <u>transfer energy</u> to components in the circuit when a <u>current</u> flows.

Kettles transfer energy <u>electrically</u> from the mains ac supply to the <u>thermal</u> energy store of the heating element inside the kettle. 	Energy is transferred <u>electrically</u> from the <u>battery</u> of a handheld fan to the <u>kinetic</u> energy store of the fan's motor.

3) Of course, <u>no</u> appliance transfers <u>all</u> energy completely usefully. The <u>higher</u> the <u>current</u>, the more energy is transferred to the <u>thermal</u> energy stores of the components (and then the surroundings). You can calculate the <u>efficiency</u> of any electrical appliance — see p.26.

Energy Transferred Depends on the Power

1) The <u>total</u> energy transferred by an appliance depends on <u>how long</u> the appliance is on for and its <u>power</u>.

2) The <u>power</u> of an appliance is the energy that it <u>transfers per second</u>. So the <u>more</u> energy it transfers in a given time, the <u>higher</u> its power.

3) The amount of <u>energy transferred by electrical work</u> is given by:

Energy transferred (J) = Power (W) × Time (s) $E = Pt$

This equation should be familiar from page 23.

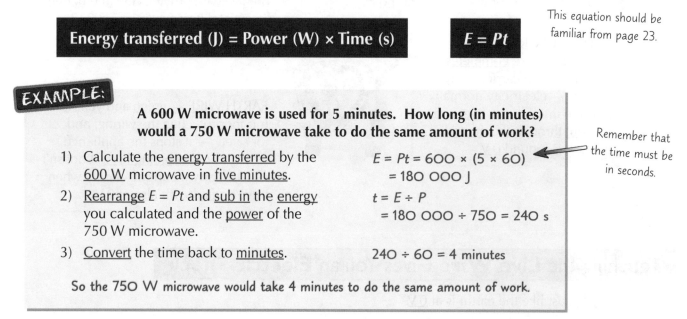

EXAMPLE:

A 600 W microwave is used for 5 minutes. How long (in minutes) would a 750 W microwave take to do the same amount of work?

1) Calculate the <u>energy transferred</u> by the 600 W microwave in <u>five minutes</u>.

$E = Pt = 600 × (5 × 60)$
$= 180\ 000\ J$

Remember that the time must be in seconds.

2) <u>Rearrange</u> $E = Pt$ and <u>sub in</u> the <u>energy</u> you calculated and the <u>power</u> of the 750 W microwave.

$t = E ÷ P$
$= 180\ 000 ÷ 750 = 240\ s$

3) <u>Convert</u> the time back to <u>minutes</u>.

$240 ÷ 60 = 4$ minutes

So the 750 W microwave would take 4 minutes to do the same amount of work.

4) Appliances are often given a <u>power rating</u> — they're labelled with the <u>maximum</u> safe power that they can operate at. You can usually take this to be their <u>maximum operating power</u>.

5) The power rating tells you the <u>maximum</u> amount of <u>energy</u> transferred between stores <u>per second</u> when the appliance is in use.

6) This helps customers choose between models — the <u>lower</u> the power rating, the <u>less</u> electricity an appliance uses in a given time and so the <u>cheaper</u> it is to run.

7) But a higher power <u>doesn't</u> necessarily mean that it transfers <u>more</u> energy <u>usefully</u>. An appliance may be <u>more powerful</u> than another, <u>but less efficient</u>, meaning that it might still only transfer the <u>same amount</u> of energy (or even <u>less</u>) to useful stores (see p.26).

More on Power

As you've seen, the power of a device tells you how much energy it transfers per second.
In electrical systems, there are a load of useful formulas you can use to calculate energy and power.

Potential Difference is **Energy Transferred** per **Charge Passed**

1) When an electrical charge goes through a change
   in potential difference, energy is transferred.

2) Energy is supplied to the charge at the power source
   to 'raise' it through a potential.

3) The charge gives up this energy when it 'falls' through any
   potential drop in components elsewhere in the circuit.

4) The formula is really simple:

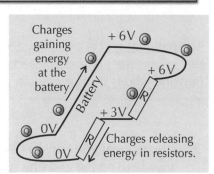

Charge flow (C)

Energy transferred (J) ——— $E = QV$ ——— Potential difference (V)

5) That means that a battery with a bigger pd will supply more energy to the circuit for every
   coulomb of charge which flows round it, because the charge is raised up "higher" at the start.

> **EXAMPLE:**
>
> **The motor in an electric toothbrush is attached to a 3 V battery.**
> **140 C of charge passes through the circuit as it is used.**
> **Calculate the energy transferred.**
>
> $E = QV = 140 \times 3 = 420$ J

This energy is transferred to the kinetic energy store of the motor, as well as to the thermal energy stores of the surroundings.

Power Also Depends on **Current** and **Potential Difference**

1) As well as energy transferred in a given time, the power of an appliance can be found with:

Power (W) = Potential difference (V) × Current (A) $P = VI$

> **EXAMPLE:** **A 1.0 kW hair dryer is connected to a 230 V supply. Calculate the**
> **current through the hair dryer. Give your answer to two significant figures.**
>
> 1) Rearrange the equation for current. $I = P \div V$
> 2) Make sure your units are correct.   1.0 kW = 1000 W
> 3) Then just stick in the numbers that you have. $I = 1000 \div 230 = 4.34... = 4.3$ A (to 2 s.f.)

2) You can also find the power if you don't know the potential difference.   Resistance (Ω)
   To do this, stick $V = IR$ from page 38 into $P = VI$, which gives you: ⟶ $P = I^2R$

Power is measured in watts, W — one W is equal to one J/s...

Remember, the power rating of an electrical appliance is the amount of energy transferred to the appliance
per second, not the amount that it transfers to useful energy stores. Two appliances with the same power
rating won't necessarily work as well as each other — it'll depend on their efficiencies (see page 26).

The National Grid

The <u>national grid</u> is a giant web of wires that covers <u>the whole of Britain</u>, getting electricity from power stations to homes everywhere. Whoever you pay for your electricity, it's the national grid that gets it to you.

Electricity is Distributed via the National Grid

1) The <u>national grid</u> is a giant system of <u>cables</u> and <u>transformers</u> that covers the UK and connects <u>power stations</u> to <u>consumers</u> (anyone who is using electricity).

2) The <u>national grid</u> transfers electrical power from <u>power stations</u> anywhere on the grid (the <u>supply</u>) to anywhere else on the grid where it's needed (the <u>demand</u>) — e.g. <u>homes</u> and <u>industry</u>.

Electricity Production has to Meet Demand

1) <u>Throughout the day</u>, electricity usage (the <u>demand</u>) changes. Power stations have to produce <u>enough</u> electricity for everyone to have it when they need it.

2) They can predict when the most electricity will be used though. Demand increases when people <u>get up</u> in the morning, <u>come home</u> from <u>school</u> or <u>work</u> and when it starts to get <u>dark</u> or <u>cold</u> outside. <u>Popular events</u> like a sporting final being shown on TV could also cause a peak in demand.

3) Power stations often run at well below their <u>maximum power output</u>, so there's <u>spare</u> capacity to cope with a <u>high demand</u>, even if there's an unexpected shut-down of another station.

4) Lots of <u>smaller</u> power stations that can start up quickly are also kept in standby just in case.

Energy demands are ever increasing...

The <u>national grid</u> has been working since the 1930s and has gone through <u>many changes</u> and <u>updates</u> since then to meet <u>increasing energy demands</u>. Using <u>energy-efficient appliances</u> and switching unneeded lights off are some ways we might ensure that <u>supply and demand</u> stay in balance. It'll do wonders for your electricity bills too, as I'm sure your parents often remind you.

The National Grid

To transfer electricity <u>efficiently</u>, the national grid makes use of some clever tech called <u>transformers</u>.

The National Grid Uses a **High pd** and a **Low Current**

1) To transmit the <u>huge</u> amount of <u>power</u> needed, you need either a <u>high potential difference</u> or a <u>high current</u> (as $P = VI$, page 51).

2) The <u>problem</u> with a <u>high current</u> is that you lose <u>loads of energy</u> as the wires <u>heat up</u> and energy is transferred to the <u>thermal</u> energy store of the <u>surroundings</u>.

Remember that power is the energy transferred in a given time, so a higher power means more energy transferred.

3) It's much <u>cheaper</u> to <u>boost the pd</u> up <u>really high</u> (to 400 000 V) and keep the current <u>relatively low</u>.

4) For a given <u>power</u>, increasing the pd <u>decreases</u> the <u>current</u>, which decreases the <u>energy lost</u> by heating the wires and the surroundings. This makes the national grid an <u>efficient</u> way of transferring energy.

Potential Difference is Changed by a **Transformer**

1) To get the potential difference to 400 000 V to transmit power requires <u>transformers</u> as well as <u>big pylons</u> with <u>huge insulators</u> — but it's <u>still cheaper</u>.

2) The transformers have to <u>step</u> the potential difference <u>up</u> at one end, for <u>efficient transmission</u>, and then bring it back down to <u>safe, usable levels</u> at the other end.

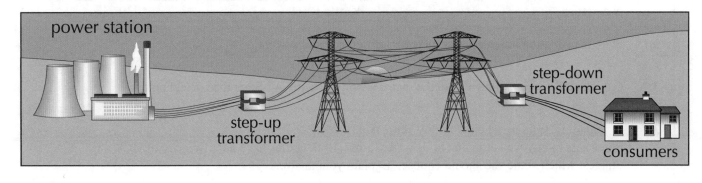

3) The <u>potential difference</u> is <u>increased</u> ('<u>stepped up</u>') using a <u>step-up transformer</u>.

4) It's then <u>reduced</u> again ('<u>stepped down</u>') for domestic use using a <u>step-down transformer</u>.

The national grid — it's a powerful thing...

The key to the <u>efficiency</u> of the <u>national grid</u> is the power equation, <u>$P = VI$</u> (see page 51). Since <u>power</u> is <u>proportional</u> to both <u>potential difference</u> and <u>current</u>, if you have a <u>constant</u> power, but <u>increase</u> the potential difference using a transformer, the current must <u>decrease</u>. And vice versa.

Warm-Up & Exam Questions

Who knew there was so much to learn about electricity in the home and across the country?
See if it's switched on a lightbulb in your brain by trying out these questions.

Warm-Up Questions

1) Name the three wires in a three-core cable that connect electrical appliances to the mains supply.
2) What is the main energy transfer when electric current flows through an electric kettle?
3) What is the equation linking power, current and resistance?
4) What is the national grid?

Exam Questions

1 Appliances with a metal casing are usually connected to the mains using a three-core cable. *(Grade 4-6)*

1.1 Mains electricity provides alternating current.
Define alternating current.

[1 mark]

1.2 An electrical cable has become frayed so that the metal part of the live wire is exposed.
Explain why you would get an electric shock if you touched it.

[3 marks]

2 The national grid transmits electricity from power stations to homes and businesses all over the country. *(Grade 6-7)*
Explain why the national grid uses step-up transformers.

[3 marks]

3 **Table 1** shows the power and potential difference ratings for two kettles. *(Grade 6-7)*

Table 1

	Power (kW)	Potential Difference (V)
Kettle A	2.8	230
Kettle B	3.0	230

3.1 State the equation linking power, potential difference and current.

[1 mark]

3.2 Calculate the current drawn from the mains supply by kettle A. State the correct unit.

[4 marks]

3.3 A student is deciding whether to buy kettle A or kettle B.
She wants to buy the kettle that boils water faster. Both kettles have an efficiency of 90%.
Suggest which kettle she should choose. Explain your answer.

[2 marks]

4 A current of 0.5 A passes through a torch bulb. The torch is powered by a 3.0 V battery. *(Grade 7-9)*

4.1 The torch is on for half an hour.
Calculate the amount of energy transferred from the battery in this time.

[4 marks]

4.2 Calculate how much charge passes through the torch in half an hour.

[3 marks]

Revision Summary for Topic 2

You've made it through <u>Topic 2</u> — time to put yourself through your paces and check it's all sunk in.
- Try these questions and <u>tick off each one</u> when you <u>get it right</u>.
- When you've done <u>all the questions</u> under a heading and are <u>completely happy</u> with it, tick it off.

Circuit Basics (p.37-40) ☑

1) Define current and state an equation that links current, charge and time, with units for each. ☑
2) What is meant by potential difference and resistance in a circuit? ☑
3) Draw the circuit symbols for: a cell, a lamp, a diode, a fuse and an LDR. ☑
4) What is the equation that links potential difference, current and resistance? ☑
5) What is an ohmic conductor? ☑
6) Explain how you would investigate how the length of a wire affects its resistance. ☑
7) Draw a circuit that could be used to investigate how the resistance of a filament bulb changes with the current through it. ☑
8) Name one linear component and one non-linear component. ☑

Circuit Devices and Types of Circuit (p.42-47) ☑

9) Explain how the resistance of an LDR varies with light intensity. ☑
10) What happens to the resistance of a thermistor as it gets colder? ☑
11) True or false? Potential difference is shared between components in a series circuit. ☑
12) True or false? The current is constant in a series circuit. ☑
13) True or false? The potential difference across each component connected in parallel is different. ☑
14) Explain why adding resistors in parallel decreases the total resistance of a circuit, but adding them in series increases the total resistance. ☑
15) Describe an experiment that could be carried out to investigate how adding resistors in series and parallel affects the total resistance of a circuit. ☑

Electricity in the Home (p.49-53) ☑

16) True or false? Mains supply electricity is an alternating current. ☑
17) What is the potential difference and the frequency of the UK mains supply? ☑
18) Name and give the colours of the three wires in a three-core cable. ☑
19) Give the potential differences for the three wires in a three-core mains cable. ☑
20) Explain why touching a live wire is dangerous. ☑
21) State three equations that can be used to calculate electrical power. ☑
22) What is the power rating of an appliance? ☑
23) Explain why electricity is transferred by the national grid at a high pd but low current. ☑
24) What are the functions of step-up and step-down transformers? ☑

Particle Model

The <u>particle model</u> is simpler than it sounds. It says that everything is made up of <u>lots of tiny particles</u> and describes how those particles behave in the three states of matter — <u>solids</u>, <u>liquids</u> and <u>gases</u>.

The **Particle Model** can Explain the **Three States of Matter**

1) In the <u>particle model</u>, you can think of the particles that make up matter as <u>tiny balls</u>. You can explain the ways that matter behaves in terms of how these tiny balls move, and the forces between them.

2) The <u>three states of matter</u> are <u>solid</u> (e.g. ice), <u>liquid</u> (e.g. water) and <u>gas</u> (e.g. water vapour). The <u>particles</u> of a substance in each state are the same — only the <u>arrangement</u> and <u>energy</u> of the particles are different.

Solids

1) <u>Strong forces</u> of attraction hold the particles <u>close together</u> in a <u>fixed</u>, <u>regular</u> arrangement.

2) The particles don't have much <u>energy</u> so they <u>can</u> only <u>vibrate</u> about their <u>fixed</u> positions.

3) The <u>density</u> is generally <u>highest</u> in this state as the particles are <u>closest together</u>.

Liquids

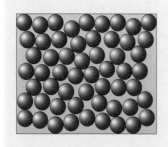

1) There are <u>weaker forces</u> of attraction between the particles.

2) The particles are <u>close together</u>, but can <u>move past each other</u>, and form <u>irregular</u> arrangements.

3) For any given substance, in the liquid state its particles will have <u>more energy</u> than in the solid state (but less energy than in the gas state).

4) They move in <u>random directions</u> at <u>low speeds</u>.

5) Liquids are generally <u>less dense</u> than solids.

Gases

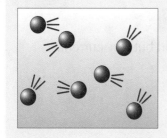

1) There are <u>almost no</u> forces of attraction between the particles.

2) For any given substance, in the gas state its particles will have <u>more energy</u> than in the solid state or the liquid state.

3) They are <u>free to move</u>, and travel in <u>random directions</u> and at <u>high speeds</u>.

4) Gases have <u>low</u> densities.

REVISION TIP

The higher their kinetic energy, the faster particles move...

Learn those diagrams above and make sure that you can describe the <u>arrangement</u> and <u>movement</u> of particles in solids, liquids and gases — it could earn you a few easy marks in the exam.

Density

Density tells you how much <u>mass</u> is packed into a given <u>volume</u> of space. You need to be able to work it out, as well as carry out <u>practicals</u> to work out the densities of different solids and liquids. Lucky you.

Density is a Measure of Compactness

Density is a measure of the '<u>compactness</u>' of a substance. It relates the <u>mass</u> of a substance to how much <u>space</u> it takes up (i.e. it's a substance's <u>mass</u> per <u>unit volume</u>). The <u>units</u> of <u>density</u> are <u>kg/m³</u> (the <u>mass</u> is in <u>kg</u> and the <u>volume</u> is in <u>m³</u>).

$$\text{Density (kg/m}^3\text{)} = \frac{\text{Mass (kg)}}{\text{Volume (m}^3\text{)}}$$

You might also see density given in <u>g/cm³</u>.
(1 g/cm³ = 1000 kg/m³)

1) The <u>density</u> of an <u>object</u> depends on what it's <u>made of</u>.

2) A <u>dense</u> material has its particles <u>packed tightly</u> together. The particles in a <u>less dense</u> material are more <u>spread out</u> — if you <u>compressed</u> the material, its particles would move <u>closer together</u>, and it would become <u>more dense</u>. (You <u>wouldn't</u> be changing its <u>mass</u>, but you <u>would</u> be <u>decreasing</u> its <u>volume</u>.)

3) This means that density varies between different <u>states of matter</u> (see previous page). <u>Solids</u> are generally <u>denser</u> than <u>liquids</u>, and <u>gases</u> are usually <u>less dense</u> than <u>liquids</u>.

You Need to be Able to Measure Density in Different Ways

To Find the Density of a Solid Object

PRACTICAL

1) Use a <u>balance</u> to measure its <u>mass</u> (see p.133).

2) For some solid shapes, you can find the <u>volume</u> using a <u>formula</u>. E.g. the volume of a cube is just width × height × length.

Make sure you know the formulas for the volumes of basic shapes.

3) For a trickier shaped-solid, you can find its volume by <u>submerging</u> it in a <u>eureka can</u> filled with water. The water <u>displaced</u> by the object will be <u>transferred</u> to the <u>measuring cylinder</u>:

full eureka can → → solid object → measuring cylinder

4) Record the <u>volume</u> of water in the measuring cylinder. This is the <u>volume</u> of the <u>object</u>.

5) Plug the object's <u>mass</u> and <u>volume</u> into the <u>formula</u> above to find its <u>density</u>.

To Find the Density of a Liquid

PRACTICAL

1) Place a <u>measuring cylinder</u> on a balance and <u>zero</u> the balance (see p.133).

2) Pour <u>10 ml</u> of the liquid into the measuring cylinder and record the liquid's <u>mass</u>.

3) Pour <u>another 10 ml</u> into the measuring cylinder and record the <u>total volume</u> and <u>mass</u>. Repeat this process until the measuring cylinder is <u>full</u>.

4) For each measurement, use the <u>formula</u> to find the <u>density</u>. (Remember that 1 ml = 1 cm³.)

5) Finally, take an <u>average</u> of your calculated densities to get an accurate value for the <u>density</u> of the <u>liquid</u>.

Internal Energy and Changes of State

This page is all about heating things. Take a look at your <u>specific heat capacity</u> notes (p.20) before you start — you need to understand it and be able to be able to use $\Delta E = mc\Delta\theta$ for this topic too I'm afraid.

Internal Energy is Stored by the Particles That Make Up a System

1) The particles in a system <u>vibrate</u> or <u>move around</u> — they have energy in their <u>kinetic energy stores</u>.

2) They also have energy in their <u>potential energy stores</u> due to their <u>positions</u> — don't worry about this.

3) The <u>energy stored</u> in a system is stored by its <u>particles</u> (atoms and molecules). The <u>internal energy</u> of a system is the <u>total energy</u> that its particles have in their <u>kinetic</u> and <u>potential</u> energy stores.

4) <u>Heating</u> the system <u>transfers</u> energy to its particles (they gain energy in their <u>kinetic stores</u> and move <u>faster</u>), increasing the <u>internal energy</u>.

5) This leads to a <u>change in temperature</u> or a <u>change in state</u>. If the <u>temperature</u> changes, the size of the change depends on the <u>mass</u> of the substance, what it's <u>made of</u> (its <u>specific heat capacity</u>) and the <u>energy input</u>. Make sure you remember all of the stuff on specific heat capacity from p.20, particularly how to use the <u>formula</u>.

6) A <u>change in state</u> occurs if the substance is <u>heated enough</u> — the particles will have enough energy in their <u>kinetic energy stores</u> to <u>break the bonds</u> holding them together.

A Change of State Conserves Mass

1) When you <u>heat</u> a <u>liquid</u>, it <u>boils</u> (or <u>evaporates</u>) and becomes a <u>gas</u>. When you <u>heat</u> a <u>solid</u>, it <u>melts</u> and becomes a <u>liquid</u>. These are both <u>changes of state</u>.

2) The state can also change due to <u>cooling</u>. The particles <u>lose energy</u> and <u>form bonds</u>.

3) The changes of state are:

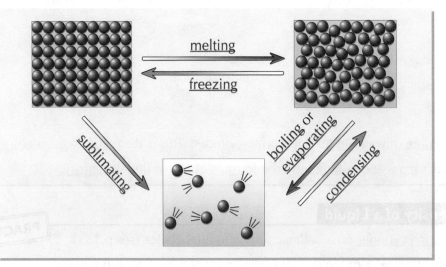

4) A <u>change of state</u> is a <u>physical</u> change (rather than a chemical change). This means you <u>don't</u> end up with a new substance — it's the <u>same substance</u> as you started with, just in a <u>different form</u>.

5) If you <u>reverse</u> a change of state (e.g. freeze a substance that has been melted), the substance will <u>return</u> to its original form and get back its <u>original properties</u>.

6) The <u>number of particles</u> doesn't change — they're just <u>arranged differently</u>. This means <u>mass is conserved</u> — none of it is lost when the substance changes state.

Specific Latent Heat

The <u>energy needed</u> to change the state of a substance is called <u>latent heat</u>. This is exciting stuff I tell you...

A Change of State Requires Energy

When a substance is <u>melting</u> or <u>boiling</u>, you're still putting in <u>energy</u> and so <u>increasing</u> the <u>internal energy</u>, but the energy's used for <u>breaking intermolecular bonds</u> rather than raising the temperature. There are <u>flat spots</u> on the heating graph where <u>energy</u> is being <u>transferred</u> by heating but not being used to change the temperature.

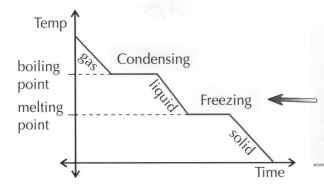

When a substance is <u>condensing</u> or <u>freezing</u>, bonds are <u>forming</u> between particles, which <u>releases</u> energy. This means the <u>internal energy</u> <u>decreases</u>, but the <u>temperature doesn't go down</u> until all the substance has turned to liquid (condensing) or a solid (freezing). The <u>flat parts</u> of the graph show this energy transfer.

The energy needed to change the state of a substance is called latent heat.

Specific Latent Heat is the Energy Needed to Change State

1) The <u>specific latent heat</u> (SLH) of a substance is the <u>amount of energy</u> needed to <u>change 1 kg</u> of it from <u>one state to another without changing its temperature</u>.

2) For <u>cooling</u>, specific latent heat is the energy <u>released</u> by a change in state.

3) Specific latent heat is <u>different</u> for <u>different materials</u>, and for changing between <u>different states</u>.

4) The specific latent heat for changing between a <u>solid</u> and a <u>liquid</u> (<u>melting</u> or <u>freezing</u>) is called the <u>specific latent heat of fusion</u>. The specific latent heat for changing between a <u>liquid</u> and a <u>gas</u> (<u>evaporating</u>, <u>boiling</u> or <u>condensing</u>) is called the <u>specific latent heat of vaporisation</u>.

There's a Formula for Specific Latent Heat

You can work out the <u>energy needed</u> (or <u>released</u>) when a substance of mass m changes state using this <u>formula</u>:

Don't get confused with specific heat capacity (p.20), which relates to a temperature rise of 1 °C. Specific latent heat is about changes of state where there's no temperature change.

Energy (E) = Mass (m) × Specific Latent Heat (L)

$$\frac{E}{m \times L}$$

Energy is given in <u>joules</u> (<u>J</u>), mass is in <u>kg</u> and SLH is in <u>J/kg</u>.

EXAMPLE:

The specific latent heat of vaporisation for water (boiling) is 2 260 000 J/kg. How much energy is needed to completely boil 1.50 kg of water at 100 °C?

1) Just plug the numbers into the <u>formula</u>.

$E = mL$
$= 1.50 × 2\ 260\ 000$

2) The units are <u>joules</u> because it's <u>energy</u>.

$= 3\ 390\ 000$ J

Topic 3 — Particle Model of Matter

Particle Motion in Gases

The particle model helps explain how temperature, pressure, volume and energy in kinetic stores are all related. And this page is here to explain it all to you. I bet you're just itching to find out more...

Colliding Gas Particles Create **Pressure**

1) Particles in gases (and liquids to a certain extent, but you don't need to worry about them) are free to move around.

2) As gas particles move about at high speeds, they bang into each other and whatever else happens to get in the way. When they collide with something, they exert a force on it.

particles collide with the container

net force at right angles to surface

3) Pressure is the force exerted per unit area.

4) So in a sealed container, the outward gas pressure is the total force exerted by all of the particles in the gas on a unit area of the container walls.

Average Energy in **Kinetic Stores** is Related to **Temperature**

1) The particles in a gas are constantly moving with random directions and speeds. If you increase the temperature of a gas, you transfer energy into the kinetic energy stores of its particles (see page 17 for more on energy stores).

2) The temperature of a gas is related to the average energy in the kinetic energy stores of the particles in the gas. The higher the temperature, the higher the average energy.

3) So as you increase the temperature of a gas, the average speed of its particles increases. This is because the energy in the particles' kinetic energy stores is $\frac{1}{2}mv^2$ — p.19.

4) This means that, for a gas at a constant volume, increasing its temperature increases its pressure.

- As the particles are travelling quicker, it means that they hit the sides of the container more often in a given amount of time.

- Each particle also has a larger momentum (p.102) which means that they exert a larger force when they collide with the container.

These factors both increase the total force exerted on a unit area, and so increase the pressure.

Higher temperatures mean higher average energies in kinetic stores...

The particle model can be used to explain what happens when you change the temperature of a gas which is kept at a constant volume. Have a look back on page 56 for more about the particle model.

Warm-Up & Exam Questions

Once you think you've got to grips with everything in this topic, all the way through from the particle model to that stuff about gases, it's time to test yourself with these questions. Let's see how you get on.

1) Describe the particles in a liquid in terms of their arrangement, energy and movement.
2) What is density a measure of?
3) How does cooling a system affect its internal energy?
4) What is the specific latent heat of vaporisation?
5) What are the units of specific latent heat?

Exam Questions

1   Substances can exist in different states of matter.   **(Grade 4-6)**

1.1   Describe the arrangement and movement of the particles in a solid.

[2 marks]

If a substance is heated to a certain temperature it can change from a solid to a liquid.

1.2   Give the name of this process.

[1 mark]

1.3   If a liquid is heated to a certain temperature it starts to boil and become a gas.
Name the other process that causes a liquid to start to become a gas.

[1 mark]

PRACTICAL

2   A student has a collection of metal toy soldiers of different sizes made from the same metal.   **(Grade 6-7)**

2.1   Which of the following statements about the toy soldiers is true? Tick **one** box.

☐ The masses and densities of each of the toy soldiers are the same.

☐ The masses of each of the toy soldiers are the same, but their densities may vary.

☐ The densities of each of the toy soldiers are the same, but their masses may vary.

☐ The densities and masses of each toy soldier may vary.

[1 mark]

The student wants to measure the density of one of the toy soldiers.
He has a eureka can, a measuring cylinder, a mass balance and some water.

2.2   State the **two** quantities the student must measure in order to calculate the density of the toy soldier.

[2 marks]

2.3*   Describe the steps the student could take to find the density
of the toy soldier using the equipment he has.

[6 marks]

Exam Questions

3   The following question is about specific latent heat. **(Grade 6-7)**

3.1   What is the name given to the specific latent heat of a
substance when it's changing between a solid and a liquid?

[1 mark]

3.2   The energy required to convert 40.8 g of liquid methanol to gaseous methanol is 47.7 J.
Calculate the specific latent heat of vaporisation of methanol.
Use the correct equation from the Physics Equation Sheet on the inside back cover.
Give your answer in J/kg and to 3 significant figures.

[3 marks]

The energy used to change liquid methanol to gaseous methanol was supplied by heating the system.

3.3   How does the internal energy of the system change as the system is heated?
Explain your answer.

[2 marks]

3.4   Explain, using the particle model, what happens when methanol
is heated so that it changes from a liquid to a gas.

[2 marks]

4   The movement of particles in a gas can be described using the particle model. **(Grade 6-7)**

4.1   Describe the particles in a gas using the particle model.
In your answer, you should refer to the arrangement, energy and movement of the particles.

[3 marks]

A scientist is calculating the density of a gas in a sealed, rigid container.

4.2   Use the particle model to explain how gas particles create pressure in a sealed container.

[2 marks]

4.3   State the equation that links density with mass and volume.

[1 mark]

4.4   A certain gas had a mass of 8.2 g and a volume of 6.69 cm³.
Calculate the density of the gas.
Give your answer to an appropriate number of significant figures.

[4 marks]

The scientist heats the container.

4.5   What happens to the pressure of the gas within the container?
Explain your answer using the particle model.

[3 marks]

5   A student is doing an investigation into the masses
of different materials of different densities. **(Grade 7-9)**
A cube has edges of length 1.5 cm and a density of 3500 kg/m³.
Calculate the mass of the cube.

[5 marks]

Revision Summary for Topic 3

Don't let all that stuff about gas pressures in <u>Topic 3</u> put too much pressure on you. Try these questions to see whether you've really got to grips with all of that stuff about <u>states of matter</u> and the <u>particle model</u>.

- Try these questions and <u>tick off each one</u> when you <u>get it right</u>.
- When you've done <u>all the questions</u> under a heading, and are <u>completely happy</u> with it, tick it off.

Particle Model (p.56) ☑

1) What are the three states of matter? ☑
2) For each state of matter, describe the arrangement and movement of the particles. ☑

Density (p.57) ☑

3) What is the formula for density? ☑
4) Give an example of the possible units of density. ☑
5) Describe how you could find the volume of an irregular solid object. ☑
6) Briefly describe an experiment to find the density of a liquid. ☑

Internal Energy and Changes of State (p.58) ☑

7) What is internal energy? ☑
8) What happens to the particles in a substance when that substance is heated? ☑
9) Name the six changes of state. ☑
10) Is a change of state a physical change or a chemical change? ☑
11) True or false? Mass stays the same when a substance changes state. ☑

Specific Latent Heat (p.59) ☑

12) Explain the cause of the flat sections on a graph of temperature against time for a substance being heated. ☑
13) Sketch a graph of temperature against time for a gas being cooled. Your graph should show the points that the gas turns into a liquid and that the liquid turns into a solid. ☑
14) Define specific latent heat. ☑
15) What is meant by the term 'specific heat of fusion'? ☑

Particle Motion in Gases (p.60) ☑

16) Explain how a gas in a sealed container exerts a pressure on the walls of the container. ☑
17) A sample of gas is heated in a container with a fixed volume. What happens to the pressure of the gas as it is heated? ☑

Developing the Model of the Atom

All this started with a Greek chap called Democritus in the 5th Century BC. He thought that all matter, whatever it was, was made up of identical lumps called "atomos". And that's as far as it got until the 1800s...

The Plum Pudding Model was Replaced with the Nuclear Model

1) In 1804 John Dalton agreed with Democritus that matter was made up of tiny spheres ("atoms") that couldn't be broken up, but he reckoned that each element was made up of a different type of "atom".

2) Nearly 100 years later, J. J. Thomson discovered particles called electrons that could be removed from atoms. So Dalton's theory wasn't quite right (atoms could be broken up). Thomson suggested that atoms were spheres of positive charge with tiny negative electrons stuck in them like the fruit in a plum pudding — the plum pudding model.

3) That "plum pudding" theory didn't last though... In 1909, scientists in Rutherford's lab tried firing a beam of alpha particles (see p.67) at thin gold foil — this was the alpha scattering experiment. From the plum pudding model, they expected the particles to pass straight through the gold sheet, or only be slightly deflected.

4) But although most of the particles did go straight through the sheet, some were deflected more than expected, and a few were deflected back the way they had come — something the plum pudding model couldn't explain.

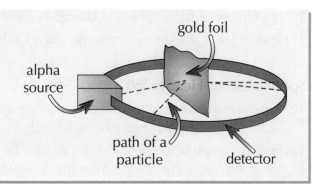

5) Because a few alpha particles were deflected back, the scientists realised that most of the mass of the atom was concentrated at the centre in a tiny nucleus. This nucleus must also have a positive charge, since it repelled the positive alpha particles.

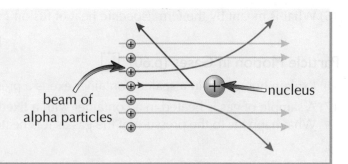

6) They also realised that because nearly all the alpha particles passed straight through, most of an atom is just empty space. This was the first nuclear model of the atom.

The gold foil experiment helped adapt the model of the atom...

Rutherford and his lab of scientists made a hypothesis, did an investigation and then analysed the data they got from it. By doing this, they showed that the plum pudding model of the atom must be wrong, so it was changed. This is a great example of the scientific method (see page 1) in action.

Developing the Model of the Atom

Rutherford and Marsden's model of the atom was a big leap forwards, but that's not the end of the story...

Bohr **Refined** Rutherford's **Nuclear Model** of the Atom

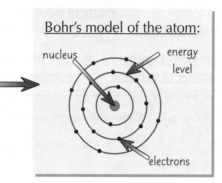

Bohr's model of the atom:

1) The nuclear model that resulted from the alpha particle scattering experiment was a positively charged nucleus surrounded by a cloud of negative electrons.

2) Niels Bohr said that electrons orbiting the nucleus do so at certain distances called energy levels. His theoretical calculations agreed with experimental data.

3) Evidence from further experiments changed the model to have a nucleus made up of a group of particles (protons) which all had the same positive charge that added up to the overall charge of the nucleus.

4) About 20 years after the idea of a nucleus was accepted, in 1932, James Chadwick proved the existence of the neutron, which explained the imbalance between the atomic and mass numbers (see next page).

Our **Current Model** of the **Atom**

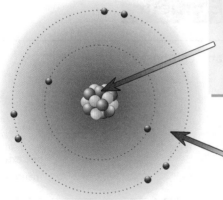

The nucleus is tiny but it makes up most of the mass of the atom. It contains protons (which are positively charged — they have a +1 relative charge) and neutrons (which are neutral, with a relative charge of 0) — which gives it an overall positive charge. Its radius is about 10 000 times smaller than the radius of the atom.

The rest of the atom is mostly empty space. Negative electrons (which have a relative charge of –1) whizz round the outside of the nucleus really fast. They give the atom its overall size — the radius of an atom is about 1×10^{-10} m.

We're currently pretty happy with this model, but there's no saying it won't change. Just like for the plum pudding model, new experiments sometimes mean we have to change or completely get rid of current models.

Number of Protons **Equals** Number of Electrons

1) In atoms, the number of protons = the number of electrons, as protons and electrons have an equal but opposite charge and atoms have no overall charge.

2) Electrons in energy levels can move within (or sometimes leave) the atom. If they gain energy by absorbing EM radiation (p.112) they move to a higher energy level, further from the nucleus. If they release EM radiation, they move to a lower energy level that is closer to the nucleus. If one or more outer electrons leaves the atom, the atom becomes a positively charged ion.

WORKING SCIENTIFICALLY

The model of the atom has developed over time...

Due to lots of scientists doing lots of experiments, we now have a better idea of what the atom's really like. We now know about the particles in atoms — protons, neutrons and electrons.

Isotopes

Isotopes of an element look pretty similar, but watch out — they have different numbers of neutrons.

Atoms of the Same Element have the Same Number of Protons

1) All atoms of each element have a set number of protons (so each nucleus has a given positive charge). The number of protons in an atom is its atomic number.

2) The mass number of an atom (the mass of the nucleus) is the number of protons + the number of neutrons in its nucleus.

Example: A certain oxygen atom has the chemical symbol — $^{16}_{8}O$.

Mass number ⟶ 16
Atomic number ⟶ 8 O ⟵ Element symbol (oxygen)

All atoms can be shown using this notation.

- Oxygen has an atomic number of 8, this means all oxygen atoms have 8 protons.
- This atom of oxygen has a mass number of 16. Since it has 8 protons, it must have 16 − 8 = 8 neutrons.

Isotopes are Different Forms of the Same Element

1) Isotopes of an element are atoms with the same number of protons (the same atomic number, and so the same charge on the nucleus) but a different number of neutrons (a different mass number).

Example: Carbon-12 and carbon-13 are isotopes.

$^{12}_{6}C$ $^{13}_{6}C$

one extra neutron

2) All elements have different isotopes, but there are usually only one or two stable ones.

3) The other unstable isotopes tend to decay into other elements and give out radiation as they try to become more stable. This process is called radioactive decay.

4) Radioactive substances spit out one or more types of ionising radiation from their nucleus — the ones you need to know are alpha, beta and gamma radiation (see next page).

5) They can also release neutrons (n) when they decay.

6) Ionising radiation is radiation that knocks electrons off atoms, creating positive ions. The ionising power of a radiation source is how easily it can do this.

Ionising Radiation

There are three types of ionising radiation you need to know about — these are alpha, beta and gamma.

Alpha Particles are Helium Nuclei

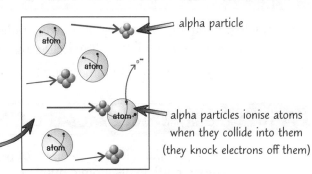

alpha particle

1) Alpha radiation is when an alpha particle (α) is emitted from the nucleus. An α-particle is two neutrons and two protons (like a helium nucleus).

2) They don't penetrate very far into materials and are stopped quickly — they can only travel a few cm in air and are absorbed by a sheet of paper.

alpha particles ionise atoms when they collide into them (they knock electrons off them)

3) Because of their size they are strongly ionising.

4) Alpha radiation has applications in the home:

Alpha radiation is used in smoke detectors — it ionises air particles, causing a current to flow. If there is smoke in the air, it binds to the ions — meaning the current stops and the alarm sounds.

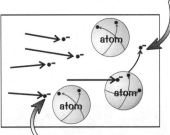

Beta Particles are High-Speed Electrons

1) A beta particle (β) is simply a fast-moving electron released by the nucleus. Beta particles have virtually no mass and a charge of –1.

2) They are moderately ionising (see right).

emitted electron

3) They also penetrate moderately far into materials before colliding and have a range in air of a few metres. They are absorbed by a sheet of aluminium (around 5 mm thick).

4) For every beta particle emitted, a neutron in the nucleus has turned into a proton.

beta particle

5) Beta radiation can be useful due to the fact that it's moderately penetrating:

Beta emitters are used to test the thickness of sheets of metal, as the particles are not immediately absorbed by the material like alpha radiation would be and do not penetrate as far as gamma rays. Therefore, slight variations in thickness affect the amount of radiation passing through the sheet.

Gamma Rays are EM Waves with a Short Wavelength

gamma ray

1) Gamma rays (γ) are waves of electromagnetic radiation (p.112) released by the nucleus.

Uses of gamma rays are on p.115.

2) They penetrate far into materials without being stopped and will travel a long distance through air.

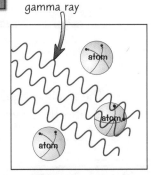

3) This means they are weakly ionising because they tend to pass through rather than collide with atoms. Eventually they hit something and do damage.

4) They can be absorbed by thick sheets of lead or metres of concrete.

Alpha particles are more ionising than beta particles...

...and beta particles are more ionising than gamma rays. Make sure you've got that clearly memorised, as well as what makes up each type of radiation, as this isn't the last you'll see of this stuff. No siree.

Nuclear Equations

Nuclear equations show radioactive decay and once you get the hang of them they're dead easy. Get going.

Mass and Atomic Numbers Have to Balance

1) Nuclear equations are a way of showing radioactive decay by using element symbols (p.66). They're written in the form: atom before decay → atom(s) after decay + radiation emitted.

2) There is one golden rule to remember: the total mass and atomic numbers must be equal on both sides.

Alpha Decay Decreases the Charge and Mass of the Nucleus

1) Remember, alpha particles are made up of two protons and two neutrons. So when an atom emits an alpha particle, its atomic number reduces by 2 and its mass number reduces by 4.

2) A proton is positively charged and a neutron is neutral, so the charge of the nucleus decreases.

3) In nuclear equations, an alpha particle can be written as a helium nucleus: ^4_2He.

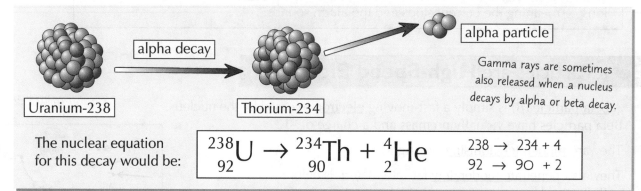

alpha decay | alpha particle

Gamma rays are sometimes also released when a nucleus decays by alpha or beta decay.

Uranium-238 | Thorium-234

The nuclear equation for this decay would be:

$$^{238}_{92}\text{U} \rightarrow {}^{234}_{90}\text{Th} + {}^4_2\text{He}$$

$$238 \rightarrow 234 + 4$$
$$92 \rightarrow 90 + 2$$

Beta Decay Increases the Charge of the Nucleus

1) When beta decay occurs, a neutron in the nucleus turns into a proton and releases a fast-moving electron (the beta particle).

2) The number of protons in the nucleus has increased by 1. This increases the positive charge of the nucleus (the atomic number).

3) Because the nucleus has lost a neutron and gained a proton during beta decay, the mass of the nucleus doesn't change (protons and neutrons have the same mass).

4) A beta particle is written as $^0_{-1}\text{e}$ in nuclear equations.

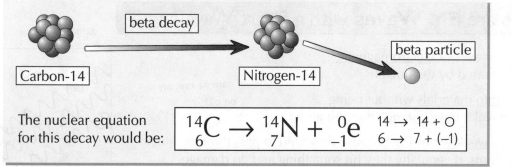

beta decay | beta particle

Carbon-14 | Nitrogen-14

The nuclear equation for this decay would be:

$$^{14}_6\text{C} \rightarrow {}^{14}_7\text{N} + {}^0_{-1}\text{e}$$

$$14 \rightarrow 14 + 0$$
$$6 \rightarrow 7 + (-1)$$

In both alpha and beta emissions, a new element will be formed, as the number of protons (atomic number) changes.

Gamma Rays Don't Change the Charge or Mass of the Nucleus

1) Gamma rays are a way of getting rid of excess energy from a nucleus.

2) This means that there is no change to the atomic mass or atomic number of the atom.

3) In nuclear equations, gamma radiation is written as γ^0_0.

Half-Life

How quickly <u>unstable nuclei</u> decay is measured using <u>activity</u> and <u>half-life</u> — two very important terms.

Radioactivity is a Totally Random Process

1) Radioactive substances give out <u>radiation</u> from the nuclei of their atoms — <u>no matter what</u>.

2) This radiation can be measured with a <u>Geiger-Muller tube and counter</u>, which records the <u>count-rate</u> — the number of radiation counts reaching it per second.

3) Radioactive decay is entirely <u>random</u>. So you <u>can't predict</u> exactly <u>which</u> nucleus in a sample will decay next, or <u>when</u> any one of them will decay.

4) But you <u>can</u> find out the <u>time</u> it takes for the <u>amount of radiation</u> emitted by a source to <u>halve</u>, this is known as the <u>half-life</u>. It can be used to make <u>predictions</u> about radioactive sources, even though their decays are <u>random</u>.

5) Half-life can be used to find the <u>rate</u> at which a source decays — its <u>ACTIVITY</u>. Activity is measured in <u>becquerels</u>, <u>Bq</u> (where 1 Bq is <u>1 decay per second</u>).

The Radioactivity of a Source Decreases Over Time

1) Each time a radioactive nucleus <u>decays</u> to become a <u>stable nucleus</u>, the activity <u>as a whole</u> will <u>decrease</u>. (<u>Older</u> sources emit <u>less</u> radiation.)

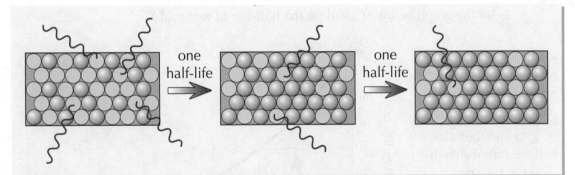

one half-life → one half-life →

2) For <u>some</u> isotopes it takes <u>just a few hours</u> before nearly all the unstable nuclei have <u>decayed</u>, whilst others last for <u>millions of years</u>.

3) The problem with trying to <u>measure</u> this is that <u>the activity never reaches zero</u>, which is why we have to use the idea of <u>half-life</u> to measure how quickly the activity <u>drops off</u>.

The <u>half-life</u> is the time taken for the <u>number of radioactive nuclei</u> in an isotope to <u>halve</u>.

4) Half-life can also be described as the time taken for the <u>activity</u>, and so count-rate, to <u>halve</u>.

Different substances have different half-lives...

Some substances take a <u>long time</u> to <u>decay</u>, giving them a <u>long half-life</u>, while others decay in the blink of an eye. For example, neodymium-144 has a half-life of 2 million billion years, while helium-5 has a half-life of 7.6×10^{-22} seconds. That's 0.00000000000000000000076 seconds. Pretty speedy eh?

Half-Life

You learnt all about what <u>half-life</u> is on the last page, but now it's time to find out how to <u>calculate</u> it. Fortunately, there's a pretty simple method you can use that involves an <u>activity-time graph</u>.

The **Radioactivity** of a Source **Decreases Over Time**

You might be asked to give the <u>decline</u> of activity or <u>count-rate</u> after a certain number of half-lives as a percentage of the original activity, like this:

> **EXAMPLE:** **The initial activity of a sample is 640 Bq. Calculate the final activity as a percentage of the initial activity after two half-lives.**
>
> 1) Find the <u>activity</u> after <u>each half-life</u>.
>
> 2) Now <u>divide</u> the <u>final activity</u> by the <u>initial</u> activity, then <u>multiply by 100</u> to make it a percentage.
>
> 1 half-life: 640 ÷ 2 = 320
> 2 half-lives: 320 ÷ 2 = 160
> (160 ÷ 640) × 100
> = 0.25 × 100
> = 25%

Always double check what the question is asking for — it may want a fraction, ratio or a percentage.

Finding the **Half-Life** of a Sample using a **Graph**

1) If you plot a graph of <u>activity against time</u> (taking into account <u>background radiation</u>), it will <u>always</u> be shaped like the one below.

2) The <u>half-life</u> is found from the graph by finding the <u>time interval</u> on the <u>bottom axis</u> corresponding to a <u>halving</u> of the <u>activity</u> on the <u>vertical axis</u>. Easy.

> **EXAMPLE:** **The activity of a sample of a radioactive material, X, is shown on the graph below. Calculate the half-life of material X.**
>
> 1) Read the <u>initial activity</u> off the graph. This is the activity when time = 0.
>
> 2) <u>Divide</u> the <u>initial activity</u> by <u>2</u> to find the value of half the initial activity.
>   80 ÷ 2 = 40
>
> 3) Find this value on the <u>y-axis</u> and read along <u>horizontally</u> to the curve.
>
> 4) Then read <u>down</u> from the curve at this point to find the half-life.
>
> *Activity in Bequerels* — 0, 10, 20, 30, 40, 50, 60, 70, 80
> *Time in hours* — 0, 4, 8, 12, 16
> ←one half-life→←one half-life→←one half-life→
>
> So the half-life of the sample is 4 hours.

You can determine half-lives from graphs...

MATHS TIP Make sure you can use <u>graphs</u> like the one above to work out <u>half-lives</u>. All you've got to do is read off the initial <u>activity</u> from the <u>y-axis</u>, then work out what half this activity would be by <u>dividing by two</u>. Then, just read off the time from the <u>x-axis</u> for this value, which is one half-life.

Irradiation and Contamination

There are two main things you need to be careful of when working with radiation — <u>exposure to radiation</u>, and <u>physical contact</u> with <u>radioactive substances</u>. It's dangerous stuff I tell you, so read with care...

There are **Risks** to Using **Radiation**

<u>Ionising radiation</u> can enter <u>living cells</u> and ionise atoms within them. This can <u>damage</u> the cells (which can cause things like <u>cancer</u>) or <u>kill</u> them off completely. That's why it's important that you know the <u>precautions</u> to take when working with any <u>sources of radiation</u>.

Exposure to Radiation is called **Irradiation**

1) Objects <u>near</u> a radioactive source are <u>irradiated</u> by it. This simply means they're <u>exposed</u> to it (we're <u>always</u> being irradiated by <u>background radiation</u> sources).

2) <u>Irradiating</u> something does <u>not</u> make it <u>radioactive</u>.

3) Keeping sources in <u>lead-lined boxes</u>, standing behind <u>barriers</u> or being in a <u>different room</u> and using <u>remote-controlled arms</u> when working with radioactive sources are all ways of reducing <u>irradiation</u>.

Contamination is Radioactive Particles **Getting onto Objects**

1) If <u>unwanted radioactive atoms</u> get onto or into an object, the object is said to be <u>contaminated</u>. E.g. if you <u>touch</u> a radioactive source without wearing <u>gloves</u>, your hands would be <u>contaminated</u>.

2) These <u>contaminating atoms</u> might then decay, releasing <u>radiation</u> which could cause you <u>harm</u>.

3) Contamination is especially dangerous because radioactive particles could get <u>inside your body</u>.

4) <u>Gloves</u> and <u>tongs</u> should be used when handling sources, to avoid particles getting stuck to your <u>skin</u> or <u>under your nails</u>. Some industrial workers wear <u>protective suits</u> to stop them <u>breathing in</u> particles.

Safety precautions can help protect against hazards from radiation...

Radiation can be pretty <u>dangerous</u> stuff, so it's important to <u>protect yourself</u> when you're working with <u>radioactive substances</u>. <u>Lead</u> is often used to line <u>storage boxes</u> and in <u>protective screens</u> because it is very good at <u>absorbing</u> radiation, so it prevents a lot of the radiation from reaching what's on the other side.

Irradiation and Contamination

Radioactive contamination and irradiation can both be pretty dangerous — but how dangerous they are depends on the type of radiation involved. Give this page a read to find out why.

Exposure to Some Sources can be More Harmful than to Others

Contamination or irradiation can cause different amounts of harm, based on the radiation type.

Irradiation

1) Outside the body, beta and gamma sources are the most dangerous. This is because beta and gamma can penetrate the body and get to delicate organs.

2) Alpha is less dangerous because it can't penetrate the skin and is easily blocked by a small air gap (p.67).

3) High levels of irradiation from all sources are dangerous, but especially from ones that emit beta and gamma.

Contamination

1) Inside the body, alpha sources are the most dangerous, because they do all their damage in a very localised area. So contamination, rather than irradiation, is the major concern when working with alpha sources.

2) Beta sources are less damaging inside the body, as radiation is absorbed over a wider area, and some passes out of the body altogether.

3) Gamma sources are the least dangerous inside the body, as they mostly pass straight out — they have the lowest ionising power, p.67.

Information About Radiation Should Be Communicated

The more we understand how different types of radiation affects our bodies, the better we can protect ourselves when using them. This is why it's so important that research about this is published. The data is peer-reviewed (see page 1) and can quickly become accepted, leading to many improvements in our use of radioactive sources.

Alpha sources are the most dangerous inside the body...

Alpha sources are the most ionising (see page 67), so if they get into the body, they can wreak havoc. Beta and gamma sources however are the most dangerous outside the body. This is because they are more penetrating than alpha sources (see page 67), so can get through the skin and cause damage to cells.

Warm-Up & Exam Questions

Atoms may be tiny, but you could bag some big marks in your exams if you know them inside-out.
Here are some questions to check just how great your understanding of atoms and radiation really is...

Warm-Up Questions

1) Describe our current, nuclear model of the atom.

2) Give the definition of the term 'isotope'.

3) Which are the most ionising — alpha particles or gamma rays?

4) Outline why beta emitters, rather than alpha or gamma emitters,
   are used to test the thickness of sheets of metal.

5) Name the type of nuclear radiation, the particles of which are electrons.

6) Name the type of nuclear radiation that is an electromagnetic wave.

7) What is the difference between radioactive contamination and irradiation?

8) Why is contamination by an alpha source more dangerous to humans than
   irradiation by an alpha source?

Exam Questions

1   Alpha, beta and gamma radiation sources were used to direct radiation at thin
     sheets of paper and aluminium. A detector was used to measure where radiation
     had passed through the sheets. The results are shown in **Figure 1**.

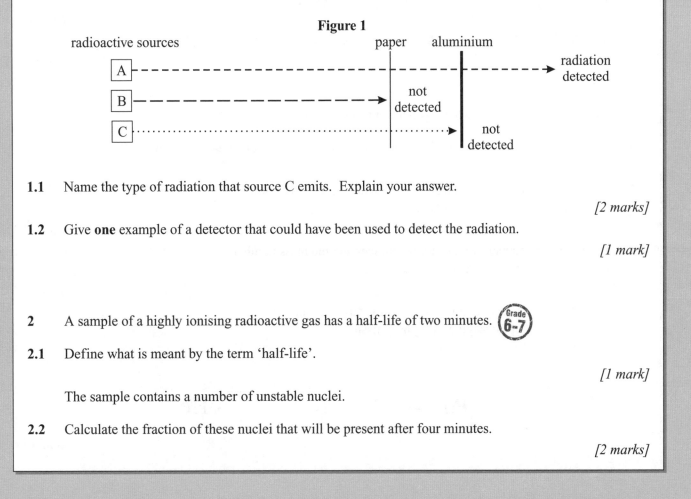

Figure 1

1.1   Name the type of radiation that source C emits. Explain your answer.

[2 marks]

1.2   Give **one** example of a detector that could have been used to detect the radiation.

[1 mark]

2   A sample of a highly ionising radioactive gas has a half-life of two minutes.

2.1   Define what is meant by the term 'half-life'.

[1 mark]

The sample contains a number of unstable nuclei.

2.2   Calculate the fraction of these nuclei that will be present after four minutes.

[2 marks]

Exam Questions

3   A radioactive isotope sample has a half-life of 40 seconds. *(Grade 6-7)*
         The initial activity of the sample is 8000 Bq.

3.1   Calculate the activity after 2 minutes. Give your answer in becquerels.

[2 marks]

3.2   After how many half-lives will the activity have fallen to 250 Bq?

[2 marks]

3.3   The radioactive source is left until its activity falls to 100 Bq.
           Calculate the final activity as a percentage of the initial activity.

[2 marks]

4   **Table 1** contains information about three atoms. *(Grade 6-7)*

Table 1

	Mass number	Atomic number
Atom A	32	17
Atom B	33	17
Atom C	32	16

4.1   Name the two types of particle that the nucleus of an atom contains.

[2 marks]

4.2   Define the term 'mass number' in the context of atoms.

[1 mark]

4.3   Which of the two atoms in **Table 1** are isotopes of the same element? Explain your answer.

[2 marks]

5   Nuclear equations show what is produced when unstable nuclei decay. *(Grade 7-9)*

5.1   Draw a symbol that can be used to represent a beta particle in a nuclear equation.

[1 mark]

5.2   Describe what happens to the atomic number and the mass number
           of an atom when it undergoes beta decay.

[2 marks]

5.3   Describe what happens to the atomic number and the mass number
           of an atom when it undergoes gamma decay.

[2 marks]

5.4   Complete the nuclear equation, shown in **Figure 2**, which shows
           a polonium isotope decaying by alpha emission.

Figure 2

$$\text{......}\atop{84}\text{Po} \longrightarrow {205\atop\text{......}}\text{Pb} + {\text{......}\atop\text{......}}\text{He}$$

[3 marks]

Revision Summary for Topic 4

Well, that's the end of <u>Topic 4</u> — hopefully it wasn't too painful. Time to see how much you've absorbed.
*   Try these questions and <u>tick off each one</u> when you <u>get it right</u>.
*   When you've done <u>all the questions</u> under a heading, and are <u>completely happy</u> with it, tick it off.

The Atomic Model (p.64-66) ☑

1) Briefly describe how the model of an atom has changed over time. ☑
2) Who provided evidence to suggest the existence of the neutron? ☑
3) Draw a sketch to show our currently accepted model of the atom. ☑
4) True or false? Atoms have no overall charge. ☑
5) What happens to an atom if it loses one or more of its outer electrons? ☑
6) Which number defines what element an atom is: the atomic number or the mass number? ☑
7) What is the atomic number of an atom? ☑
8) True or false? Isotopes have different mass numbers. ☑

Nuclear Decay and Half-life (p.67-70) ☑

9) What is radioactive decay? ☑
10) Name four things that may be emitted during radioactive decay. ☑
11) For alpha, beta and gamma radiation, give: a) their ionising power,   b) their range in air. ☑
12) Explain why alpha radiation could not be used to check the thickness of metal sheets. ☑
13) How could you represent alpha radiation in nuclear equations? ☑
14) What type of nuclear decay doesn't change the mass or charge of the nucleus? ☑
15) Name a piece of equipment that could be used to measure radiation. ☑
16) What is the activity of a source? What are its units? ☑
17) Explain how you would find the half-life of a source, given a graph of its activity over time. ☑

Irradiation and Contamination (p.71-72) ☑

18) Define irradiation and contamination. ☑
19) Compare the hazards of being irradiated by an alpha source and a gamma source. ☑

Contact and Non-Contact Forces

Just like sports, forces are either <u>contact</u> or <u>non-contact</u> and involve lots of <u>interaction</u>.

Vectors Have **Magnitude** and **Direction**

1) Force is a <u>vector quantity</u> — vector quantities have a <u>magnitude</u> and a <u>direction</u>.

2) Lots of <u>physical quantities</u> are vector quantities:

> <u>Vector quantities</u>: force, velocity, displacement, acceleration, momentum, etc.

3) Some physical quantities <u>only</u> have magnitude and <u>no direction</u>.
These are called <u>scalar quantities</u>:

> <u>Scalar quantities</u>: speed, distance, mass, temperature, time, etc.

4) Vectors are usually represented by an <u>arrow</u> — the <u>length</u> of the arrow shows the <u>magnitude</u>, and the <u>direction</u> of the arrow shows the <u>direction of the quantity</u>.

> <u>Velocity</u> is a <u>vector</u>, but <u>speed</u> is a <u>scalar</u> quantity.
> Both bikes are travelling at the same <u>speed</u>, v (the <u>length</u> of each arrow is the same).
> They have <u>different velocities</u> because they are travelling in different <u>directions</u>.

Forces Can be **Contact** or **Non-Contact**

1) A <u>force</u> is a <u>push</u> or a <u>pull</u> on an object that is caused by it <u>interacting</u> with something.

2) All forces are either <u>contact</u> or <u>non-contact</u> forces.

3) When <u>two objects</u> have to be <u>touching</u> for a force to act, that force is called a <u>contact force</u>.

> E.g. friction, air resistance, tension in ropes, normal contact force, etc.

4) If the objects <u>do not need to be touching</u> for the force to act, the force is a <u>non-contact force</u>.

> E.g. magnetic force, gravitational force, electrostatic force, etc.

5) When two objects <u>interact</u>, there is a <u>force</u> produced on <u>both</u> objects.
An <u>interaction pair</u> is a pair of forces that are <u>equal</u> and <u>opposite</u> and act on two <u>interacting</u> objects.
(This is basically Newton's Third Law — see p.95.)

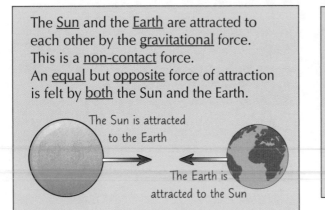

The <u>Sun</u> and the <u>Earth</u> are attracted to each other by the <u>gravitational</u> force.
This is a <u>non-contact</u> force.
An <u>equal</u> but <u>opposite</u> force of attraction is felt by <u>both</u> the Sun and the Earth.

The Sun is attracted to the Earth

The Earth is attracted to the Sun

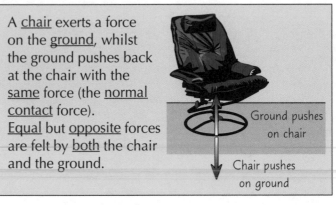

A <u>chair</u> exerts a force on the <u>ground</u>, whilst the ground pushes back at the chair with the <u>same</u> force (the <u>normal contact</u> force).
<u>Equal</u> but <u>opposite</u> forces are felt by <u>both</u> the chair and the ground.

Ground pushes on chair

Chair pushes on ground

Weight, Mass and Gravity

Gravity might seem like a rather heavy subject to tackle only a page into the topic, but you might end up finding it quite attractive. It's pretty important stuff, so make sure you understand it.

Gravitational Force is the Force of Attraction Between Masses

Gravity attracts all masses, but you only notice it when one of the masses is really really big, e.g. a planet. Anything near a planet or star is attracted to it very strongly.
This has two important effects:

> 1) On the surface of a planet, it makes all things fall towards the ground.

> 2) It gives everything a weight.

Weight and Mass are Not the Same

1) Mass is just the amount of 'stuff' in an object. For any given object this will have the same value anywhere in the universe.

2) Weight is the force acting on an object due to gravity (the pull of the gravitational force on the object). Close to Earth, this force is caused by the gravitational field around the Earth.

3) Gravitational field strength varies with location. It's stronger the closer you are to the mass causing the field, and stronger for larger masses.

4) The weight of an object depends on the strength of the gravitational field at the location of the object. This means that the weight of an object changes with its location.

5) For example, an object has the same mass whether it's on Earth or on the Moon — but its weight will be different. A 1 kg mass will weigh less on the Moon (about 1.6 N) than it does on Earth (about 9.8 N), simply because the gravitational field strength on the surface of the Moon is less.

6) Weight is a force measured in newtons. You can think of the force as acting from a single point on the object, called its centre of mass (a point at which you assume the whole mass is concentrated). For a uniform object (one that's the same density, p.57, throughout and is a regular shape), this will be at the centre of the object.

7) Weight is measured using a calibrated spring balance (or newtonmeter).

8) Mass is not a force. It's measured in kilograms with a mass balance (an old-fashioned pair of balancing scales).

centre of mass

weight

Mass and Weight are Directly Proportional

1) You can calculate the weight of an object if you know its mass (m) and the strength of the gravitational field that it is in (g):

> Weight (N) = Mass (kg) × Gravitational Field Strength (N/kg)

2) For Earth, $g \approx 9.8$ N/kg and for the Moon it's around 1.6 N/kg. Don't worry, you'll always be given a value of g to use in the exam.

3) Increasing the mass of an object increases its weight. If you double the mass, the weight doubles too, so you can say that weight and mass are directly proportional.

4) You can write this, using the direct proportionality symbol, as $W \propto m$.

Resultant Forces

When <u>multiple forces</u> act on an object, they can <u>add together</u> or <u>subtract</u> from each other until there's the equivalent of just <u>one</u> force acting in a <u>single direction</u>. This is the <u>resultant force</u>.

Free Body Diagrams Show All the Forces Acting on an Object

1) You need to be able to <u>describe</u> all the <u>forces</u> acting on an <u>isolated object</u> or a <u>system</u> (p.17) — i.e. <u>every</u> force <u>acting on</u> the object or system but <u>none</u> of the forces the object or system <u>exerts</u> on the rest of the world.

2) For example, a skydiver's <u>weight</u> acts on him pulling him towards the ground and <u>drag</u> (air resistance) also acts on him, in the <u>opposite direction</u> to his motion.

3) This can be shown using a <u>free body diagram</u> like the ones below.

4) The <u>sizes</u> of the arrows show the <u>relative magnitudes</u> of the forces and the <u>directions</u> show the directions of the forces acting on the object.

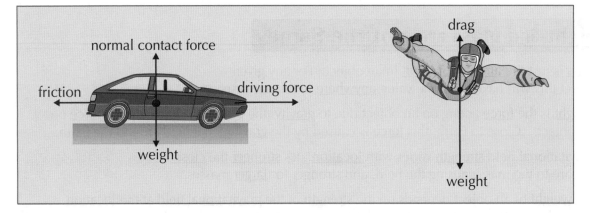

A Resultant Force is the Overall Force on a Point or Object

1) In most <u>real</u> situations there are at least <u>two forces</u> acting on an object along any direction.

2) If you have a <u>number of forces</u> acting at a single point, you can replace them with a <u>single force</u> (so long as the single force has the <u>same effect</u> as all the original forces together).

3) This single force is called the <u>resultant force</u>.
For example, there is a <u>downward resultant force</u> acting on the <u>skydiver</u> above.

4) If the forces all act along the <u>same line</u> (they're all parallel), the <u>overall effect</u> is found by <u>adding</u> those going in the <u>same</u> direction and <u>subtracting</u> any going in the opposite direction.

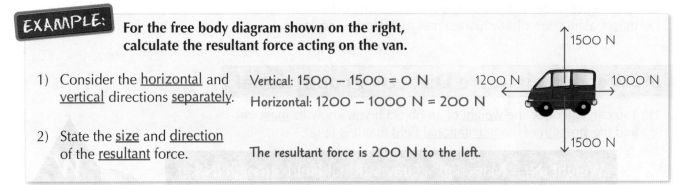

EXAMPLE: **For the free body diagram shown on the right, calculate the resultant force acting on the van.**

1) Consider the <u>horizontal</u> and <u>vertical</u> directions <u>separately</u>.

Vertical: 1500 − 1500 = 0 N
Horizontal: 1200 − 1000 N = 200 N

2) State the <u>size</u> and <u>direction</u> of the <u>resultant</u> force.

The resultant force is 200 N to the left.

The resultant force — one force with the same result as many...

You'll most often encounter a <u>resultant force</u> as the <u>difference</u> between some kind of <u>driving force</u> and a <u>resistive force</u>, acting in <u>opposite directions</u> along the <u>same line</u>. For example, <u>weight</u> and <u>air resistance</u> for a <u>falling</u> object. But its not always so <u>straightforward</u>. Read on for some <u>techniques</u> for tackling them.

Resultant Forces

If A **Resultant** Force **Moves** An Object, **Work is Done**

> When a <u>force</u> moves an object through a <u>distance</u>,
> <u>ENERGY IS TRANSFERRED</u> and <u>WORK IS DONE</u> on the object.

1) To make something <u>move</u> (or <u>keep</u> it moving if there are <u>frictional forces</u>), a <u>force</u> must be applied.

2) The thing <u>applying the force</u> needs a <u>source</u> of <u>energy</u> (like <u>fuel</u> or <u>food</u>).

3) The force does '<u>work</u>' to <u>move</u> the object and <u>energy</u> is <u>transferred</u> from one <u>store</u> to another (p.18).

4) Whether energy is transferred '<u>usefully</u>' (e.g. <u>lifting a load</u>) or is '<u>wasted</u>' (p.23) you can still say that '<u>work is done</u>'. '<u>Work done</u>' and '<u>energy transferred</u>' are <u>the same thing</u>.

> When you push something along a <u>rough surface</u> (like a <u>carpet</u>) you are doing work <u>against frictional</u> <u>forces</u>. Energy is being <u>transferred</u> to the <u>kinetic energy store</u> of the <u>object</u> because it starts <u>moving</u>, but some is also being transferred to <u>thermal energy stores</u> due to the friction. This causes the overall <u>temperature</u> of the object to <u>increase</u>. (Like <u>rubbing your hands together</u> to warm them up.)

5) You can find out <u>how much</u> work has been done using:

> Work done (J) = Force (N) × Distance (moved along the line of action of the force) (m)

6) <u>One joule of work</u> is done when a <u>force of one newton</u> causes an object to move a <u>distance of one metre</u>. You need to be able to <u>convert</u> joules (J) to newton metres (Nm). <u>1 J = 1 Nm</u>.

$W = Fs$

$$\frac{W}{F \times s}$$

Use **Scale Drawings** to Find **Resultant Forces**

Working out resultant forces using scale diagrams isn't too tough. Here's what to do:

1) Draw all the <u>forces</u> acting on an object, to scale, '<u>tip-to-tail</u>'.

2) Then draw a <u>straight line</u> from the start of the <u>first force</u> to the <u>end</u> of the <u>last force</u> — this is the <u>resultant force</u>.

3) Measure the <u>length</u> of the <u>resultant force</u> on the diagram to find the <u>magnitude</u> and the <u>angle</u> to find the <u>direction</u> of the force.

EXAMPLE: **A man is on an electric bicycle that has a driving force of 4 N north.**
However, the wind produces a force of 3 N east.
Find the magnitude and direction of the resultant force.

1) Start by drawing a <u>scale drawing</u> of the forces acting.

2) Make sure you choose a <u>sensible</u> <u>scale</u> (e.g. 1 cm = 1 N).

3) Draw the <u>resultant</u> from the tail of the first arrow to the tip of the last arrow.

4) Measure the <u>length</u> of the resultant with a <u>ruler</u> and use the <u>scale</u> to find the force in N.

5) Use a <u>protractor</u> to measure the direction as a <u>bearing</u>. A bearing is an angle measured clockwise from north, given as a 3 digit number, e.g. 10° = 010°.

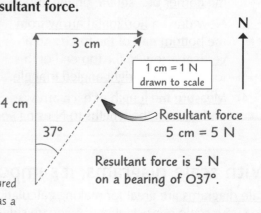

N

3 cm

1 cm = 1 N
drawn to scale

4 cm

37°

Resultant force
5 cm = 5 N

Resultant force is 5 N
on a bearing of 037°.

More on Forces

Scale diagrams are useful for more than just calculating resultant forces. You can also use them to check if forces are balanced and to split a force into component parts, as you're about to see...

An Object is in **Equilibrium** if the **Forces** on it are **Balanced**

1) If all of the forces acting on an object combine to give a resultant force of zero, the object is in equilibrium.

2) On a scale diagram, this means that the tip of the last force you draw should end where the tail of the first force you drew begins. E.g. for three forces, the scale diagram will form a triangle.

Make sure you draw the last force in the right direction. It's in the opposite direction to how you'd draw a resultant force.

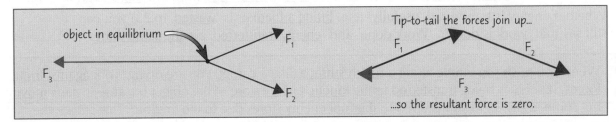

3) You might be given forces acting on an object and told to find a missing force, given that the object is in equilibrium. To do this, draw out the forces you do know (to scale and tip-to-tail), join the end of the last force to the start of the first force.

4) This line is the missing force so you can measure its size and direction.

You Can **Split** a Force into **Components**

1) Not all forces act horizontally or vertically — some act at awkward angles.

2) To make these easier to deal with, they can be split into two components at right angles to each other (usually horizontal and vertical).

3) Acting together, these components have the same effect as the single force.

4) You can resolve a force (split it into components) by drawing it on a scale grid.

EXAMPLE: Use the grid below to resolve a 10 N force, acting at 53° above the horizontal, into horizontal and vertical components. Give your answers to 1 significant figure.

1) Begin by deciding on a scale for your grid. Here, we have 1 cm² squares, so an easy scale to work with would be if 1 cm = 1 N.

2) Next, draw your force to scale on the grid and at the right angle. Aim to have at least one end of the force arrow at the corner of a square on the grid.

3) Now draw a horizontal arrow from the bottom end of the force and a vertical arrow to the top end of the force to form a right angled triangle.

4) Measure the length of each arrow, and convert the lengths to N using your scale.

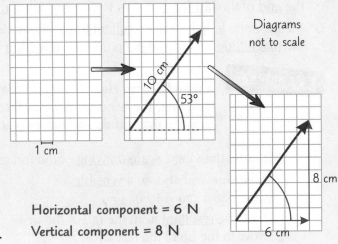

Diagrams not to scale

Horizontal component = 6 N
Vertical component = 8 N

With scale diagrams, it's important to keep things in proportion...

Scale diagrams are great for making calculations with forces, but you need to be careful. Make sure you keep your scale consistent (e.g. 1 square side = 1 N) and that you draw the forces in the correct direction.

Warm-Up & Exam Questions

Now you've learnt the basics of forces, it's time to act on your new knowledge.
Give these questions a whack and test how well you've forced those facts into your brain.

Warm-Up Questions

1) A tennis ball is dropped from a height.
   Name one contact force and one non-contact force that act on the ball as it falls.
2) Give an example of a vector quantity and a scalar quantity.
3) State the units of: a) gravitational field strength,   b) mass,   c) weight.
4) How can you tell if a set of forces are balanced using a scale diagram?

Exam Questions

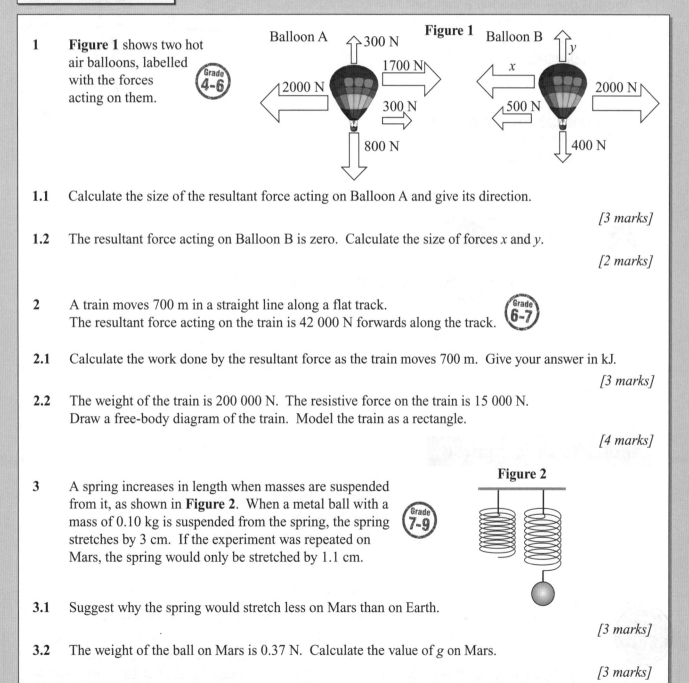

1   **Figure 1** shows two hot air balloons, labelled with the forces acting on them.

Grade 4-6

1.1   Calculate the size of the resultant force acting on Balloon A and give its direction.

[3 marks]

1.2   The resultant force acting on Balloon B is zero. Calculate the size of forces *x* and *y*.

[2 marks]

2   A train moves 700 m in a straight line along a flat track.
        The resultant force acting on the train is 42 000 N forwards along the track.

Grade 6-7

2.1   Calculate the work done by the resultant force as the train moves 700 m. Give your answer in kJ.

[3 marks]

2.2   The weight of the train is 200 000 N. The resistive force on the train is 15 000 N.
          Draw a free-body diagram of the train. Model the train as a rectangle.

[4 marks]

3   A spring increases in length when masses are suspended from it, as shown in **Figure 2**. When a metal ball with a mass of 0.10 kg is suspended from the spring, the spring stretches by 3 cm. If the experiment was repeated on Mars, the spring would only be stretched by 1.1 cm.

Grade 7-9

Figure 2

3.1   Suggest why the spring would stretch less on Mars than on Earth.

[3 marks]

3.2   The weight of the ball on Mars is 0.37 N. Calculate the value of *g* on Mars.

[3 marks]

Forces and Elasticity

Forces don't just make objects <u>move</u>, they can also make them <u>change shape</u>. Whether they change shape <u>temporarily</u> or <u>permanently</u> depends on <u>the object</u> and the forces applied.

Stretching, Compressing or Bending Transfers Energy

1) When you apply a force to an object you may cause it to <u>stretch</u>, <u>compress</u> or <u>bend</u>.

2) To do this, you need <u>more than one</u> force acting on the object — otherwise the object would simply <u>move</u> in the direction of the <u>applied force</u>, instead of changing shape.

3) <u>Work is done</u> when a force stretches or compresses an object and causes energy to be transferred to the <u>elastic potential energy</u> store of the object.

4) If it is <u>elastically deformed</u> (see below), <u>ALL</u> this energy is transferred to the object's <u>elastic potential energy store</u> (see p.19).

Elastic Deformation

1) An object has been <u>elastically deformed</u> if it can <u>go back</u> to its <u>original shape</u> and <u>length</u> after the force has been removed.

2) Objects that can be elastically deformed are called <u>elastic objects</u> (e.g. a spring).

Inelastic Deformation

1) An object has been <u>inelastically deformed</u> if it <u>doesn't</u> return to its <u>original shape</u> and <u>length</u> after the force has been removed.

Elastic objects are only elastic up to a certain point...

Remember the difference between <u>elastic deformation</u> and <u>inelastic deformation</u>. If an <u>object</u> has been <u>elastically deformed</u>, it will <u>return</u> to its <u>original shape</u> when you <u>remove the force</u>. If it's been <u>inelastically deformed</u>, its shape will have been <u>changed permanently</u> — for example, an over- stretched spring will stay stretched even after your remove the force.

Forces and Elasticity

Springs obey a really handy little <u>equation</u> that relates the <u>force</u> on them to their <u>extension</u> — for a while at least. Thankfully, you can <u>plot a graph</u> to see where this equation is <u>valid</u>.

Extension is **Directly Proportional** to **Force**...

If a spring is supported at the top and a weight is attached to the bottom, it <u>stretches</u>.

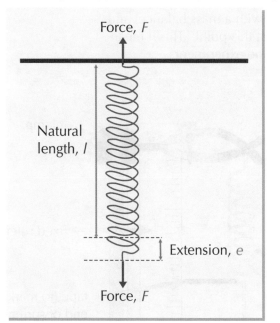

1) The <u>extension</u> of a stretched spring (or certain other elastic objects) is <u>directly proportional</u> to the load or <u>force</u> applied — so $F \propto e$.

2) This is the equation:

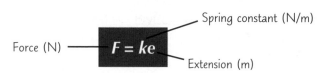

Force (N) —— $\boxed{F = ke}$ —— Spring constant (N/m)

Extension (m)

3) The <u>spring constant</u>, k, depends on the <u>material</u> that you are stretching — a <u>stiffer</u> spring has a <u>greater</u> spring constant.

4) The equation also works for <u>compression</u> (where e is just the <u>difference</u> between the <u>natural</u> and <u>compressed</u> lengths — the <u>compression</u>).

...But this **Stops Working** when the **Force** is **Great Enough**

There's a <u>limit</u> to the amount of force you can apply to an object for the extension to keep on increasing <u>proportionally</u>.

1) The graph shows <u>force against extension</u> for an elastic object.

2) There is a <u>maximum</u> force above which the graph <u>curves</u>, showing that extension is <u>no longer</u> proportional to force.

3) This is known as the <u>limit of proportionality</u> and is shown on the graph at the point marked P.

4) You might see graphs with these <u>axes</u> the <u>other way around</u> — extension-force graphs. The graph still starts has a straight part, but starts to <u>curve upwards</u> once you go past the limit of proportionality, instead of downwards.

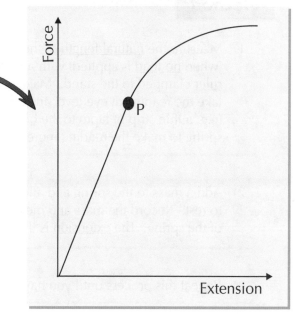

The spring constant is measured in N/m...

EXAM TIP Be careful with <u>units</u> when doing calculations with springs. Your values for <u>extension</u> will usually be in <u>centimetres</u> or <u>millimetres</u>, but the <u>spring constant</u> is measured in <u>newtons per metre</u>. So <u>convert</u> the extension into metres <u>before</u> you do any calculations, or you'll get the wrong answer.

Investigating Springs

Oh look, here's another one of those <u>Required Practicals</u>... This one looks pretty straightforward, but there are a few ways this experiment can <u>stretch</u> you. <u>Read on</u>, so you won't be past your limits in the exam.

You Can **Investigate** the Link Between **Force** and **Extension**

1) Before you start, set up the <u>apparatus</u> as shown in the diagram. Make sure you have plenty of extra masses.

2) It's a good idea to measure the <u>mass</u> of each of your masses (with a mass balance) and calculate its <u>weight</u> (the <u>force</u> applied) using $W = mg$ (p.77) at this point. This'll mean you don't have to do a load of calculations in the middle of the experiment.

Before you launch into the investigation, you could do a quick <u>pilot experiment</u> to check your masses are an appropriate size for your investigation:

* Using an <u>identical spring</u> to the one you'll be testing, <u>load</u> it with <u>masses</u> one at a time up to a total of <u>five</u>. Measure the <u>extension each time</u> you add another mass.

* Work out the <u>increase</u> in the extension of the spring for <u>each</u> of your masses. If any of them cause a <u>bigger increase</u> in extension than the previous masses, you've gone past the spring's <u>limit of proportionality</u>. If this happens, you'll need to use <u>smaller masses</u>, or else you won't get enough measurements for your graph.

clamp

spring

fixed ruler

tape (to mark end of spring)

hanging mass

extra masses

weighted stand

Method

1) Measure the <u>natural length</u> of the spring (when <u>no load</u> is applied) with a <u>millimetre ruler</u> clamped to the stand. Make sure you take the reading at eye level and add a <u>marker</u> (e.g. a thin strip of tape) to the <u>bottom</u> of the spring to make the reading more accurate.

2) Add a mass to the spring and allow the spring to come to <u>rest</u>. Record the mass and measure the new <u>length</u> of the spring. The <u>extension</u> is the change in length.

To check whether the deformation is elastic or inelastic, you can remove each mass temporarily and check to see if the spring goes back to the previous extension.

3) <u>Repeat</u> this process until you have enough measurements (no fewer than 6).

Extension is the change in length due to an applied force...

Make sure you know how to calculate the <u>extension of a spring</u>. It's <u>not</u> the just the <u>length</u> of the spring, it's the <u>difference</u> between the <u>stretched length</u> and the <u>original, unstretched length</u>. The extension when <u>no force</u> is acting on a spring should always be <u>zero</u> — unless the spring has been <u>inelastically deformed</u>.

Investigating Springs **PRACTICAL**

Once you've collected all your <u>data</u>, you need to know what to do with it. Fortunately this page is all about how to use the <u>results</u> from the <u>practical</u> on the last page to work out things like the <u>spring constant</u>.

You Can **Plot** Your **Results** on a **Force-Extension Graph**

Once you've collected your results using the method on the last page, you can <u>plot</u> a <u>force-extension graph</u> of your results. It will only start to <u>curve</u> if you <u>exceed</u> the <u>limit of proportionality</u>, but don't worry if yours doesn't (as long as you've got the straight line bit).

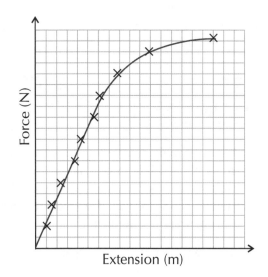

- When the line of best fit is a <u>straight line</u> it means there is a <u>linear</u> relationship between force and extension (they're <u>directly proportional</u>, see page 88). $F = ke$, so the <u>gradient</u> of the straight line is equal to k, the <u>spring constant</u>.

- When the line begins to <u>bend</u>, the relationship is now <u>non-linear</u> between force and extension — the spring <u>stretches more</u> for each unit increase in force.

You Can **Work Out Energy** Stored for **Linear** Relationships

1) As long as a spring is not stretched <u>past</u> its <u>limit of proportionality</u>, <u>work done</u> in stretching (or compressing) a spring can be found using:

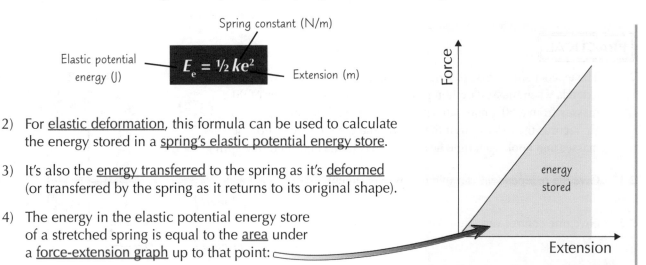

Spring constant (N/m)

Elastic potential energy (J) — $E_e = \frac{1}{2}ke^2$ — Extension (m)

2) For <u>elastic deformation</u>, this formula can be used to calculate the energy stored in a <u>spring's elastic potential energy store</u>.

3) It's also the <u>energy transferred</u> to the spring as it's <u>deformed</u> (or transferred by the spring as it returns to its original shape).

4) The energy in the elastic potential energy store of a stretched spring is equal to the <u>area</u> under a <u>force-extension graph</u> up to that point:

energy stored

The force-extension graph curves at the limit of proportionality...

In reality, you may not always see the <u>curved part</u> in your force-extension graph for this experiment. This may be because you may not have added <u>enough masses</u> to your spring to reach, and go past, the <u>limit of proportionality</u>. But you can still use the <u>gradient</u> of your straight line to calculate the <u>spring constant</u>.

Warm-Up & Exam Questions

It's time to stretch those thinking muscles with another round of questions. Give these a go to test the limits of your newly extended knowledge of springs and elasticity.

Warm-Up Questions

1) True or false? An object which is elastically deformed will not return to its original shape when the force is removed.

2) State the formula linking force, extension and spring constant.

3) What is meant by the limit of proportionality of a spring?

4) Why is it a good idea to do a pilot experiment before starting an experiment on spring extension?

Exam Questions

1 A student wants to investigate how a particular spring extends when a force is applied to it. **Grade 4-6** He plots a graph of force against extension, see **Figure 1**, using the results from his experiment. He then writes a summary of his results. Complete the passage below, using appropriate words to fill in the gaps.

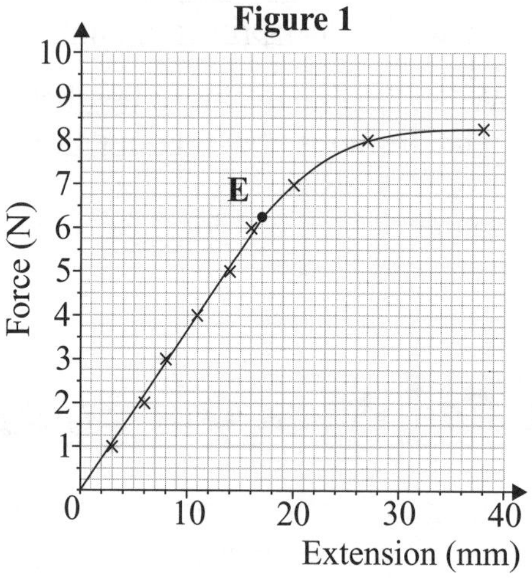

Applying a force to the spring causes it to change

....

Up to the point **E** shown on the graph, the extension

of the spring is directly .... to the

applied force. In this region the spring also returns

to its original shape every time the force is removed.

This is known as .... behaviour.

[3 marks]

Figure 1

(Graph: Force (N) on y-axis from 0 to 10, Extension (mm) on x-axis from 0 to 40, with point **E** marked.)

PRACTICAL

2 The teacher shows his students an experiment to show how a spring extends when masses are hung from it. He hangs a number of 90 g masses from a 50 g hook attached to the base of the spring. **Grade 6-7** He records the extension of the spring and the total weight of the masses and hook each time he adds a mass to the bottom of the spring.

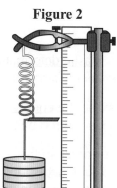

Figure 2

2.1 Give the independent variable in this experiment

[1 mark]

2.2 Give **one** control variable in this experiment.

[1 mark]

When a force of 4 N is applied to the spring, the spring extends elastically by 2.5 cm.

2.3 Calculate the spring constant of the spring.

[4 marks]

2.4 The teacher applies a 15 N force to the spring. When he removes the force, the spring is 7 cm long. The original length of the spring was 5 cm. Describe what has happened to the spring.

[1 mark]

Distance, Displacement, Speed and Velocity

There are a lot of very similar <u>variables</u> on this page, but they're <u>different</u> in some <u>very important</u> ways, so prepare to pay extra close attention. It's down to whether they're a <u>vector</u> or a <u>scalar</u> quantity.

Distance is Scalar, Displacement is a Vector

1) <u>Distance</u> is just <u>how far</u> an object has moved. It's a <u>scalar</u> quantity (p.76) so it doesn't involve <u>direction</u>.

2) Displacement is a <u>vector</u> quantity. It measures the distance and direction in a <u>straight line</u> from an object's <u>starting point</u> to its <u>finishing point</u> — e.g. the plane flew 5 metres <u>north</u>. The direction could be <u>relative to a point</u>, e.g. <u>towards the school</u>, or a <u>bearing</u> (a <u>three-digit angle from north</u>, e.g. <u>035˚</u>).

3) If you walk 5 m <u>north</u>, then 5 m <u>south</u>, your <u>displacement</u> is <u>0 m</u> but the <u>distance</u> travelled is <u>10 m</u>.

Speed and Velocity are Both How Fast You're Going

1) <u>Speed and velocity</u> both measure <u>how fast</u> you're going, but <u>speed</u> is a <u>scalar</u> and <u>velocity</u> is a <u>vector</u>:

<u>Speed</u> is just <u>how fast</u> you're going (e.g. 30 mph or 20 m/s) with no regard to the direction.
<u>Velocity</u> is speed in a given <u>direction</u>, e.g. 30 mph north or 20 m/s, 060°.

2) This means you can have objects travelling at a <u>constant speed</u> with a <u>changing velocity</u>. This happens when the object is <u>changing direction</u> whilst staying at the <u>same speed</u>. An object moving in a <u>circle</u> at a <u>constant speed</u> has a <u>constantly changing</u> velocity, as the direction is <u>always changing</u> (e.g. a <u>car</u> going around a <u>roundabout</u>).

3) If you want to <u>measure</u> the <u>speed</u> of an object that's moving with a <u>constant speed</u>, you should <u>time</u> how long it takes the object to travel a certain <u>distance</u>, e.g. using a <u>ruler</u> and a <u>stopwatch</u>. You can then <u>calculate</u> the object's <u>speed</u> from your measurements using this <u>formula</u>:

$$s = vt$$ distance travelled (m) = speed (m/s) × time (s)

4) Objects <u>rarely</u> travel at a <u>constant speed</u>. E.g. when you <u>walk</u>, <u>run</u> or travel in a <u>car</u>, your speed is <u>always changing</u>. For these cases, the formula above gives the <u>average</u> (<u>mean</u>) speed during that time.

You Need to Know Some Typical Everyday Speeds

1) Whilst every person, train, car etc. is <u>different</u>, there is usually a <u>typical speed</u> that each object travels at. <u>Remember</u> these typical speeds for everyday objects:

A person <u>walking</u> — <u>1.5 m/s</u>	A <u>car</u> — <u>25 m/s</u>
A person <u>running</u> — <u>3 m/s</u>	A <u>train</u> — <u>55 m/s</u>
A person <u>cycling</u> — <u>6 m/s</u>	A <u>plane</u> — <u>250 m/s</u>

2) Lots of different things can <u>affect</u> the speed something travels at. For example, the speed at which a person can <u>walk</u>, <u>run</u> or <u>cycle</u> depends on their <u>fitness</u>, their <u>age</u>, the <u>distance travelled</u> and the <u>terrain</u> (what kind of <u>land</u> they're moving over, e.g. roads, fields) as well as many other factors.

3) It's not only the speed of <u>objects</u> that varies. The speed of <u>sound</u> (<u>330 m/s</u> in <u>air</u>) <u>changes</u> depending on what the sound waves are <u>travelling</u> through, and the <u>speed of wind</u> is affected by many factors.

4) Wind speed can be affected by things like <u>temperature</u>, atmospheric <u>pressure</u> and if there are any large <u>buildings</u> or structures nearby (e.g. forests reduce the speed of the air travelling through them).

Acceleration

Acceleration is the rate of change of velocity. For cases of constant acceleration, there's a really useful equation you can use to calculate all sorts of variables of motion.

Acceleration is How Quickly You're Speeding Up

1) Acceleration is definitely not the same as velocity or speed.
2) Acceleration is the change in velocity in a certain amount of time.
3) You can find the average acceleration of an object using:

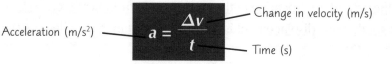

Acceleration (m/s²) — $a = \dfrac{\Delta v}{t}$ — Change in velocity (m/s) / Time (s)

EXAMPLE:
A cat accelerates at 2.5 m/s²
from 2.0 m/s to 6.0 m/s.
Find the time it takes to do this.
$t = \Delta v \div a$
$= (6.0 - 2.0) \div 2.5 = 1.6$ s

4) Deceleration is just negative acceleration (if something slows down, the change in velocity is negative).

You Need to be Able to Estimate Accelerations

You might have to estimate the acceleration (or deceleration) of an object.
To do this, you need the typical speeds from the previous page:

EXAMPLE: A car is travelling along a road, when it collides with a tree and comes to a stop. Estimate the deceleration of the car.

1) First, give a sensible speed for the car to be travelling at. — The typical speed of a car is ~25 m/s.
2) Next, estimate how long it would take the car to stop. — The car comes to a stop in ~1 s.
3) Put these numbers into the acceleration equation. — $a = \Delta v \div t$
   $= (-25) \div 1$
   $= -25$ m/s²

   The ~ symbol just means it's an approximate value (or answer).

4) The question asked for the deceleration, so you can lose the minus sign (which shows the car is slowing down): — So the deceleration is ~25 m/s²

Uniform Acceleration Means a Constant Acceleration

1) Constant acceleration is sometimes called uniform acceleration.
2) Acceleration due to gravity (g) is uniform for objects in free fall. It's roughly equal to 9.8 m/s² near the Earth's surface and has the same value as gravitational field strength (p.77).
3) You can use this equation for uniform acceleration:

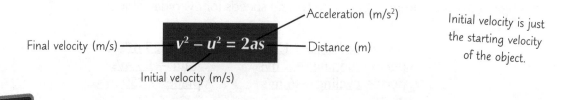

Final velocity (m/s) — $v^2 - u^2 = 2as$ — Acceleration (m/s²) / Distance (m)
Initial velocity (m/s)

Initial velocity is just the starting velocity of the object.

EXAMPLE: A van travelling at 23 m/s starts decelerating uniformly at 2.0 m/s² as it heads towards a built-up area 112 m away. What will its speed be when it reaches the built-up area?

1) First, rearrange the equation so v^2 is on one side. — $v^2 = u^2 + 2as$
2) Now put the numbers in — remember a is negative because it's a deceleration. — $v^2 = 23^2 + (2 \times -2.0 \times 112)$
   $= 81$
3) Finally, square root the whole thing. — $v = \sqrt{81} = 9$ m/s

Distance-Time Graphs

It's time for some more exciting graphs. Distance-time graphs contain a lot of information, but they can look a bit complicated. Read on to get to grips with the rules of the graphs, and all will become clear.

You Can **Show Journeys** on **Distance-Time Graphs**

If an object moves in a straight line, its distance travelled can be plotted on a distance-time graph.

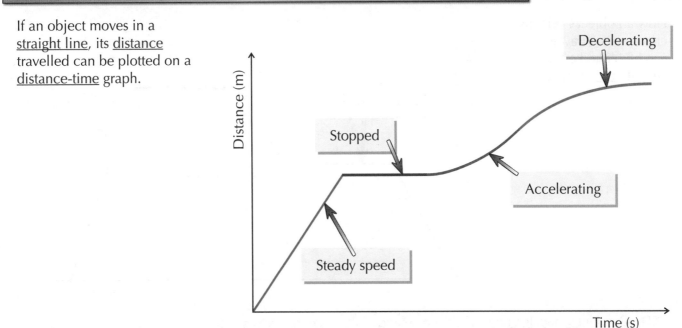

The **Shape of the Graph** Shows How the **Object** is **Moving**

1) Gradient = speed. (The steeper the graph, the faster the object is going.)
   This is because: speed = distance ÷ time = (change in vertical axis) ÷ (change in horizontal axis).

2) Flat sections are where the object's stationary — it's stopped.

3) Straight uphill sections mean it is travelling at a steady speed.

4) Curves represent acceleration or deceleration (p.88).

5) A steepening curve means the object's speeding up (increasing gradient).

6) A levelling off curve means it's slowing down (decreasing gradient).

7) If the object is changing speed (accelerating) you can find its speed at a point by finding the gradient of the tangent to the curve at that point, p.10.

Read the axes of any graph you get given carefully...

Make sure you don't get confused between distance-time graphs and velocity-time graphs. They can look similar, but tell you different things and have different rules, as you're about to find out...

Velocity-Time Graphs

Even more graphs! Just like distance-time graphs, velocity-time graphs are a great way of representing journeys. There's a lot of information in them, so make sure you know how to get the most out of them.

You Can Also Show them on a Velocity-Time Graph

How an object's velocity changes as it travels can be plotted on a velocity-time graph.

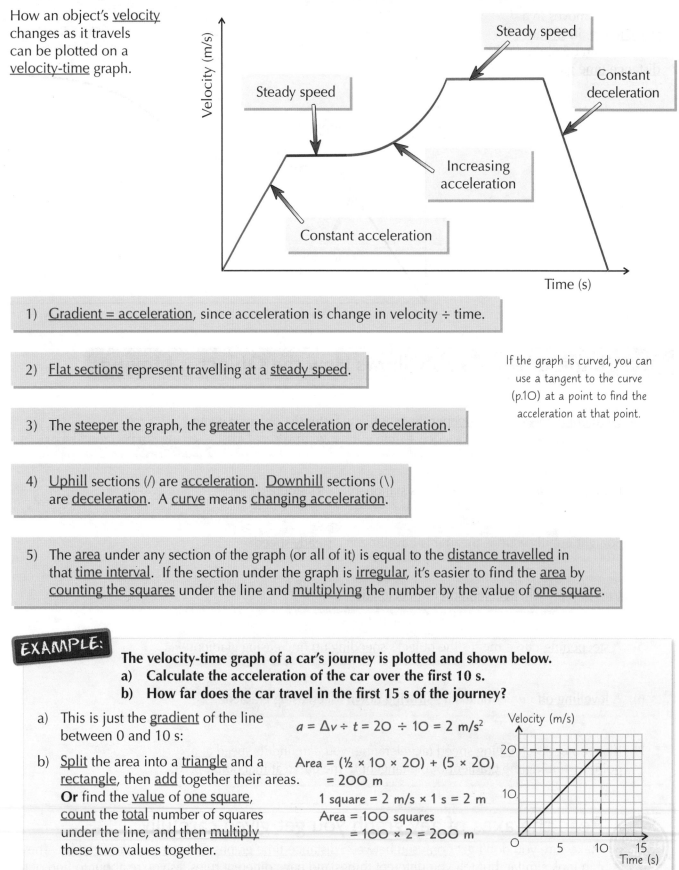

1) Gradient = acceleration, since acceleration is change in velocity ÷ time.

2) Flat sections represent travelling at a steady speed.

3) The steeper the graph, the greater the acceleration or deceleration.

4) Uphill sections (/) are acceleration. Downhill sections (\) are deceleration. A curve means changing acceleration.

If the graph is curved, you can use a tangent to the curve (p.10) at a point to find the acceleration at that point.

5) The area under any section of the graph (or all of it) is equal to the distance travelled in that time interval. If the section under the graph is irregular, it's easier to find the area by counting the squares under the line and multiplying the number by the value of one square.

EXAMPLE:

The velocity-time graph of a car's journey is plotted and shown below.
a) Calculate the acceleration of the car over the first 10 s.
b) How far does the car travel in the first 15 s of the journey?

a) This is just the gradient of the line between 0 and 10 s:

$$a = \Delta v \div t = 20 \div 10 = 2 \text{ m/s}^2$$

b) Split the area into a triangle and a rectangle, then add together their areas. **Or** find the value of one square, count the total number of squares under the line, and then multiply these two values together.

Area = (½ × 10 × 20) + (5 × 20)
= 200 m

1 square = 2 m/s × 1 s = 2 m
Area = 100 squares
= 100 × 2 = 200 m

Drag

Revision can be a bit of a <u>drag</u>, but hey, you're over halfway though the topic now.
No use <u>slowing down</u> now — however, there's quite a bit of that on this page.

Friction is Always There to Slow Things Down

1) If an object has <u>no force</u> propelling it along it will always <u>slow down and stop</u> because of <u>friction</u> (unless you're in space where there's nothing to rub against).

2) Friction always acts in the <u>opposite</u> direction to movement.

3) To travel at a <u>steady</u> speed, the driving force needs to <u>balance</u> the frictional forces.

4) You get friction between <u>two surfaces</u> in contact, or when an object passes <u>through a fluid</u> (<u>drag</u>).

Drag and Air Resistance

Air flows easily
over a streamlined car.

1) <u>Drag</u> is the <u>resistance</u> you get in a <u>fluid</u> (a gas or a liquid). <u>Air resistance</u> is a type of <u>drag</u> — it's the frictional force produced by the <u>air</u> acting on a <u>moving object</u>.

2) The most <u>important factor</u> by far in reducing drag is keeping the shape of the object <u>streamlined</u>. This is where the object is designed to allow fluid to <u>flow easily</u> across it, reducing drag.

3) Parachutes work in the <u>opposite</u> way — they want as much drag as they can get.

Drag Increases as Speed Increases

<u>Frictional forces</u> from fluids always <u>increase with speed</u>.

A car has <u>much more</u> friction to <u>work against</u> when travelling at <u>70 mph</u> compared to <u>30 mph</u>. So at 70 mph the engine has to work <u>much harder</u> just to maintain a <u>steady speed</u>.

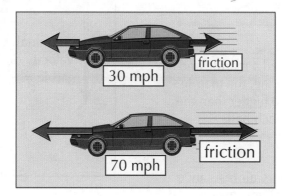

Use the right words when talking about resistive forces...

Be as <u>specific</u> as you can when talking about <u>forces</u> which act <u>against motion</u> (i.e. <u>resistive</u> <u>forces</u>). If an object is travelling through <u>air</u>, simply referring to the resistive force as 'drag' may not be enough to get you the marks — you'll need to specify the force is <u>air resistance</u>.

Terminal Velocity

If an object <u>falls</u> for long enough, it will reach its <u>terminal velocity</u>. It's all about <u>balance</u> between <u>weight</u> and <u>air resistance</u>. <u>Parachutes</u> work by <u>decreasing</u> your terminal velocity.

Objects **Falling** Through **Fluids** Reach a **Terminal Velocity**

1) When falling objects first <u>set off</u>, the force of gravity is <u>much more</u> than the <u>frictional force</u> slowing them down, so they accelerate.

2) As the <u>speed increases</u> the friction <u>builds up</u>.

3) This gradually <u>reduces</u> the <u>acceleration</u> until eventually the <u>frictional force</u> is <u>equal</u> to the <u>accelerating force</u> (so the <u>resultant force is zero</u>).

4) It will have reached its maximum speed or <u>terminal velocity</u> and will fall at a steady speed.

maximum speed or 'terminal velocity'

Velocity

Time

Terminal Velocity Depends on **Shape** and **Area**

1) Typically, the <u>less streamlined</u> an object is, the <u>lower</u> its <u>terminal velocity</u>.

2) So objects with <u>large surface areas</u> tend to have lower terminal velocities.

3) For example, if you dropped a <u>marble</u> and a <u>beach ball</u> off a tall building, the marble's terminal velocity would be <u>higher</u> than the terminal velocity of the beach ball.

4) This is because there is <u>more air resistance</u> acting on the beach ball, at any given speed.

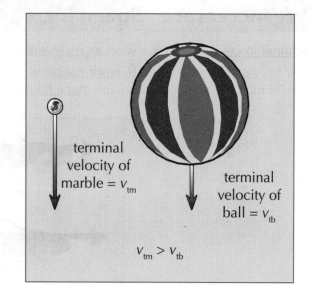

terminal velocity of marble = v_{tm}

terminal velocity of ball = v_{tb}

$v_{tm} > v_{tb}$

5) So the beach ball spends <u>less time</u> accelerating (and so doesn't <u>speed up</u> as much) before the air resistance is large enough to <u>equal</u> the accelerating force

Warm-Up & Exam Questions

Slow down, it's not time to move on to the next section just yet. First it's time to check that all the stuff you've just read is still running around your brain. Dive into these questions.

Warm-Up Questions

1) What is the difference between speed and velocity?
2) Suggest the typical speeds of: a) a person running,   b) a train,   c) a plane.
3) How is acceleration shown on a distance-time graph?
4) Describe the shape of the line on a velocity-time graph for an object travelling at a steady speed.
5) In general, how does the air resistance acting on a car change as the car's speed increases?

Exam Questions

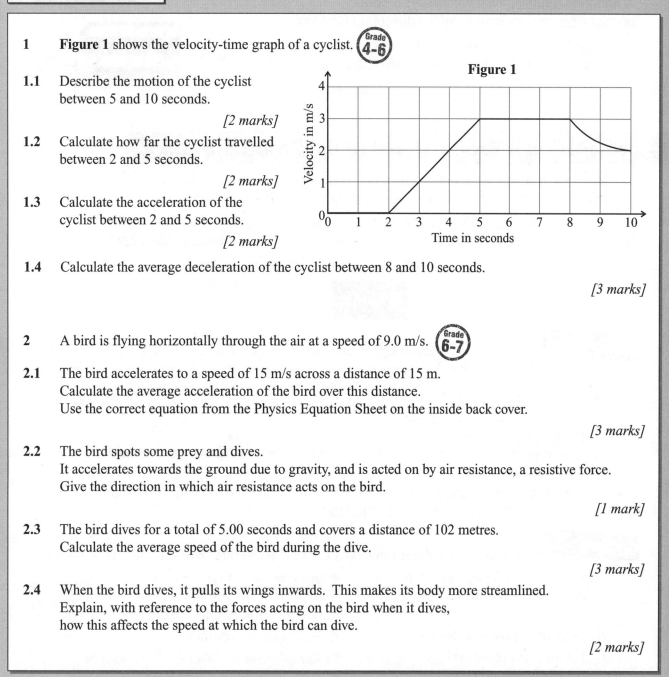

1   **Figure 1** shows the velocity-time graph of a cyclist. *Grade 4-6*

1.1   Describe the motion of the cyclist between 5 and 10 seconds.

[2 marks]

1.2   Calculate how far the cyclist travelled between 2 and 5 seconds.

[2 marks]

1.3   Calculate the acceleration of the cyclist between 2 and 5 seconds.

[2 marks]

1.4   Calculate the average deceleration of the cyclist between 8 and 10 seconds.

[3 marks]

2   A bird is flying horizontally through the air at a speed of 9.0 m/s. *Grade 6-7*

2.1   The bird accelerates to a speed of 15 m/s across a distance of 15 m.
Calculate the average acceleration of the bird over this distance.
Use the correct equation from the Physics Equation Sheet on the inside back cover.

[3 marks]

2.2   The bird spots some prey and dives.
It accelerates towards the ground due to gravity, and is acted on by air resistance, a resistive force.
Give the direction in which air resistance acts on the bird.

[1 mark]

2.3   The bird dives for a total of 5.00 seconds and covers a distance of 102 metres.
Calculate the average speed of the bird during the dive.

[3 marks]

2.4   When the bird dives, it pulls its wings inwards. This makes its body more streamlined.
Explain, with reference to the forces acting on the bird when it dives,
how this affects the speed at which the bird can dive.

[2 marks]

Newton's First and Second Laws

Way back in the 1660s, some clever chap named <u>Isaac Newton</u> worked out some <u>Laws of Motion</u>...

A **Force** is Needed to **Change Motion**

This may seem simple, but it's important. <u>Newton's First Law</u> says that a resultant force (p.78) is needed to make something <u>start moving</u>, <u>speed up</u> or <u>slow down</u>:

> If the resultant force on a <u>stationary</u> object is <u>zero</u>, the object will <u>remain stationary</u>. If the <u>resultant force</u> on a moving object is <u>zero</u>, it'll just carry on moving at the <u>same velocity</u> (same speed <u>and</u> direction).

So, when a train or car or bus or anything else is <u>moving</u> at a <u>constant velocity</u>, the resistive and driving <u>forces</u> on it must all be <u>balanced</u>. The velocity will only change if there's a <u>non-zero</u> resultant force acting on the object.

1) A non-zero <u>resultant</u> force will always produce <u>acceleration</u> (or deceleration) in the <u>direction of the force</u>.

2) This "<u>acceleration</u>" can take <u>five</u> different forms: <u>starting</u>, <u>stopping</u>, <u>speeding up</u>, <u>slowing down</u> and <u>changing direction</u>.

3) On a free body diagram, the <u>arrows</u> will be <u>unequal</u>.

Acceleration is **Proportional** to the **Resultant Force**

1) The <u>larger</u> the <u>resultant force</u> acting on an object, the <u>more</u> the object accelerates — the force and the acceleration are <u>directly proportional</u>. You can write this as $F \propto a$.

2) Acceleration is also <u>inversely proportional</u> to the <u>mass</u> of the object — so an object with a <u>larger</u> mass will accelerate <u>less</u> than one with a smaller mass (for a <u>fixed resultant force</u>).

3) There's an incredibly <u>useful formula</u> that describes <u>Newton's Second Law</u>:

Resultant force (N) — $F = ma$ — Acceleration (m/s²) / Mass (kg)

EXAMPLE: **A van of mass of 2080 kg has an engine that provides a driving force of 5200 N. At 70 mph the drag force acting on the van is 5148 N. Find its acceleration at 70 mph.**

1) Work out the <u>resultant force</u> on the van. (Drawing a <u>free body diagram</u> may help.)

Resultant force = 5200 − 5148 = 52 N

2) <u>Rearrange</u> $F = ma$ and stick in the <u>values</u> you know.

$a = F \div m$
$= 52 \div 2080 = 0.025$ m/s²

You can use <u>Newton's Second Law</u> to get an idea of the forces involved in everyday transport. Large <u>forces</u> are needed to produce large <u>accelerations</u>:

EXAMPLE: **Estimate the resultant force on a car as it accelerates from rest to a typical speed.**

1) Estimate the <u>acceleration</u> of the car, using <u>typical</u> speeds from page 87.

A typical speed of a car is ~25 m/s. It takes ~10 s to reach this. So $a = \Delta v \div t = 25 \div 10 = 2.5$ m/s²

The ~ means approximately.

2) <u>Estimate</u> the <u>mass</u> of the car.

Mass of a car is ~1000 kg.

3) Put these numbers into <u>Newton's Second Law</u>.

So using $F = ma = 1000 \times 2.5 = 2500$ N
So the resultant force is ~2500 N

Inertia and Newton's Third Law

Newton's Third Law and inertia sound pretty straightforward, but things can quickly get confusing...

Inertia is the Tendency for Motion to Remain Unchanged

1) Until acted upon by a resultant force, objects at rest stay at rest and
    objects moving at a steady speed will stay moving at that speed (Newton's First Law).
    This tendency to continue in the same state of motion is called inertia.

2) An object's inertial mass measures how difficult it is to change the velocity of an object.

3) Inertial mass can be found using Newton's Second Law of $F = ma$ (see the last page).
    Rearranging this gives $m = F \div a$, so inertial mass is just the ratio of force over acceleration.

Newton's Third Law — Interaction Pairs are Equal and Opposite

Newton's Third Law says:

> When two objects interact, the forces they
> exert on each other are equal and opposite.

1) If you push something, say a shopping trolley, the trolley will push back against you, just as hard.

2) And as soon as you stop pushing, so does the trolley. Kinda clever really.

3) So far so good. The slightly tricky thing to get your head round is this
    — if the forces are always equal, how does anything ever go anywhere?
    The important thing to remember is that the two forces are acting on different objects.

When skater A pushes on skater B, she feels an equal and opposite force from skater B's hand (the 'normal contact' force). Both skaters feel the same sized force, in opposite directions, and so accelerate away from each other.

Skater A will be accelerated more than skater B, though, because she has a smaller mass — remember $a = F \div m$.

An example of Newton's Third Law in an equilibrium situation is a man pushing against a wall. As the man pushes the wall, there is a normal contact force acting back on him. These two forces are the same size. As the man applies a force and pushes the wall, the wall 'pushes back' on him with an equal force.

Normal contact force

Push

It can be easy to get confused with Newton's Third Law when an object is in equilibrium. E.g. a book resting on a table is in equilibrium. The weight of the book is equal to the normal contact force. The weight of the book pulls it down, and the normal reaction force from the table pushes it up. This is NOT Newton's Third Law. These forces are different types and they're both acting on the book.

The pairs of forces due to Newton's Third Law in this case are:

1) The weight of book is pulled down by gravity from Earth (W_B)
    and the book also pulls back up on the Earth (W_E).

2) The normal contact force from the table pushing up on the book (N_B) and
    the normal contact force from the book pushing down on the table (N_T).

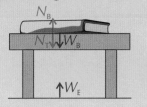

PRACTICAL Investigating Motion

Here comes another Required Practical. This one's all about testing Newton's Second Law. It uses some nifty bits of kit that you may not have seen before, so make sure you follow the instructions closely.

You can **Investigate** how **Mass** and **Force** Affect Acceleration

It's time for an experiment that tests Newton's 2nd Law, $F = ma$ (p.94).

1) Set up the apparatus shown above. Set up the trolley so it holds a piece of card with a gap in the middle that will interrupt the signal on the light gate twice. If you measure the length of each bit of card that will pass through the light gate and input this into the software, the light gate can measure the velocity for each bit of card. It can use this to work out the acceleration of the trolley.

2) Connect the trolley to a piece of string that goes over a pulley and is connected on the other side to a hook (that you know the mass of and can add more masses to).

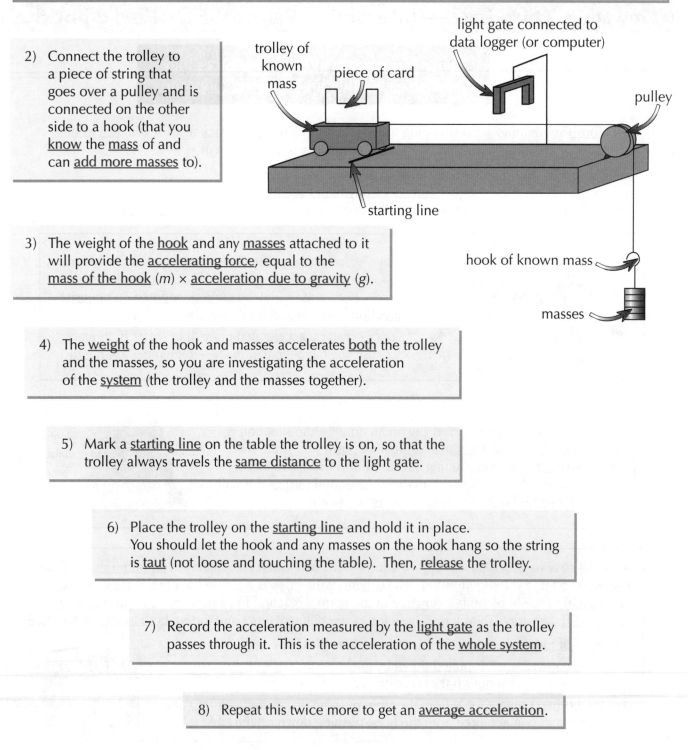

3) The weight of the hook and any masses attached to it will provide the accelerating force, equal to the mass of the hook (m) × acceleration due to gravity (g).

4) The weight of the hook and masses accelerates both the trolley and the masses, so you are investigating the acceleration of the system (the trolley and the masses together).

5) Mark a starting line on the table the trolley is on, so that the trolley always travels the same distance to the light gate.

6) Place the trolley on the starting line and hold it in place. You should let the hook and any masses on the hook hang so the string is taut (not loose and touching the table). Then, release the trolley.

7) Record the acceleration measured by the light gate as the trolley passes through it. This is the acceleration of the whole system.

8) Repeat this twice more to get an average acceleration.

Investigating Motion

Now you've set up the equipment, and you're used to how it works, it's time to start adjusting your variables. Take care with the method here — there are some important points you don't want to miss.

Varying Mass and Force

1) To investigate the effect of mass, add masses to the trolley, one at a time, to increase the mass of the system.

2) Don't add masses to the hook, or you'll change the force.

3) Record the average acceleration for each mass.

The friction between the trolley and the bench might affect your acceleration measurements. You could use an air track to reduce this friction (a track which hovers a trolley on jets of air).

To investigate the effect of force, you need to keep the total mass of the system the same, but change the mass on the hook.

1) To do this, start with all the masses loaded onto the trolley, and transfer the masses to the hook one at a time, to increase the accelerating force (the weight of the hanging masses).

2) The mass of the system stays the same as you're only transferring the masses from one part of the system (the trolley) to another (the hook).

3) Record the average acceleration for each force.

Newton's Second Law Can Explain the Results

1) Newton's Second Law can be written as $F = ma$. Here, F = weight of the hanging masses, m = mass of the whole system and a = acceleration of the system.

2) By adding masses to the trolley, the mass of the whole system increases, but the force applied to the system stays the same. This should lead to a decrease in the acceleration of the trolley, as $a = F \div m$.

3) By transferring masses to the hook, you are increasing the accelerating force without changing the mass of the whole system. So increasing the force should lead to an increase in the acceleration of the trolley.

PRACTICAL TIP

This experiment has a lot of steps, so don't speed through it...

Make sure the string is the right length and there's enough space for the hanging masses to fall. There needs to be enough space so that the masses don't hit the floor before the trolley has passed through the light gate fully — if they hit the floor, the force won't be applied the whole way through the trolley's journey, so you won't get an accurate measurement for the speed.

Warm-Up & Exam Questions

Now you've gotten yourself on the right side of the law(s of motion), it's time to put your knowledge on trial. Have a go at cross-examining these questions.

1) What is the resultant force on an object moving at a constant velocity?

2) Boulders A and B are accelerated from 0 m/s to 5 m/s in 10 s. Boulder A required a force of 70 N, and Boulder B required a force of 95 N. Which boulder has the greater inertial mass?

3) True or False? Two interacting objects exert equal and opposite forces on each other.

4) In a trolley-and-pulley system, as in the practical on page 96, where should you put masses to increase the mass of the system without increasing the force on the trolley?

Exam Questions

1 Dahlia's cricket bat has a mass of 1.2 kg. (Grade 4-6)
She uses it to hit a ball with a mass of 160 g forwards with a force of 500 N.

1.1 State the force that the ball exerts on the bat. Explain your answer.

[2 marks]

1.2 Which is greater — the acceleration of the bat or the ball? Explain your answer.

[2 marks]

Figure 1

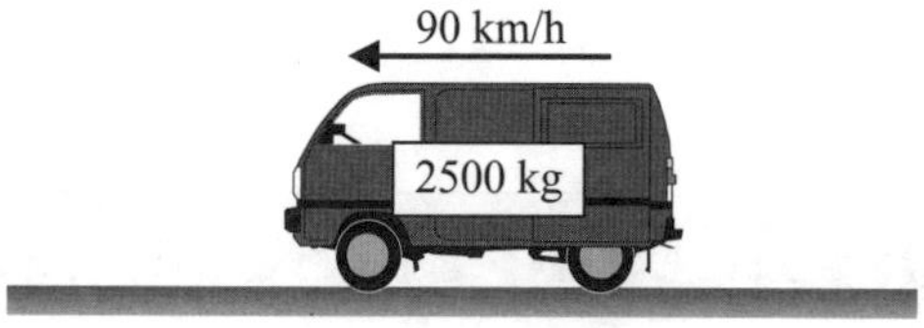

90 km/h

2500 kg

2 A camper van has a mass of 2500 kg.
It is driven along a straight,
level road at a constant speed   (Grade 6-7)
of 90.0 kilometres per hour.

2.1 A headwind begins blowing with a force of 200 N, causing the van to slow down.
Calculate the van's deceleration.

[3 marks]

The van begins travelling at a constant speed before colliding with a stationary 10.0 kg traffic cone.
The traffic cone accelerates in the direction of the van's motion with an acceleration of 29.0 m/s^2.

2.2 Calculate the force applied to the traffic cone by the van.

[2 marks]

2.3 Calculate the deceleration of the van during the collision.
Assume all of the force applied by the cone to the van causes the deceleration.

[3 marks]

PRACTICAL

3* Stefan is investigating how acceleration varies with force.
He has a 1 kg trolley, attached by a pulley to a 0.5 kg hanging hook.   (Grade 7-9)
He also has eight 100 g masses. When the hook is released, the trolley rolls
along a table, and passes through a light gate which calculates its acceleration.

Describe an experiment that Stefan can perform using this equipment to investigate the relationship between force and acceleration.

[4 marks]

Stopping Distances

Knowing what affects <u>stopping distances</u> is especially useful for everyday life, as well as the exam.

Stopping Distance is the Sum of Two Distances

1) In an <u>emergency</u> (e.g. a <u>hazard</u> ahead in the road), a driver may perform an <u>emergency stop</u>. This is where <u>maximum force</u> is applied by the <u>brakes</u> in order to stop the car in the <u>shortest possible distance</u>. The <u>longer</u> it takes to perform an <u>emergency stop</u>, the <u>higher the risk</u> of crashing into whatever's in front.

2) The distance it takes to stop a car in an emergency (its <u>stopping distance</u>) is found by:

> Stopping Distance = Thinking Distance + Braking Distance

3) The <u>thinking distance</u> — how far the car travels during the driver's <u>reaction time</u> (the time <u>between</u> the driver <u>seeing</u> a hazard and <u>applying the brakes</u>).

4) The <u>braking distance</u> — the distance taken to stop under the <u>braking force</u> (once the brakes are applied).

Typical car braking distances are: 14 m at 30 mph, 55 m at 60 mph and 75 m at 70 mph.

Many Factors Affect Your Total Stopping Distance

<u>Thinking distance</u> is affected by:
*   Your <u>speed</u> — the <u>faster</u> you're going the <u>further</u> you'll travel during the <u>time</u> you take to <u>react</u>.
*   Your <u>reaction time</u> — the longer your reaction time (see next page), the longer your <u>thinking distance</u>. This can be affected by <u>tiredness</u>, <u>drugs</u> or <u>alcohol</u>. <u>Distractions</u> can affect your <u>ability</u> to <u>react</u>.

<u>Braking distance</u> is affected by:
*   Your <u>speed</u> — for a <u>given</u> braking force, the <u>faster</u> a vehicle travels, the <u>longer</u> it takes to stop (p.101).
*   The <u>weather</u> or <u>road surface</u> — if it is <u>wet</u> or <u>icy</u>, or there are <u>leaves</u> or <u>oil</u> on the road, there is <u>less grip</u> (and so less <u>friction</u>) between a vehicle's tyres and the road, which can cause tyres to <u>skid</u>.
*   The <u>condition</u> of your <u>tyres</u> — if the tyres of a vehicle are <u>bald</u> (they don't have <u>any tread left</u>) then they cannot <u>get rid of water</u> in wet conditions. This leads to them <u>skidding</u> on top of the water.
*   How good your <u>brakes</u> are — if brakes are <u>worn</u> or <u>faulty</u>, they won't be able to apply as much <u>force</u> as well-maintained brakes, which could be dangerous when you need to brake hard.

You need to be able to <u>describe</u> the <u>factors</u> affecting stopping distance and how this affects <u>safety</u> — especially in an <u>emergency</u>.

> For example: <u>Icy</u> conditions increase the chance of <u>skidding</u> (and so increase the stopping distance) so driving <u>too close</u> to other cars in icy conditions is <u>unsafe</u>. The <u>longer</u> your stopping distance, the <u>more space</u> you need to leave <u>in front</u> in order to stop <u>safely</u>.

<u>Speed limits</u> are really important because <u>speed</u> affects the stopping distance so much.

Stopping distance = thinking distance + braking distance.
The exam might ask you to give factors, <u>other than speed</u>, which affect <u>thinking</u> or <u>braking</u> <u>distances</u>, so make sure you know <u>all the factors</u> that affect each of these and <u>what their effects are</u>.

Reaction Times

Reaction times are an <u>important factor</u> in <u>thinking distances</u>. They're also super easy to <u>test</u> for yourself. Read on for a simple <u>experiment</u> you can do in the lab.

You can **Measure** Reaction Times with the **Ruler Drop Test**

<u>Everyone's</u> reaction time is different, but a typical reaction time is between <u>0.2</u> and <u>0.9 s</u> and many different <u>factors</u> affect it (see previous page).

You can do <u>simple experiments</u> to investigate your reaction time, but as reaction times are <u>so short</u>, you haven't got a chance of measuring one with a <u>stopwatch</u>. One way of measuring reaction times is to use a <u>computer-based test</u> (e.g. <u>clicking a mouse</u> when the screen changes colour). Another is the <u>ruler drop test</u>. Here's how to carry it out:

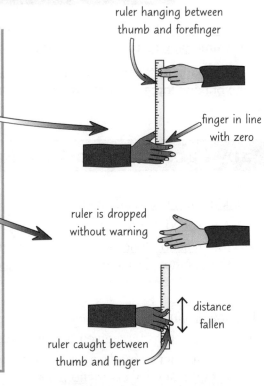

ruler hanging between thumb and forefinger

finger in line with zero

ruler is dropped without warning

distance fallen

ruler caught between thumb and finger

1) Sit with your arm resting on the edge of a table (this should stop you moving your arm up or down during the test). Get someone else to hold a ruler so it <u>hangs between</u> your thumb and forefinger, lined up with <u>zero</u>. You may need a <u>third person</u> to be at <u>eye level with the ruler</u> to check it's lined up.

2) Without giving any warning, the person holding the ruler should <u>drop it</u>. Close your thumb and finger to try to <u>catch the ruler as quickly as possible</u>.

3) The measurement on the ruler at the point where it is caught is <u>how far</u> the ruler dropped in the time it takes you to react.

4) The <u>longer</u> the <u>distance</u>, the <u>longer</u> the <u>reaction time</u>.

5) You can calculate <u>how long</u> the ruler falls for (the <u>reaction</u> time) because <u>acceleration due to gravity is constant</u> (roughly 9.8 m/s²).

E.g. say you catch the ruler at 20 cm. From p.88 you know: $v^2 - u^2 = 2as$.

$u = 0$, $a = 9.8$ m/s² and $s = 0.2$ m, so: $v = \sqrt{2 \times 9.8 \times 0.2 + 0}$ = <u>2.0 m/s (to 2 s.f.)</u>

v is equal to the <u>change in velocity</u> of the ruler.

From page 88 you also know: $a = \Delta v \div t$ so $t = \Delta v \div a = 2.0 \div 9.8 = 0.2$ s (to 1 s.f.) This gives your <u>reaction time</u>.

6) It's <u>pretty hard</u> to do this experiment <u>accurately</u>, so you should do a lot of <u>repeats</u>. The results will be better if the ruler falls <u>straight down</u> — you might want to add a <u>blob of modelling clay</u> to the bottom to stop it from waving about.

7) Make sure it's a <u>fair test</u> — use the <u>same ruler</u> for each repeat, and have the <u>same person</u> dropping it.

8) You could try to investigate some factors affecting reaction time, e.g. you could introduce <u>distractions</u> by having some <u>music</u> playing or by having someone <u>talk to you</u> while the test takes place (see the previous page for more on the factors affecting reaction time).

9) Remember to still do lots of <u>repeats</u> and calculate the <u>mean</u> reaction time with distractions, which you can <u>compare</u> to the mean reaction time <u>without</u> distractions.

Braking Distances

So you know the basics of <u>stopping distances</u> now, but how do the brakes actually work to <u>slow down a car</u>? Well, it's all down to <u>friction</u> and <u>transferring energy</u> away from the wheels to the brakes.

Braking Relies on **Friction** Between the **Brakes** and **Wheels**

1) When the brake pedal is pushed, this causes brake pads to be <u>pressed</u> onto the wheels. This contact causes <u>friction</u>, which <u>causes work to be done</u>.

2) The work done between the brakes and the wheels transfers <u>energy</u> from the <u>kinetic energy stores</u> of the <u>wheels</u> to the <u>thermal energy stores</u> of the <u>brakes</u>. The brakes <u>increase</u> in <u>temperature</u>.

3) The <u>faster</u> a vehicle is going, the more energy it has in its <u>kinetic</u> store, so the <u>more work</u> needs to be done to stop it. This means that a <u>greater braking force</u> is needed to make it stop within a <u>certain distance</u>.

4) A larger <u>braking force</u> means a <u>larger deceleration</u>. Very large decelerations can be <u>dangerous</u> because they may cause brakes to <u>overheat</u> (so they don't work as well) or could cause the vehicle to <u>skid</u>.

You Can **Estimate** the **Braking Force** Required to **Stop**

You can <u>estimate</u> the <u>braking force</u> required to make a vehicle <u>decelerate</u> and <u>come to a stop</u>. As you're only estimating the force, this is a place where you may well need to use <u>typical values</u>:

> **EXAMPLE:**
>
> **A car travelling at a typical speed makes an emergency stop to avoid hitting a hazard 25 m ahead.**
> **Estimate the braking force needed to produce this deceleration.**
>
> *For a refresher on typical speed values, head back to page 87.*
>
> 1) Assume the deceleration is <u>uniform</u>, and <u>rearrange</u> $v^2 - u^2 = 2as$ to find the deceleration.
>
> $v = {\sim}25$ m/s $\quad m = {\sim}1000$ kg.
> $a = (v^2 - u^2) \div 2s = (0^2 - 25^2) \div (2 \times 25) = -12.5$
>
> 2) Then use $\underline{F = ma}$, with $m = {\sim}1000$ kg.
>
> $F = ma$
> $F = 1000 \times 12.5 = 12\ 500$ N, so F is ${\sim}12\ 500$ N

Typical values, always there when you need them...

Make sure you <u>memorise</u> the <u>typical speed values</u> on page 87. It shouldn't matter if they're slightly off, but they need to be of <u>roughly the right size</u>, or your calculations won't make sense. If you're asked about a <u>vehicle</u> that you don't know the <u>typical speed</u> or <u>mass</u> of, try to use those you do know as a <u>guide</u>. For example, a <u>bus</u> will have a <u>greater typical mass</u> than a car (1000 kg) but a <u>slightly smaller typical speed</u> than a car (25 m/s), as it's <u>bigger</u> and travels on <u>slower</u> routes.

Momentum

A <u>large rugby player</u> running very <u>fast</u> has much <u>more momentum</u> than a <u>skinny</u> bloke out for a Sunday afternoon <u>stroll</u>. Momentum's something that <u>all moving objects have</u>, so you better get your head around it.

Momentum = Mass × Velocity

Momentum is mainly about how much 'oomph' an object has. It's a <u>property</u> that <u>all moving objects have</u>.

1) The <u>greater</u> the <u>mass</u> of an object, or the <u>greater</u> its <u>velocity</u>, the <u>more momentum</u> the object has.

2) Momentum is a <u>vector</u> quantity — it has size <u>and</u> direction.

3) You can <u>work out</u> the momentum of an object using:

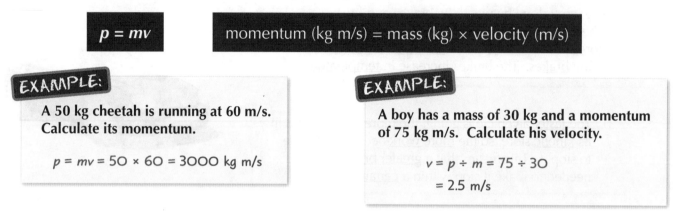

$$p = mv$$

momentum (kg m/s) = mass (kg) × velocity (m/s)

EXAMPLE:

A 50 kg cheetah is running at 60 m/s. Calculate its momentum.

$p = mv = 50 × 60 = 3000$ kg m/s

EXAMPLE:

A boy has a mass of 30 kg and a momentum of 75 kg m/s. Calculate his velocity.

$v = p ÷ m = 75 ÷ 30$
$= 2.5$ m/s

Momentum Before = Momentum After

In a <u>closed system</u>, the total momentum <u>before</u> an event (e.g. a collision) is the same as <u>after</u> the event. This is called <u>conservation of momentum</u>.

A closed system is just a fancy way of saying that no external forces act.

In snooker, balls of the <u>same size</u> and <u>mass</u> collide with each other. Each collision is an <u>event</u> where the <u>momentum</u> of <u>each ball changes</u>, but the <u>overall</u> momentum <u>stays the same</u> (momentum is <u>conserved</u>).

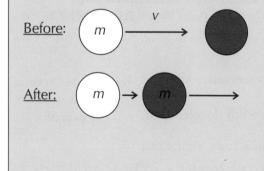

Before:

After:

The red ball is <u>stationary</u>, so it has <u>zero momentum</u>. The white ball is moving with a velocity v, so has a <u>momentum</u> of $p = mv$.

The white ball hits the red ball, causing it to <u>move</u>. The red ball now has <u>momentum</u>. The white ball <u>continues</u> moving, but at a much <u>smaller velocity</u> (and so a much <u>smaller momentum</u>).

The <u>combined</u> momentum of the red and white ball is equal to the <u>original</u> momentum of the white ball, mv.

A <u>moving car</u> hits into the back of a <u>parked car</u>. The crash causes the two cars to <u>lock together</u>, and they <u>continue moving</u> in the direction that the original moving car was travelling, but at a <u>lower velocity</u>.

<u>Before:</u> The momentum was equal to mass of moving car × its velocity.
<u>After:</u>   The <u>mass</u> of the moving object has <u>increased</u>, but its momentum is equal to the momentum <u>before the collision</u>. So an <u>increase</u> in <u>mass</u> causes a <u>decrease</u> in <u>velocity</u>.

If the momentum <u>before</u> an event is <u>zero</u>, then the momentum <u>after</u> will also be <u>zero</u>. E.g. in an <u>explosion</u>, the momentum before is zero. After the explosion, the pieces fly off in <u>different directions</u>, so that the total momentum <u>cancels out</u> to <u>zero</u>.

Warm-Up & Exam Questions

Time to apply the brakes for a second and put your brain through an MOT. Try out these questions.
If you can handle these, your exam should be clear of hazards.

Warm-Up Questions

1) What is meant by 'thinking distance'?
2) What must be added to the thinking distance to find the total stopping distance of a car?
3) Give an example of how poor weather can affect your ability to stop a car before hitting a hazard.
4) Describe an experiment you could carry out, using a ruler, to measure the reaction time of an individual.
5) What energy transfer occurs when a car brakes?
6) Calculate the momentum of a 2.5 kg rabbit running through a garden at 10 m/s.
7) What is meant by the conservation of momentum?
8) What is the total momentum before and after an explosion?

Exam Question

1 A van is travelling along a flat road. (Grade 4-6)

1.1 The van driver spots a hazard ahead and makes an emergency stop.
The van comes to a stop in 58 m, and travels 41 m in the time between applying the brakes and stopping.
Calculate the thinking distance during this emergency stop.

[2 marks]

1.2 The next morning, there is a heavy frost on the road.
Explain how the braking distance of the van may be affected by these conditions.

[2 marks]

The van is fitted with a new set of brakes and new tyres.

1.3 State how this will affect the thinking distance and the braking distance of the van.

[2 marks]

2 In a demolition derby, cars drive around an arena and crash into each other. (Grade 6-7)

2.1 Give the equation linking momentum, velocity and mass.

[1 mark]

2.2 One car has a mass of 650 kg and a velocity of 15.0 m/s.
Calculate the momentum of the car.

[2 marks]

The car collides with the back of a stationary car with a mass of 750 kg.
The two cars stick together.

2.3 Give the momentum of the two cars after the collision.

[1 mark]

2.4 Explain how the speed of the two cars moving together after the
collision differs from the speed of the moving car before the collision.

[2 marks]

Revision Summary for Topic 5

That wraps up <u>Topic 5</u> — time to put yourself to the test and find out <u>how much you really know</u>.
- Try these questions and <u>tick off each one</u> when you <u>get it right</u>.
- When you've done <u>all the questions</u> under a heading and are <u>completely happy</u> with it, tick it off.

Forces and Work Done (p.76-80) ☑

1) Explain the difference between scalar and vector quantities, and contact and non-contact forces. ☑
2) What is the formula for calculating the weight of an object? ☑
3) What is a free body diagram? ☑
4) Give the formula for calculating the work done by a force. ☑
5) Describe the forces acting on an object in equilibrium. ☑

Springs and Stretching (p.82-85) ☑

6) What is the difference between an elastic and an inelastic deformation? ☑
7) How do you find the spring constant from a linear force-extension graph? ☑
8) What is the area under the linear part of a force-extension graph of an object equal to? ☑

Motion (p.87-97) ☑

9) What is the difference between displacement and distance? ☑
10) Define acceleration in terms of velocity and time. ☑
11) What does the term 'uniform acceleration' mean? ☑
12) What does the gradient represent for:
    a) a distance-time graph?
    b) a velocity-time graph? ☑
13) What is terminal velocity? ☑
14) Why do objects reach terminal velocity? ☑
15) State Newton's three laws of motion. ☑
16) What is inertia? ☑

Car Safety and Momentum (p.99-102) ☑

17) What is the stopping distance of a vehicle? How can it be calculated? ☑
18) Give two things that affect a person's reaction time. ☑
19) What is an average reaction time? ☑
20) Give two examples of methods that could be used to test a person's reaction time. ☑
21) State four things that can affect the braking distance of a vehicle. ☑
22) Is momentum a vector or a scalar quantity? ☑

Wave Basics

Waves <u>transfer energy</u> from one place to another <u>without</u> transferring any <u>matter</u> (stuff).

Waves Transfer **Energy** in the **Direction** they are **Travelling**

When waves travel through a medium, the <u>particles</u> of the medium <u>oscillate</u> and <u>transfer energy</u> between each other. BUT overall, the particles stay in the <u>same place</u> — <u>only energy</u> is transferred.

> For example, if you drop a twig into a calm pool of water, <u>ripples</u> form on the water's surface. The ripples <u>don't</u> carry the <u>water</u> (or the twig) away with them though.
>
> Similarly, if you strum a <u>guitar string</u> and create <u>sound waves</u>, the sound waves don't carry the <u>air</u> away from the guitar and create a <u>vacuum</u>.

Waves have **Amplitude**, **Wavelength** and **Frequency**

1) The <u>amplitude</u> of a wave is the <u>maximum displacement</u> of a point on the wave from its <u>undisturbed position</u>.

2) The <u>wavelength</u> is the distance between the <u>same point</u> on two <u>adjacent</u> waves (e.g. between the <u>trough</u> of one wave and the <u>trough</u> of the wave <u>next to it</u>).

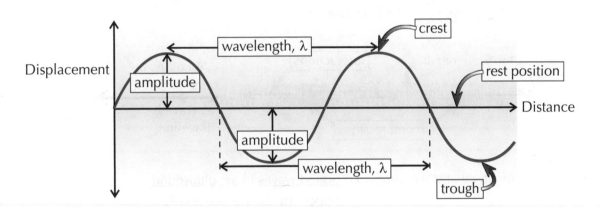

3) <u>Frequency</u> is the <u>number of complete waves</u> passing a certain point <u>per second</u>. Frequency is measured in <u>hertz</u> (Hz). 1 Hz is <u>1 wave per second</u>.

The period of a wave is the amount of <u>time</u> it takes for a <u>full cycle</u> of the wave to pass a point. You can find it from the <u>frequency</u> of the wave using the <u>formula</u>:

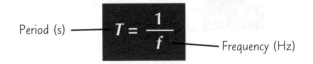

Period (s) —— $$T = \frac{1}{f}$$ —— Frequency (Hz)

The only thing a wave transfers is energy...

REVISION TIP

It's <u>really</u> important that you understand this stuff <u>really</u> well, or the rest of this topic will simply be a blur. Make sure you can sketch the <u>wave diagram</u> above and can <u>label</u> all the features from memory. Then check you know all the <u>definitions</u> and the <u>equation</u> linking period and frequency.

Transverse and Longitudinal Waves

All waves are either <u>transverse</u> or <u>longitudinal</u>. Read on to find out more...

Transverse Waves Have Perpendicular Vibrations

In <u>transverse waves</u>, the oscillations (vibrations) are <u>perpendicular</u> (at 90°) to the <u>direction</u> of energy transfer.
A spring wiggled from <u>side to side</u> gives a <u>transverse wave</u>:

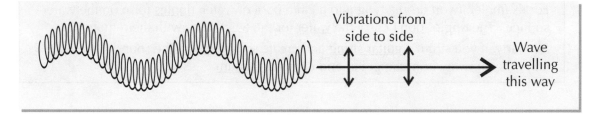

<u>Most waves</u> are transverse, including:

1) <u>All electromagnetic waves</u>, e.g. light (page 112).
2) <u>Ripples</u> and waves in <u>water</u> (page 107).
3) A wave on a <u>string</u> (page 108).

Water waves, shock waves and waves in springs and ropes are all examples of mechanical waves.

Longitudinal Waves Have Parallel Vibrations

In <u>longitudinal waves</u>, the oscillations are <u>parallel</u> to the <u>direction</u> of energy transfer.
If you push the end of a spring, you get a longitudinal wave.

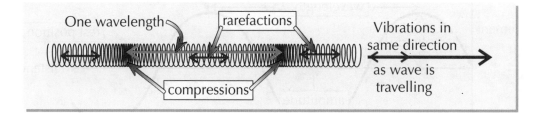

Other examples of longitudinal waves are:

1) <u>Sound waves</u> in air, <u>ultrasound</u>.
2) <u>Shock waves</u>, e.g. some seismic waves.

Wave Speed = Frequency × Wavelength

The <u>wave speed</u> is the speed at which <u>energy is being transferred</u> (or the speed the <u>wave</u> is moving at).
The <u>wave equation</u> applies to <u>all waves</u>:

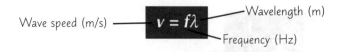

Wave speed (m/s) — $v = f\lambda$ — Wavelength (m), Frequency (Hz)

EXAMPLE:
A radio wave has a frequency of 12.0×10^6 Hz. Find its wavelength.
(The speed of radio waves in air is 3.0×10^8 m/s.)

1) To find λ, you need to <u>rearrange</u> the equation $v = f\lambda$. $\lambda = v \div f$
2) <u>Substitute</u> in the values for v and f to calculate λ. $= (3.0 \times 10^8) \div (12.0 \times 10^6) = 25$ m

Experiments with Waves

Measuring the <u>speed of waves</u> isn't that simple. It calls for crafty methods...

Use an **Oscilloscope** to Measure the **Speed** of **Sound**

By attaching a <u>signal generator</u> to a speaker you can generate sounds with a specific <u>frequency</u>.
You can use <u>two microphones</u> and an <u>oscilloscope</u> to find the <u>wavelength</u> of the sound waves generated.

1) Set up the oscilloscope so the <u>detected waves</u> at each microphone are shown as <u>separate waves</u>.

2) Start with <u>both microphones</u> next to the speaker, then slowly <u>move one away</u> until the two waves are <u>aligned</u> on the display, but have moved <u>exactly one wavelength apart</u>.

3) Measure the <u>distance between the microphones</u> to find one <u>wavelength</u> (λ).

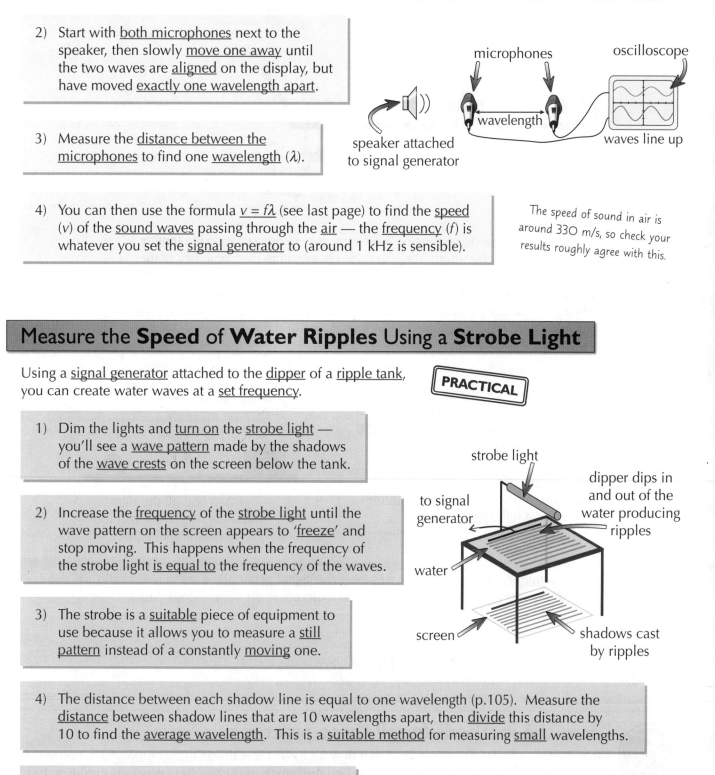

4) You can then use the formula <u>$v = f\lambda$</u> (see last page) to find the <u>speed</u> (v) of the <u>sound waves</u> passing through the <u>air</u> — the <u>frequency</u> (f) is whatever you set the <u>signal generator</u> to (around 1 kHz is sensible).

The speed of sound in air is around 330 m/s, so check your results roughly agree with this.

Measure the **Speed** of **Water Ripples** Using a **Strobe Light**

Using a <u>signal generator</u> attached to the <u>dipper</u> of a <u>ripple tank</u>, you can create water waves at a <u>set frequency</u>.

PRACTICAL

1) Dim the lights and <u>turn on</u> the <u>strobe light</u> — you'll see a <u>wave pattern</u> made by the shadows of the <u>wave crests</u> on the screen below the tank.

2) Increase the <u>frequency</u> of the <u>strobe light</u> until the wave pattern on the screen appears to '<u>freeze</u>' and stop moving. This happens when the frequency of the strobe light <u>is equal to</u> the frequency of the waves.

3) The strobe is a <u>suitable</u> piece of equipment to use because it allows you to measure a <u>still pattern</u> instead of a constantly <u>moving</u> one.

4) The distance between each shadow line is equal to one wavelength (p.105). Measure the <u>distance</u> between shadow lines that are 10 wavelengths apart, then <u>divide</u> this distance by 10 to find the <u>average wavelength</u>. This is a <u>suitable method</u> for measuring <u>small</u> wavelengths.

5) Use $v = f\lambda$ to calculate the <u>speed</u> of the waves.

PRACTICAL   Experiments with Waves

One more <u>wave experiment</u> coming up. This time, it's to do with <u>waves on strings</u>.

You can Use the **Wave Equation** for Waves on **Strings**

In this practical, you create a wave on a string. Again, you use a <u>signal generator</u>, but this time you attach it to a <u>vibration transducer</u> which converts the signals to vibrations.

1) Set up the equipment shown below, then <u>turn on</u> the signal generator and vibration transducer. The string will start to <u>vibrate</u>.

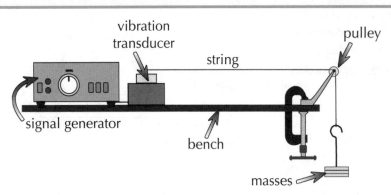

This set-up is suitable for investigating waves on a string because it's easy to see and measure the wavelength (and frequency).

2) You can adjust the <u>frequency</u> setting on the signal generator to change the <u>length</u> of the wave created on the string. You should keep adjusting the frequency of the signal generator until there appears to be a <u>clear wave</u> on the string. This happens when a <u>whole number</u> of half-wavelengths fit exactly on the string (you want at least four or five half-wavelengths ideally). The frequency you need will depend on the <u>length</u> of string between the <u>pulley</u> and the <u>transducer</u>, and the <u>masses</u> you've used.

3) You need to measure the <u>wavelength</u> of the wave. The best way to do this <u>accurately</u> is to measure the length of all the <u>half-wavelengths</u> on the string <u>in one go</u>, then <u>divide</u> by the total number of half-wavelengths to get the <u>mean half-wavelength</u> (see p.8 for more on calculating the mean). You can then <u>double</u> this value to get a <u>full wavelength</u>.

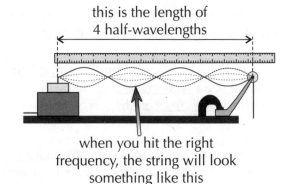

this is the length of 4 half-wavelengths

when you hit the right frequency, the string will look something like this

4) The <u>frequency</u> of the wave is whatever the <u>signal generator</u> is set to (you could also measure it with a strobe, as in the experiment on the previous page).

5) You can find the <u>speed</u> of the wave using $v = f\lambda$.

Learn the methods for all these practicals...

These experiments seem complicated, but they all have a few things <u>in common</u>. First, you set the <u>frequency</u> on the signal generator, then find the length of the resulting wave (this tends to be the fiddly bit). You can then use the <u>equation</u> $v = f\lambda$ to find the <u>wave speed</u>. That's about it.

Refraction

Refraction is when light waves are <u>bent</u> when they enter a <u>new media</u> (which is a posh word for material).

All Waves Can be **Absorbed, Transmitted** or **Reflected**

When a wave arrives at a <u>boundary</u> between two <u>different materials</u>, <u>three</u> things can happen:

1) The wave is <u>absorbed</u> by the second material — this <u>transfers energy</u> to the <u>material's energy stores</u>. Often, the energy is transferred to a <u>thermal</u> energy store, which leads to <u>heating</u> (this is how a microwave works, see page 114).

2) The wave is <u>transmitted</u> through the second material — the waves <u>carry on travelling</u> through the new material. This often leads to <u>refraction</u> (more on this below). This can be used in <u>communications</u> (p.113) as well as in the lenses of <u>glasses</u> and <u>cameras</u>.

3) The wave is <u>reflected</u> — this is where the incoming wave is neither <u>absorbed</u> nor <u>transmitted</u>, but instead is '<u>sent back</u>' away from the second material.

What actually happens depends on the <u>wavelength</u> of the wave and the <u>properties</u> of the <u>materials</u> involved.

Refraction — Waves **Changing Direction** at a **Boundary**

1) When a wave crosses a <u>boundary</u> between two materials it <u>changes speed</u>.

2) If the wave is travelling <u>along the normal</u> it will <u>change speed</u>, but it's <u>NOT refracted</u>.

3) If the wave hits the boundary at an <u>angle</u> it <u>changes direction</u> — it's <u>refracted</u>.

4) The wave bends <u>towards the normal</u> if it <u>slows down</u>. It bends <u>away</u> from the normal if it <u>speeds up</u>.

5) <u>How much</u> it's refracted by depends on how much the wave <u>speeds up</u> or <u>slows down</u>, which usually depends on the <u>density</u> of the two materials (usually the <u>higher</u> the density of a material, the <u>slower</u> a wave travels through it).

6) The <u>optical density</u> of a material is a measure of <u>how quickly light</u> can travel through it — the <u>higher</u> the optical density, the <u>slower</u> light waves travels through it.

7) The <u>wavelength</u> of a wave changes when it is refracted, but the <u>frequency stays the same</u>.

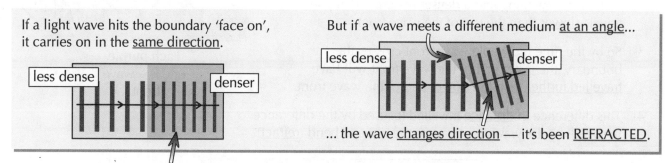

If a light wave hits the boundary 'face on', it carries on in the <u>same direction</u>.

But if a wave meets a different medium <u>at an angle</u>...

less dense   denser

less dense   denser

... the wave <u>changes direction</u> — it's been <u>REFRACTED</u>.

The wave fronts (see next page) being closer together shows a change in wavelength (and so a change in velocity).

Hitting a boundary at an angle leads to refraction...

If you can't remember <u>which way</u> a wave bends when it hits an optically denser material at an angle, imagine a skier skiing from some nice smooth snow onto some rough ground at an angle. The ski hitting the rough ground first <u>slows down first</u>, so they will swing towards that side.

Refraction

Refraction is a really important property of waves, but it can be tricky to get your head around.
Thankfully, there's a load of ways to show refraction in diagrams, to help you visualise what's going on.

You can Construct a Ray Diagram to show Refraction

Rays are straight lines that are perpendicular to wave fronts. They show the direction a wave is travelling in.
You can construct a ray diagram for a refracted light ray.

1) First, draw the boundary between your two materials and the normal (a line at 90° to the boundary).

2) Draw an incident ray that meets the normal at the boundary. The angle between the ray and the normal is the angle of incidence. (If you're given this angle, make sure to draw it carefully with a protractor.)

incoming ray

angle of incidence

boundary

normal

3) Now draw the refracted ray on the other side of the boundary. If the second material is optically denser than the first, the refracted ray bends towards the normal (like on the right). The angle between the refracted ray and the normal (the angle of refraction) is smaller than the angle of incidence. If the second material is less optically dense, the angle of refraction is larger than the angle of incidence.

normal

angle of refraction

refracted ray

You can also Explain Refraction using Wave Front Diagrams

1) A wave front is a line showing all of the points on a wave that are in the same position as each other after a given number of wavelengths.

2) When a wave crosses a boundary at an angle, only part of a wave front crosses the boundary at first. If it's travelling into a denser material, that part travels slower than the rest of the wave front.

3) So by the time the whole wave front crosses the boundary, the faster part of the wave front will have travelled further than the slower part of the wave front.

4) This difference in distance travelled (caused by the difference in speed) by the wave front causes the wave to bend (refract).

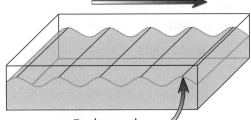

Wave travels this way

Each purple line is a wave front.

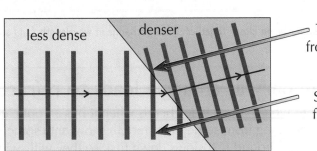

less dense   denser

This part of the wave front travels slower than the rest.

So this part of the wave front will have travelled further by the time it crosses the boundary.

Warm-Up & Exam Questions

Now to check what's actually stuck in your mind over the last six pages...

Warm-Up Questions

1) Describe the direction of vibrations in a longitudinal wave.
2) Give the formula for calculating the speed of a wave.
3) Outline a method you could use to measure the speed of water waves in a ripple tank.
4) True or false? A wave entering a new medium along the path of the normal won't be refracted.

Exam Questions

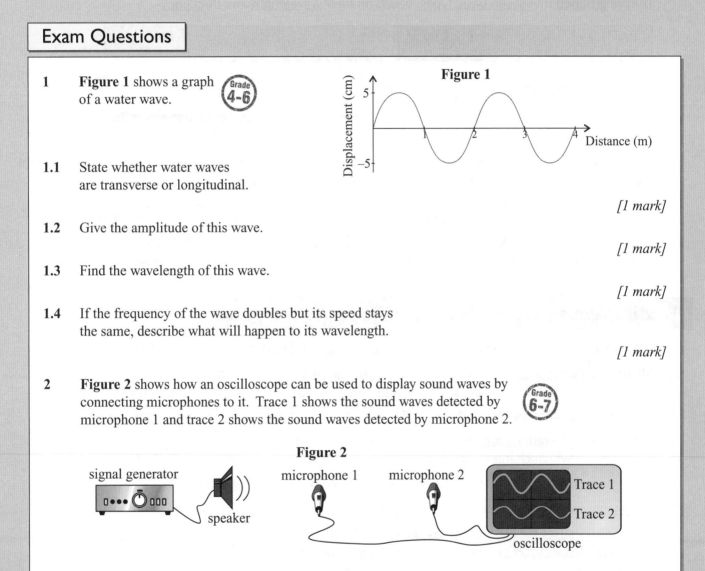

1 **Figure 1** shows a graph of a water wave. *(Grade 4-6)*

Figure 1

1.1 State whether water waves are transverse or longitudinal.

[1 mark]

1.2 Give the amplitude of this wave.

[1 mark]

1.3 Find the wavelength of this wave.

[1 mark]

1.4 If the frequency of the wave doubles but its speed stays the same, describe what will happen to its wavelength.

[1 mark]

2 **Figure 2** shows how an oscilloscope can be used to display sound waves by connecting microphones to it. Trace 1 shows the sound waves detected by microphone 1 and trace 2 shows the sound waves detected by microphone 2. *(Grade 6-7)*

Figure 2

signal generator   microphone 1   microphone 2

speaker   Trace 1   Trace 2

oscilloscope

A student begins with both microphones at equal distances from the speaker and the signal generator set at a fixed frequency. He gradually moves microphone 2 away from the speaker, which causes trace 2 to move. He stops moving microphone 2 when both traces line up again as shown in **Figure 2**. He then measures the distance between the microphones.

2.1 Explain how his measurement could be used to work out the speed of sound in air.

[2 marks]

2.2 With the signal generator set to 50 Hz, the distance between the microphones was measured as 6.8 m. Calculate the speed of sound in air. Give the correct unit.

[3 marks]

Electromagnetic Waves and Uses of EM Waves

The differences between <u>types</u> of <u>electromagnetic</u> (<u>EM</u>) waves make them useful to us in different ways.

There's a **Continuous Spectrum** of **EM Waves**

1) All EM waves are <u>transverse</u> waves (p.106) that transfer energy <u>from a source</u> to an <u>absorber</u>. E.g. a <u>hot object</u> transfers energy by emitting <u>infrared radiation</u>, which is <u>absorbed</u> by the surrounding <u>air</u>.

Electromagnetic waves aren't vibrations of particles, they're vibrations of electric and magnetic fields. This means they can travel through a vacuum.

2) All EM waves travel at the <u>same speed</u> through <u>air</u> or a <u>vacuum</u> (space).

3) Electromagnetic waves form a <u>continuous spectrum</u> over a range of frequencies. They're <u>grouped</u> into <u>seven basic types</u>, based on their <u>wavelength</u> and <u>frequency</u>.

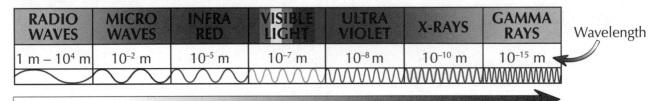

RADIO WAVES	MICRO WAVES	INFRA RED	VISIBLE LIGHT	ULTRA VIOLET	X-RAYS	GAMMA RAYS	Wavelength
$1\,m - 10^4\,m$	$10^{-2}\,m$	$10^{-5}\,m$	$10^{-7}\,m$	$10^{-8}\,m$	$10^{-10}\,m$	$10^{-15}\,m$	

INCREASING FREQUENCY AND DECREASING WAVELENGTH

4) The human eye can only detect a <u>tiny part</u> of the EM spectrum — the only part we can see is <u>visible light</u>.

5) There is such a large <u>range of frequencies</u> because EM waves are <u>generated</u> by a <u>variety</u> of changes in <u>atoms</u> and their <u>nuclei</u>. E.g. changes in the <u>nucleus</u> of an atom creates <u>gamma rays</u> (p.67). This also explains why atoms can <u>absorb</u> a range of frequencies — each one causes a <u>different change</u>.

6) EM waves travel at <u>different speeds</u> in <u>different materials</u> (which can lead to <u>refraction</u>).

7) Because of their <u>different properties</u>, different EM waves are used for <u>different purposes</u>.

Radio Waves are Made by **Oscillating Charges**

Head on over to page 49 for more on ac.

1) <u>EM waves</u> are made up of <u>oscillating electric and magnetic fields</u>.

2) <u>Alternating currents</u> (<u>ac</u>) (p.49) are made up of <u>oscillating</u> charges. As the charges oscillate, they produce <u>oscillating electric and magnetic fields</u>, i.e. <u>electromagnetic waves</u>.

3) The <u>frequency</u> of the <u>waves</u> produced will be equal to the <u>frequency</u> of the <u>alternating current</u>.

4) You can produce <u>radio waves</u> using an alternating current in an electrical circuit. The object in which charges (electrons) oscillate to <u>create</u> the radio waves is called a <u>transmitter</u>.

5) When transmitted radio waves reach a <u>receiver</u>, the radio waves are <u>absorbed</u>.

6) The <u>energy</u> transferred by the waves is <u>transferred</u> to the <u>electrons</u> in the material of the receiver.

7) This energy causes the electrons to <u>oscillate</u> and, if the receiver is part of a <u>complete electrical circuit</u>, it generates an <u>alternating current</u> (p.49).

8) This current has the <u>same frequency</u> as the <u>radio waves</u> that generated it.

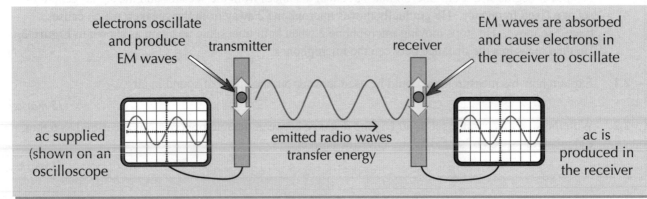

electrons oscillate and produce EM waves — transmitter

EM waves are absorbed and cause electrons in the receiver to oscillate — receiver

ac supplied (shown on an oscilloscope

emitted radio waves transfer energy

ac is produced in the receiver

Uses of EM Waves

Radio waves and microwaves are both types of EM waves, and they're both used for communications. Their exact properties determine which sort of communications they're used for.

Radio Waves are Used Mainly for Communication

1) Radio waves are EM radiation with wavelengths longer than about 10 cm.

2) Long-wave radio waves (wavelengths of 1 – 10 km) can be transmitted from London, say, and received halfway round the world. That's because long wavelengths diffract (bend) around the curved surface of the Earth. Long-wave radio wavelengths can also diffract around hills, into tunnels and all sorts.

3) This makes it possible for radio signals to be received even if the receiver isn't in line of the sight of the transmitter.

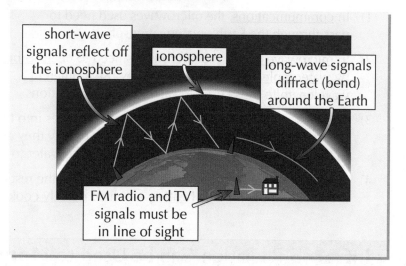

short-wave signals reflect off the ionosphere

ionosphere

long-wave signals diffract (bend) around the Earth

FM radio and TV signals must be in line of sight

4) Short-wave radio signals (wavelengths of about 10 m – 100 m) can, like long-wave, be received at long distances from the transmitter. That's because they are reflected (see p.109) from the ionosphere — an electrically charged layer in the Earth's upper atmosphere.

5) Bluetooth® uses short-wave radio waves to send data over short distances between devices without wires (e.g. wireless headsets so you can use your phone while driving a car).

6) Medium-wave signals (well, the shorter ones) can also reflect from the ionosphere, depending on atmospheric conditions and the time of day.

7) The radio waves used for TV and FM radio transmissions have very short wavelengths. To get reception, you must be in direct sight of the transmitter — the signal doesn't bend or travel far through buildings.

Microwaves are Used by Satellites

Communication to and from satellites (including satellite TV signals and satellite phones) uses microwaves. But you need to use microwaves which can pass easily through the Earth's watery atmosphere.

For satellite TV, the signal from a transmitter is transmitted into space...

... where it's picked up by the satellite receiver dish orbiting thousands of kilometres above the Earth. The satellite transmits the signal back to Earth in a different direction...

... where it's received by a satellite dish on the ground. There is a slight time delay between the signal being sent and received because of the long distance the signal has to travel.

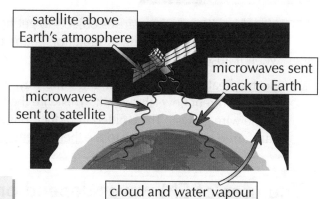

satellite above Earth's atmosphere

microwaves sent back to Earth

microwaves sent to satellite

cloud and water vapour

Uses of EM Waves

Each type of EM wave covers a <u>spectrum</u> of <u>wavelengths</u> and <u>frequencies</u> itself. So the <u>properties</u> of, say, a microwave from one end of the range may <u>differ</u> from those of a microwave from the <u>other end</u> of the range.

Microwave Ovens Use a **Different Wavelength** from **Satellites**

1) In <u>communications</u>, the microwaves used need to <u>pass through</u> the Earth's watery atmosphere.

2) In <u>microwave ovens</u>, the microwaves need to be <u>absorbed</u> by <u>water molecules</u> in food — so they use a <u>different</u> wavelength to those used in satellite communications.

3) The microwaves penetrate up to a few centimetres into the food before being <u>absorbed</u> and <u>transferring</u> the energy they are carrying to the <u>water molecules</u> in the food, causing the water to <u>heat up</u>.

4) The water molecules then <u>transfer</u> this energy to the rest of the molecules in the food <u>by heating</u> — which <u>quickly cooks</u> the food.

Infrared Radiation Can be Used to **Monitor Temperature**...

1) <u>Infrared</u> (IR) radiation is <u>given out</u> by all <u>objects</u> — and the <u>hotter</u> the object, the <u>more</u> IR radiation it gives out.

2) <u>Infrared cameras</u> can be used to detect infrared radiation and <u>monitor temperature</u>. The camera detects the IR radiation and turns it into an <u>electrical signal</u>, which is <u>displayed on a screen</u> as a picture. The <u>hotter</u> an object is, the <u>brighter</u> it appears. E.g. <u>energy transfer</u> from a house's <u>thermal energy store</u> can be detected using <u>infrared cameras</u>.

Different <u>colours</u> represent different <u>amounts</u> of <u>IR radiation</u> being detected. Here, the <u>redder</u> the colour, the <u>more</u> infrared radiation is being detected.

...Or **Increase** it

1) <u>Absorbing</u> IR radiation causes objects to get <u>hotter</u>. <u>Food</u> can be <u>cooked</u> using IR radiation — the <u>temperature</u> of the food increases when it <u>absorbs</u> IR radiation, e.g. from a toaster's heating element.

2) <u>Electric heaters</u> heat a room in the same way. Electric heaters contain a <u>long piece of wire</u> that <u>heats up</u> when a current flows through it. This wire then <u>emits</u> lots of <u>infrared radiation</u> (and a little <u>visible light</u> — the wire <u>glows</u>). The emitted IR radiation is <u>absorbed</u> by objects and the air in the room — energy is transferred <u>by the IR waves</u> to the <u>thermal energy stores</u> of the objects, causing their <u>temperature</u> to <u>increase</u>.

The uses of EM waves depend on their properties...

Differences in wavelength, frequency and energy between types of EM wave give them <u>different properties</u>. For example, some types of EM wave are <u>very harmful</u> (see page 116). Luckily, radio waves are considered <u>safe</u> to beam round the world. IR radiation is generally fairly safe, although too much of it will burn you.

Uses of EM Waves

Here are just a few more uses of EM waves — complete with the all-important <u>reasons</u> why they're used.

Fibre Optic Cables Use Visible Light to Transmit Data

1) <u>Optical fibres</u> are thin <u>glass or plastic fibres</u> that can <u>carry data</u> (e.g. from telephones or computers) over long distances as pulses of <u>visible light</u>.

2) They work because of <u>reflection</u> (p.109). The light rays are <u>bounced back and forth</u> until they reach the end of the fibre.

3) Light is not easily <u>absorbed</u> or <u>scattered</u> as it travels along a fibre.

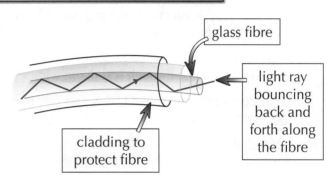

glass fibre

light ray bouncing back and forth along the fibre

cladding to protect fibre

Ultraviolet Radiation Gives You a Suntan

1) <u>Fluorescence</u> is a property of certain chemicals, where <u>ultra-violet</u> (<u>UV</u>) radiation is <u>absorbed</u> and then <u>visible light</u> is <u>emitted</u>. That's why fluorescent colours look so <u>bright</u> — they actually <u>emit light</u>.

2) <u>Fluorescent lights</u> generate <u>UV radiation</u>, which is absorbed and <u>re-emitted as visible light</u> by a layer of <u>phosphorus</u> on the inside of the bulb. They're <u>energy-efficient</u> (p.26) so they're good to use when light is needed for <u>long periods</u> (like in your <u>classroom</u>).

3) <u>Security pens</u> can be used to <u>mark</u> property with your name (e.g. laptops). Under <u>UV light</u> the ink will <u>glow</u> (fluoresce), but it's <u>invisible</u> otherwise. This can help the police <u>identify</u> your property if it's stolen.

4) <u>Ultraviolet radiation (UV)</u> is produced by the Sun, and exposure to it is what gives people a <u>suntan</u>.

5) When it's <u>not sunny</u>, some people go to <u>tanning salons</u> where <u>UV lamps</u> are used to give them an artificial <u>suntan</u>. However, overexposure to UV radiation can be <u>dangerous</u> (fluorescent lights emit very little UV — they're totally safe).

There's more on the dangers of UV on p.116.

X-rays and Gamma Rays are Used in Medicine

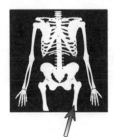

The <u>brighter bits</u> are where <u>fewer X-rays</u> get through. This is a <u>negative image</u>. The plate starts off <u>all white</u>.

There's more on gamma rays on p.67.

1) <u>Radiographers</u> in <u>hospitals</u> take <u>X-ray 'photographs'</u> of people to see if they have any <u>broken bones</u>.

2) X-rays pass <u>easily through flesh</u> but not so easily through <u>denser material</u> like <u>bones</u> or <u>metal</u>. So it's the amount of radiation that's <u>absorbed</u> (or <u>not absorbed</u>) that gives you an X-ray image.

3) <u>Radiographers</u> use <u>X-rays</u> and <u>gamma rays</u> to treat people with <u>cancer</u> (radiotherapy). This is because high doses of these rays <u>kill all living cells</u> — so they are carefully <u>directed</u> towards cancer cells, to avoid killing too many normal, <u>healthy cells</u>.

4) <u>Gamma radiation</u> can also be used as a <u>medical tracer</u> — this is where a <u>gamma-emitting source</u> is injected into the patient, and its <u>progress</u> is followed around the body. Gamma radiation is well <u>suited</u> to this because it can <u>pass out</u> through the body to be <u>detected</u>.

5) <u>Both</u> X-rays and gamma rays can be <u>harmful</u> to people (p.116), so radiographers wear <u>lead aprons</u> and stand behind a <u>lead screen</u> or <u>leave the room</u> to keep their exposure to them to a minimum.

Dangers of Electromagnetic Waves

Okay, so you know how <u>useful</u> electromagnetic radiation can be — well, it can also be pretty <u>dangerous</u>.

Some **EM Radiation** Can be **Harmful** to **People**

1) When EM radiation enters <u>living tissue</u>, like <u>you</u>, it's often harmless, but sometimes it creates havoc. The effects of each type of radiation are based on <u>how much energy the wave transfers</u>.

2) <u>Low frequency</u> waves, like <u>radio waves</u>, don't transfer much energy and so mostly <u>pass through soft tissue</u> without being absorbed.

3) <u>High frequency</u> waves like <u>UV</u>, <u>X-rays</u> and <u>gamma rays</u> all transfer <u>lots</u> of energy and so can cause <u>lots of damage</u>.

4) <u>UV radiation</u> damages surface cells, which can lead to <u>sunburn</u> and cause <u>skin</u> to <u>age prematurely</u>. Some more serious effects are <u>blindness</u> and an <u>increased risk of skin cancer</u>.

5) <u>X-rays</u> and <u>gamma rays</u> are types of <u>ionising radiation</u>. (They carry enough energy to <u>knock electrons off of atoms</u>.) This can cause <u>gene mutation or cell destruction</u>, and <u>cancer</u>.

You Can **Measure Risk** Using the **Radiation Dose** in **Sieverts**

1) Whilst UV radiation, X-rays and gamma rays can all be <u>harmful</u>, they are also very <u>useful</u> (see page 115). <u>Before</u> any of these types of EM radiation are used, people look at whether the <u>benefits outweigh the health risks</u>.

2) For example, the <u>risk</u> of a person involved in a car accident then developing cancer from having an X-ray photograph taken, is <u>much smaller</u> than the potential health risk of not finding and treating their injuries.

Radiation doses can be calculated for all types of radiation, not just UV, X-rays and gamma rays.

3) <u>Radiation dose</u> (measured in <u>sieverts</u>) is a measure of the <u>risk</u> of harm from the body being exposed to radiation.

4) This is <u>not</u> a measure of the <u>total amount</u> of radiation that has been <u>absorbed</u>.

5) The risk depends on the <u>total amount of radiation</u> absorbed <u>and</u> how <u>harmful</u> the <u>type</u> of radiation is.

6) A sievert is pretty big, so you'll often see doses in <u>millisieverts</u> (mSv), where <u>1000 mSv = 1 Sv</u>.

Risk can be **Different** for **Different Parts** of the **Body**

A CT scan uses <u>X-rays</u> and a <u>computer</u> to build up a picture of the inside of a patient's body. The table shows the <u>radiation dose</u> received by two <u>different parts</u> of a patient's body when having CT scans.

	Radiation dose (mSv)
Head	2.0
Chest	8.0

If a patient has a CT scan on their <u>chest</u>, they are <u>four times more likely</u> to suffer damage to their genes (and their <u>added risk</u> of harm is <u>four times higher</u>) than if they had a <u>head</u> scan.

The risks and benefits of radiation exposure must be balanced...

<u>Ionising radiation</u> can be <u>dangerous</u>, but the risk can be worth taking. From 1920-1970, <u>X-ray machines</u> were installed in shoe shops for use in <u>shoe fittings</u>. But when people realised radiation was harmful, they were phased out. The <u>risks</u> far <u>outweighed</u> the <u>benefits</u> of using X-rays rather than tape measures...

Infrared Radiation and Temperature

Infrared radiation is what you feel as <u>heat</u>. It's easy to think that only really hot objects, like the glowing bars on an electric fire, give out infrared radiation, but that's <u>not</u> at all true as you'll soon discover...

Every Object Absorbs and Emits Infrared Radiation

<u>All objects</u> are <u>continually emitting</u> and <u>absorbing infrared</u> (IR) radiation.

1) Infrared radiation is emitted from the <u>surface</u> of an object.

2) The <u>hotter</u> an object is, the <u>more</u> infrared radiation it radiates in a given time.

3) An object that's <u>hotter</u> than its surroundings <u>emits more</u> <u>IR radiation</u> than it <u>absorbs</u> as it <u>cools down</u> (e.g. a cup of tea left on a table). And an object that's <u>cooler</u> than its surroundings <u>absorbs</u> more IR radiation than it <u>emits</u> as it <u>warms up</u> (e.g. a cold glass of water on a sunny day).

4) Objects at a <u>constant temperature</u> emit infrared radiation at the <u>same rate</u> that they are <u>absorbing it</u>.

5) <u>Some colours</u> and <u>surfaces absorb</u> and <u>emit</u> radiation better than others. For example, a <u>black</u> surface is <u>better</u> at absorbing and emitting radiation than a <u>white</u> one, and a <u>matt</u> surface is <u>better</u> at absorbing and emitting radiation than a <u>shiny</u> one.

The hot chocolate (and the mug) is warmer than the air around it, so it gives out more IR radiation than it absorbs, which cools it down.

You Can Investigate Absorption with the Melting Wax Trick

The amount of infrared radiation <u>absorbed</u> by different materials also depends on the <u>material</u>. You can do an experiment to show this, using a <u>Bunsen burner</u> and some <u>candle wax</u>.

PRACTICAL

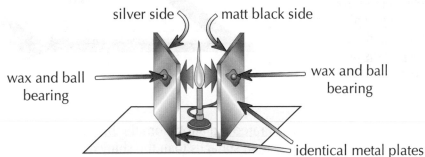

silver side   matt black side

wax and ball bearing

wax and ball bearing

identical metal plates

1) Set up the equipment as shown above. Two <u>ball bearings</u> are each stuck to <u>one side</u> of a <u>metal plate</u> with solid pieces of <u>candle wax</u>. The other sides of these plates are then faced towards the <u>flame</u>.

2) The sides of the plates that are facing towards the flame each have a different <u>surface colour</u> — one is <u>matt black</u> and the other is <u>silver</u>.

3) The ball bearing on the black plate will <u>fall first</u> as the black surface <u>absorbs more</u> infrared radiation — <u>transferring</u> more energy to the <u>thermal energy store</u> of the wax. This means the wax on the <u>black</u> plate melts <u>before</u> the wax on the <u>silver</u> plate.

PRACTICAL Investigating Emission

Time for another <u>Required Practical</u>. In this one, you'll meet a fun, new piece of kit called a <u>Leslie Cube</u>. Read on to find out more about how you can use this equipment to investigate <u>infrared radiation emissions</u>.

You Can Investigate **Emission** With a **Leslie Cube**

A <u>Leslie cube</u> is a <u>hollow</u>, <u>watertight</u>, metal cube made of e.g. aluminium, whose four <u>vertical faces</u> have <u>different</u> <u>surfaces</u> (for example, matt black paint, matt white paint, shiny metal and dull metal). You can use them to <u>investigate IR radiation emitted</u> by different surfaces:

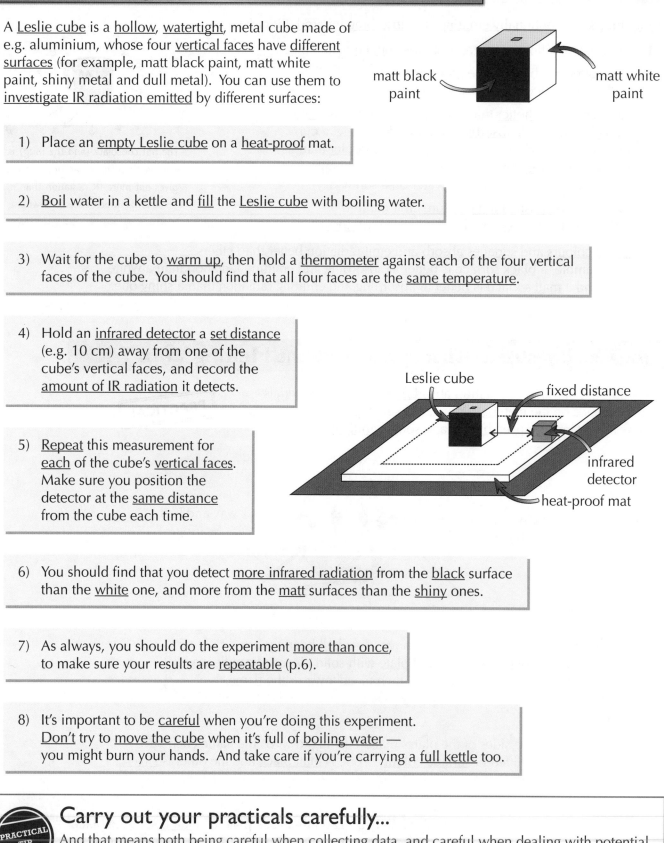

matt black paint

matt white paint

1) Place an <u>empty Leslie cube</u> on a <u>heat-proof</u> mat.

2) <u>Boil</u> water in a kettle and <u>fill</u> the <u>Leslie cube</u> with boiling water.

3) Wait for the cube to <u>warm up</u>, then hold a <u>thermometer</u> against each of the four vertical faces of the cube. You should find that all four faces are the <u>same temperature</u>.

4) Hold an <u>infrared detector</u> a <u>set distance</u> (e.g. 10 cm) away from one of the cube's vertical faces, and record the <u>amount of IR radiation</u> it detects.

Leslie cube

fixed distance

infrared detector

heat-proof mat

5) <u>Repeat</u> this measurement for <u>each</u> of the cube's <u>vertical faces</u>. Make sure you position the detector at the <u>same distance</u> from the cube each time.

6) You should find that you detect <u>more infrared radiation</u> from the <u>black</u> surface than the <u>white</u> one, and more from the <u>matt</u> surfaces than the <u>shiny</u> ones.

7) As always, you should do the experiment <u>more than once</u>, to make sure your results are <u>repeatable</u> (p.6).

8) It's important to be <u>careful</u> when you're doing this experiment. <u>Don't</u> try to <u>move the cube</u> when it's full of <u>boiling water</u> — you might burn your hands. And take care if you're carrying a <u>full kettle</u> too.

PRACTICAL TIP Carry out your practicals carefully...

And that means both being careful when <u>collecting data</u>, and careful when dealing with potential <u>hazards</u>. Watch out when you're pouring or carrying <u>boiling water</u>, and make sure any water or equipment has <u>cooled down</u> enough before you start handling it after your experiment is done.

Warm-Up & Exam Questions

There's quite a few different sorts of electromagnetic waves — and you never know which ones might come up in the exams... So check which you're still a bit hazy on with these questions.

Warm-Up Questions

1) Which type of EM wave has the highest frequency?
2) Explain how an alternating current produces radio waves.
3) Explain how microwaves heat food.
4) What are optical fibres used for in phone lines?
5) Why is ionising radiation dangerous?
6) If an object is hotter than its surroundings, does it emit more or less IR radiation than it absorbs?
7) What specialised piece of apparatus is used to investigate IR radiation emissions from surfaces?

Exam Questions

1 EM radiation can be harmful but also useful. (Grade 4-6)

1.1 Give **one** practical use of ultraviolet radiation.

[1 mark]

1.2 Give **one** hazard associated with ultraviolet radiation.

[1 mark]

1.3 Gamma rays can be used in medical tracers to check that your body is working correctly. Explain how medical tracers work.

[3 marks]

1.4 Explain why gamma rays are suitable for use in medical tracers.

[1 mark]

2 **Figure 1** shows a transmitter which is transmitting a communications signal. There is a receiver for the signal inside the house. There is a mountain between the transmitter and the house. (Grade 6-7)

Figure 1

2.1 Explain why radio waves would be more suitable than light to send the transmission.

[2 marks]

2.2 The home owner decides to get satellite TV installed. State what type of electromagnetic radiation is used to send signals to satellites and explain why it is suitable.

[2 marks]

2.3 Describe how satellite TV signals are transmitted from a transmitter on the ground to the house.

[2 marks]

Exam Questions

PRACTICLE

3 A student is investigating the infrared radiation emitted by different surfaces using a Leslie Cube, as shown in **Figure 2**. The student records how long it takes the temperature on each thermometer to increase by 5 °C.

(Grade 7-9)

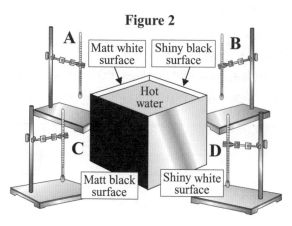

Figure 2

3.1 Suggest **one** thing the student should do to make the experiment a fair test.

[1 mark]

The student's results are displayed in **Figure 3**.

Infrared emission is affected by both the texture and colour of a surface.

3.2 Write down a conclusion from the data in **Figure 3** about how texture affects infrared radiation emission.

[1 mark]

3.3 Write down a conclusion from the data in **Figure 3** about how colour affects infrared radiation emission.

[1 mark]

3.4 The water used in the experiment was initially at boiling point, 100 °C. The experiment is repeated using water at 60 °C. Predict how this would affect the results. Explain your prediction.

[2 marks]

3.5 Another student suggests that using digital thermometers connected to data loggers to measure the temperatures would improve the investigation. The digital thermometers measure temperature in °C to two decimal places. Give **two** reasons why this student is correct.

[2 marks]

Revision Summary for Topic 6

And that's the end of Topic 6 — give yourself a pat on the back before seeing how much you've learnt.
- Try these questions and tick off each one when you get it right.
- When you've done all the questions under a heading and are completely happy with it, tick it off.

Wave Properties (p.105-110) ☑

1) Define the following features of a wave:
   a) amplitude,
   b) wavelength,
   c) frequency,
   d) period ☑
2) Describe the difference between transverse and longitudinal waves and give an example of each. ☑
3) Describe an experiment to measure the speed of ripples on water. ☑
4) A wave moves from material A into material B, and bends towards the normal as it crosses the boundary. In which material does the wave travel faster? ☑
5) Draw a diagram showing a light ray crossing, at an angle, into a medium in which it slows down. ☑

Uses of Electromagnetic Waves (p.112-115) ☑

6) True or false? All electromagnetic waves are transverse. ☑
7) What kind of current is used to generate radio waves in an antenna? ☑
8) Explain why microwaves are suitable for satellite communication. ☑
9) Give one use of infrared radiation. ☑
10) What type of radiation is used to transmit a signal in an optical fibre? ☑
11) Name the type of radiation produced by the lamps in tanning beds. ☑

Dangers of Electromagnetic Waves (p.116) ☑

12) What does the term 'ionising radiation' mean? ☑
13) What is 1 Sv in mSv? ☑

Investigating Infrared Radiation (p.117-118) ☑

14) Compare the IR radiation absorption and emission rates for an object at constant temperature. ☑
15) How could you use a Leslie cube to investigate IR radiation emitted by different surfaces? ☑

Magnets

I think magnetism is an <u>attractive</u> subject, but don't get <u>repelled</u> by the exam — <u>revise</u>.

Magnets Produce **Magnetic Fields**

1) All magnets have <u>two poles</u> — <u>north</u> (or north seeking) and <u>south</u> (or south seeking).

2) All magnets produce a <u>magnetic field</u> — a region where <u>other magnets</u> or <u>magnetic materials</u> (e.g. iron, steel, nickel and cobalt) experience a <u>force</u>. (This is a <u>non-contact force</u> — see page 76.)

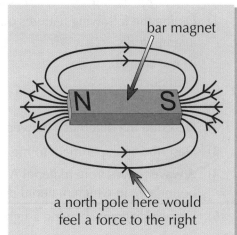

bar magnet

a north pole here would
feel a force to the right

3) You can show a magnetic field by drawing <u>magnetic field lines</u>.

4) The lines always go from <u>north to south</u> and they show <u>which way</u> a force would act on a north pole if it was put at that point in the field.

5) The <u>closer together</u> the lines are, the <u>stronger</u> the magnetic field. The <u>further away</u> from a magnet you get, the <u>weaker</u> the field is.

6) The magnetic field is <u>strongest</u> at the <u>poles</u> of a magnet. This means that the <u>magnetic forces</u> are also <u>strongest</u> at the poles.

7) The force between a <u>magnet</u> and a <u>magnetic material</u> is <u>always attractive</u>, no matter the pole.

8) If the two poles of a magnet are put <u>near</u> each other, they will exert a <u>force</u> on each other. This force can be <u>attractive</u> or <u>repulsive</u>. Two poles that are the same (these are called <u>like poles</u>) will <u>repel</u> each other. Two <u>unlike</u> poles will <u>attract</u> each other.

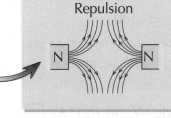

Repulsion   Attraction

Compasses Show the **Direction** of Magnetic Fields

1) Inside a compass is a tiny <u>bar magnet</u> (the needle). The <u>north</u> pole of this magnet is attracted to the south pole of any other magnet it is near. So the compass needle <u>points</u> in the direction of the magnetic field it is in.

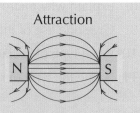

The north pole of the magnet in the
compass points along the field line
towards the south pole of the bar magnet.

2) You can move a compass around a magnet and <u>trace</u> the needle's position on some paper to build up a picture of what the magnetic field <u>looks like</u>.

3) When they're not near a magnet, compass needles always point <u>north</u>. This is because the <u>Earth</u> generates its own <u>magnetic field</u>, which shows that the <u>inside</u> (core) of the Earth must be <u>magnetic</u>.

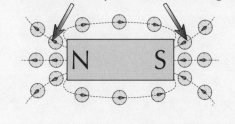

A bar magnet's magnetic field lines go from north to south...

...no matter which direction the magnet is pointing. You can see the shape of a <u>magnetic field</u> using <u>compasses</u> or <u>iron filings</u>. Iron filings will give you a pretty pattern — but they won't show you the <u>direction</u> of the <u>magnetic field</u>. That's where compasses really shine. They're also a lot easier to clear up.

Magnetism

Permanent magnets are great, but it would be <u>really</u> handy to be able to turn a magnetic field <u>on</u> and <u>off</u>. Well, it turns out that when <u>electric current</u> flows it <u>produces a magnetic field</u>...

Magnets Can be **Permanent** or **Induced**

1) There are <u>two types</u> of magnet — <u>permanent</u> magnets and <u>induced</u> magnets.

2) <u>Permanent</u> magnets produce their <u>own</u> magnetic field.

3) <u>Induced</u> magnets are magnetic materials that <u>turn into</u> a magnet when they're put into a magnetic field.

4) The force between permanent and induced magnets is always <u>attractive</u> (see magnetic materials on the previous page).

5) When you <u>take away</u> the magnetic field, induced magnets quickly <u>lose</u> most or all of their magnetism.

N permanent magnet S   magnetic material

The magnetic material becomes magnetised when it is brought near the bar magnet. It has its own poles and magnetic field:

N permanent magnet S   N induced magnet S

induced poles

A **Moving Charge** Creates a Magnetic Field

1) When a <u>current flows</u> through a <u>wire</u>, a <u>magnetic field</u> is created <u>around</u> the wire.

2) The field is made up of <u>concentric circles</u> perpendicular to the wire, with the wire in the centre.

3) You can see this by placing a <u>compass</u> near a <u>wire</u> that is carrying a <u>current</u>. As you move the compass, it will <u>trace</u> the direction of the magnetic field.

4) Changing the <u>direction</u> of the <u>current</u> changes the direction of the <u>magnetic field</u> — use the <u>right-hand thumb rule</u> to work out which way it goes.

5) The <u>strength</u> of the magnetic field produced <u>changes</u> with the <u>current</u> and the <u>distance</u> from the wire. The <u>larger</u> the current through the wire, or the <u>closer</u> to the wire you are, the <u>stronger</u> the field is.

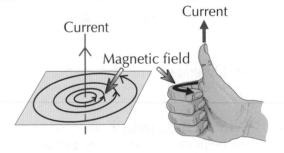

<u>The Right-Hand Thumb Rule</u>
Using your right hand, point your <u>thumb</u> in the direction of <u>current</u> and <u>curl</u> your fingers. The direction of your <u>fingers</u> is the direction of the <u>field</u>.

Just point your thumb in the direction of the current...

...and your fingers show the direction of the field. Remember, it's always your <u>right thumb</u>. Not your left. You'll use your left hand on page 127 though, so it shouldn't feel left out...

Electromagnets

Electric currents can create magnetic fields (see previous page). We can use this to make magnets that can be switched on and off — these are electromagnets.

A **Solenoid** is a Coil of Wire

1) You can <u>increase</u> the <u>strength</u> of the magnetic field that a wire produces by <u>wrapping</u> the wire into a <u>coil</u> called a <u>solenoid</u>.

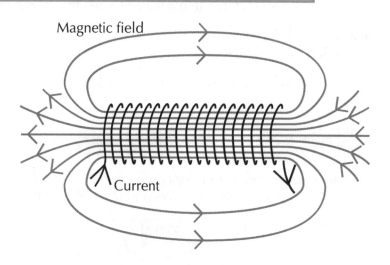

Magnetic field

Current

2) This happens because the field lines around each loop of wire <u>line up</u> with each other. This results in <u>lots</u> of field lines <u>pointing in the same direction</u> that are <u>very close</u> to each other. As you saw on page 122, the closer together field lines are, the <u>stronger</u> the field is.

3) The magnetic field <u>inside</u> a solenoid is <u>strong</u> and <u>uniform</u> (it has the <u>same strength</u> and <u>direction</u> at every point in that region).

4) <u>Outside</u> the coil, the magnetic field is just like the one round a <u>bar magnet</u>.

5) You can <u>increase</u> the field strength of the solenoid <u>even more</u> by putting a block of <u>iron</u> in the <u>centre</u> of the coil. This <u>iron core</u> becomes an <u>induced</u> magnet whenever current is flowing.

6) If you <u>stop</u> the current, the magnetic field <u>disappears</u>.

7) A <u>solenoid with an iron core</u> is called an <u>ELECTROMAGNET</u> (a magnet whose magnetic field can be turned <u>on</u> and <u>off</u> with an <u>electric current</u>).

Fields around electromagnets and bar magnets are the same shape

Electromagnets pop up in lots of different places — they're used in <u>electric bells</u>, <u>car ignition circuits</u> and some <u>security doors</u>. Electromagnets aren't all the same strength though — how <u>strong</u> they are depends on stuff like the number of <u>turns</u> of wire there are and the <u>size</u> of the <u>current</u> going through the wire.

Warm-Up & Exam Questions

It's time for another page of questions to check your knowledge retention. If you can do the warm-up questions without breaking into a sweat, then see how you get on with the exam questions below.

Warm-Up Questions

1) Draw a diagram to show the magnetic field around a single bar magnet.
2) Describe the magnetic field around a current-carrying wire.
3) What is a solenoid?

Exam Questions

1 A student draws the magnetic field lines between four bar magnets, as shown in **Figure 1**. *Grade 6-7*

Figure 1

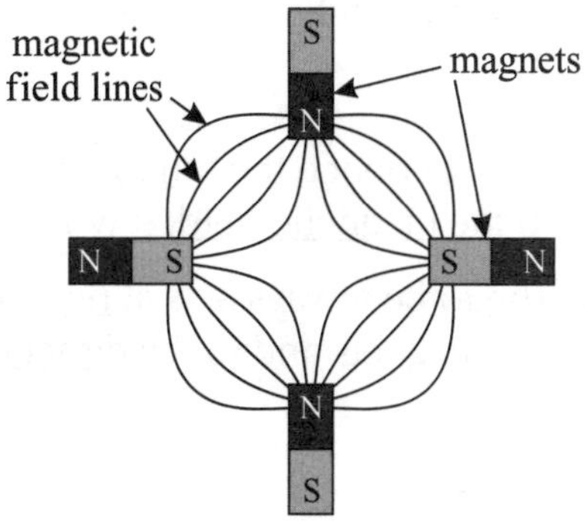

1.1 Describe an experiment that the student could have done to show this magnetic field pattern.

[2 marks]

The student arranges two of the magnets as shown in **Figure 2**.

Figure 2

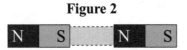

1.2 Describe the magnetic field lines in the shaded region between the dotted lines.

[1 mark]

1.3 State whether there will be a force of attraction, repulsion, or no force between the two magnets. Explain your answer.

[2 marks]

2 Arnold is making an electromagnet using a current-carrying solenoid and a core. *Grade 6-7*

2.1 Complete **Figure 3** of the solenoid to show the magnetic field inside and around it.

[2 marks]

Figure 3

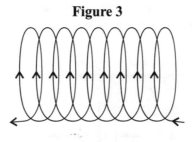

2.2 Suggest a material that would be suitable for the core.

[1 mark]

Arnold uses his electromagnet to pick up some paper clips, as shown in **Figure 4**.

Figure 4

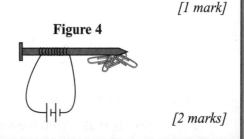

2.3 State what happens when the current is turned off, and explain why this happens.

[2 marks]

The Motor Effect

Passing an electric current through a wire produces a magnetic field around the wire (p.123). If you put that wire into a magnetic field, the <u>two magnetic fields interact</u>, which can exert a force on the wire.

A **Current** in a Magnetic Field Experiences a **Force**

When a <u>current-carrying</u> wire (or any other <u>conductor</u>) is put between magnetic poles,
the <u>magnetic field</u> around the wire <u>interacts</u> with the magnetic field it has been placed in.
This causes the magnet and the conductor to <u>exert a force on each other</u>.
This is called the <u>motor effect</u> and can cause the <u>wire</u> to <u>move</u>.

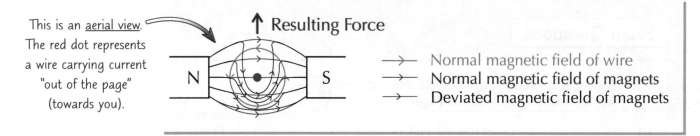

This is an <u>aerial view</u>.
The red dot represents
a wire carrying current
"out of the page"
(towards you).

↑ Resulting Force

N   S

→ Normal magnetic field of wire
→ Normal magnetic field of magnets
→ Deviated magnetic field of magnets

1) To experience the <u>full force</u>, the <u>wire</u> has to be at <u>90°</u> to the <u>magnetic field</u>. If the wire runs <u>parallel</u> to the <u>magnetic field</u>, it won't experience <u>any force at all</u>. At angles in between, it'll feel <u>some</u> force.

2) The force always acts at <u>right angles</u> to the <u>magnetic field</u> of the magnets and to the <u>direction of the current</u> in the wire.

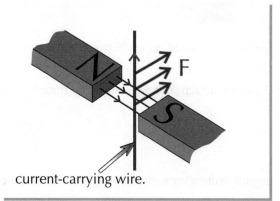

current-carrying wire.

3) A good way of showing the direction of the force is to apply a current to a set of <u>rails</u> inside a <u>horseshoe magnet</u> (shown below). A bar is placed on the rails, which <u>completes the circuit</u>. This generates a <u>force</u> that <u>rolls the bar</u> along the rails.

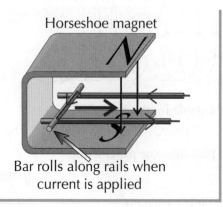

Horseshoe magnet

Bar rolls along rails when
current is applied

*The motor effect is used in lots of appliances that use movement —
see page 128.*

4) The magnitude (strength) of the force <u>increases</u> with the <u>strength</u> of the <u>magnetic field</u>.

5) The force also <u>increases</u> with the amount of <u>current</u> passing through the conductor.

The Motor Effect

You Can Find the **Size** of the **Force**...

The force acting on a conductor in a magnetic field depends on three things:

1) The magnetic flux density — how many field lines there are in a region.
   This shows the strength of the magnetic field (p.122).

2) The size of the current through the conductor.

3) The length of the conductor that's in the magnetic field.

When the current is at 90° to the magnetic field it is in, the
force acting on it can be found using the equation on the right.

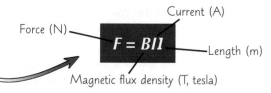
Force (N)
Current (A)
$$F = BIl$$
Length (m)
Magnetic flux density (T, tesla)

... and **Which Way** it's Acting

You can find the direction of the force with Fleming's left-hand rule.

1) Using your left hand, point your First finger
   in the direction of the Field.

2) Point your seCond finger in the direction of the Current.

3) Your thuMb will then point in the
   direction of the force (Motion).

thuMb
Motion
First finger
Field
seCond finger
Current

Fleming's left-hand rule shows that if either the current or the magnetic field is reversed,
then the direction of the force will also be reversed. This can be used to find the direction
of the force in all sorts of things — like motors, as shown on the next page.

EXAMPLE:

**In the diagram on the right, in which
direction does the force act on the wire?**

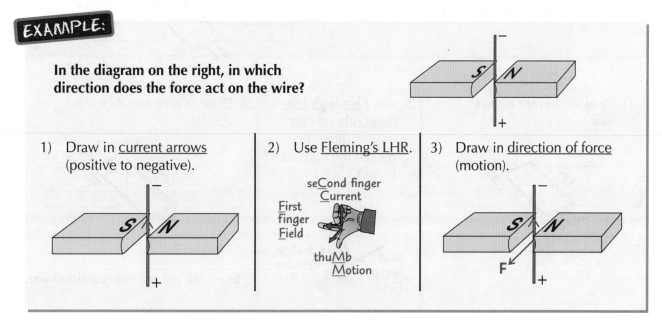

1) Draw in current arrows
   (positive to negative).

2) Use Fleming's LHR.

   seCond finger
   Current
   First
   finger
   Field
   thuMb
   Motion

3) Draw in direction of force
   (motion).

EXAM TIP

Fleming's left-hand rule can really come in handy...

Use the left-hand rule in the exam. You might look a bit silly, but it makes getting those marks so
much easier. So don't get tripped up — your First finger corresponds to the direction of the Field,
your seCond finger points in the direction of the Current, and finally your thuMb points in the
direction of the force (or Motion). If you can remember that, then those marks will come easily.

Electric Motors

Electric motors use the <u>motor effect</u> (see pages 126-127) to get them (and keep them) <u>moving</u>.
This is one of the favourite exam topics of all time. Read it. Understand it. Learn it. Lecture over.

A Current-Carrying **Coil** of Wire **Rotates** in a Magnetic Field

1) The diagram on the right shows a <u>basic dc motor</u>.
<u>Forces</u> act on the two <u>side arms</u> of a <u>coil</u> of
wire that's carrying a <u>current</u>.

2) These forces are just the <u>usual forces</u> which
act on <u>any current</u> in a <u>magnetic field</u> (p.127).

3) Because the coil is on an <u>axle</u> and the
forces act <u>one up</u> and <u>one down</u>, it <u>rotates</u>.

4) The <u>split-ring commutator</u> is a clever way of
<u>swapping</u> the contacts <u>every half turn</u> to
keep the motor rotating in the <u>same direction</u>.

5) The direction of the motor can be <u>reversed</u> either by
swapping the <u>polarity</u> of the <u>dc supply</u> (reversing the <u>current</u>)
or swapping the <u>magnetic poles</u> over (reversing the <u>field</u>).

6) You can use <u>Fleming's left-hand rule</u> to work out which way the coil will <u>turn</u>.

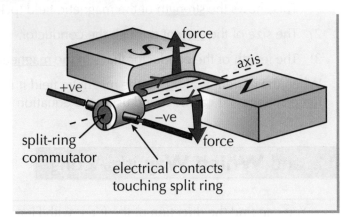

split-ring commutator

electrical contacts touching split ring

Direct current (dc) is current that only flows in one direction.

EXAMPLE:

Is the coil turning clockwise or anticlockwise?

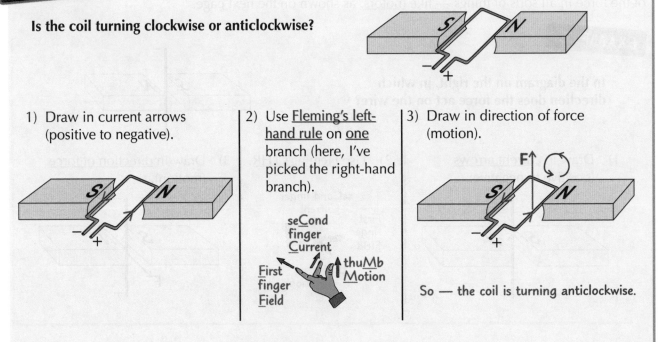

1) Draw in current arrows (positive to negative).

2) Use <u>Fleming's left-hand rule</u> on <u>one</u> branch (here, I've picked the right-hand branch).

seCond finger Current

First finger Field

thuMb Motion

3) Draw in direction of force (motion).

So — the coil is turning anticlockwise.

The motor effect has a lot of important applications...

Electric motors are <u>important components</u> in a lot of <u>everyday items</u>. Food mixers, DVD players, and
anything that has a fan (hair dryers, laptops, etc) use electric motors to keep things turning.

Warm-Up & Exam Questions

Time to test your knowledge — as usual, check you can do the basics, then get stuck into some lovely exam questions. Don't forget to go back and check up on any niggling bits you can't do.

Warm-Up Questions

1) What is the motor effect?
2) In Fleming's left-hand rule, what's represented by the first finger, the second finger and the thumb?
3) Give two changes that can be made to make a dc motor run in reverse.

Exam Questions

1 **Figure 1** shows an aerial view of a current-carrying wire in a magnetic field. *Grade 4-6*
The circle represents the wire carrying current out of the page, towards you.

Figure 1

N ○ S

1.1 On **Figure 1**, draw an arrow to show the direction of the force acting on the current-carrying wire.

[1 mark]

1.2 Describe what would happen to the force acting on the current-carrying wire if the direction of the current was reversed.

[1 mark]

1.3 Describe how the size of the force acting on the wire would change if the wire was at 30° to the magnetic field.

[1 mark]

1.4 Describe how the size of the force acting on the wire would change if the wire ran parallel to the magnetic field.

[1 mark]

2 A student is building a simple dc motor.
He starts by putting a loop of current-carrying wire that is free to rotate about an axis in a magnetic field, as shown in **Figure 2**. *Grade 7-9*
The magnetic field between the poles has a magnetic flux density of 0.2 T.

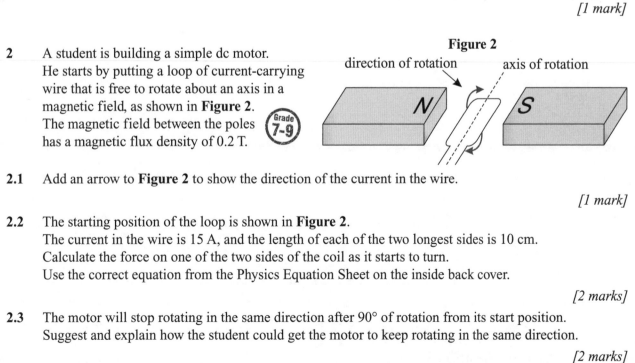

Figure 2

direction of rotation   axis of rotation

N   S

2.1 Add an arrow to **Figure 2** to show the direction of the current in the wire.

[1 mark]

2.2 The starting position of the loop is shown in **Figure 2**.
The current in the wire is 15 A, and the length of each of the two longest sides is 10 cm.
Calculate the force on one of the two sides of the coil as it starts to turn.
Use the correct equation from the Physics Equation Sheet on the inside back cover.

[2 marks]

2.3 The motor will stop rotating in the same direction after 90° of rotation from its start position.
Suggest and explain how the student could get the motor to keep rotating in the same direction.

[2 marks]

Revision Summary for Topic 7

That wraps up <u>Topic 7</u> — time to put yourself to the test and find out <u>how much you really know</u>.
- Try these questions and <u>tick off each one</u> when you <u>get it right</u>.
- When you've done <u>all the questions</u> under a heading and are <u>completely happy</u> with it, tick it off.

Magnetism (p.122-123) ☑
1) What is a magnetic field? ☑
2) Give three magnetic materials. ☑
3) In what direction do magnetic field lines point? ☑
4) True or false? The force between a magnet and a magnetic material is always repulsive. ☑
5) Describe how you could use a compass to show the direction of
   a bar magnet's magnetic field lines. ☑
6) Describe the behaviour of a compass needle that is far away from any magnets. ☑
7) What happens to an induced magnet when it is moved far away from a permanent magnet? ☑
8) How can you work out the direction of the magnetic field around a current-carrying wire
   without using a compass? ☑

Basic Electromagnetism (p.124) ☑
9) Why does adding an iron core to a solenoid increase the strength of its magnetic field? ☑
10) Describe an electromagnet. ☑

The Motor Effect (p.126-128) ☑
11) Explain why a current-carrying conductor in a magnetic field experiences a force. ☑
12) State the equation for calculating the size of this force. ☑
13) Name three ways you could increase the force on a current-carrying wire in a magnetic field. ☑
14) What is Fleming's left-hand rule used for? ☑
15) Explain how a basic dc motor works. ☑

Measuring Lengths and Angles

Get your lab coat on, it's time to find out about the skills you'll need in experiments.
First things first — make sure you're using appropriate equipment and know how to use it correctly.

Measure **Most Lengths** with a **Ruler**

1) In most cases a bog-standard centimetre ruler can be used to measure length. It depends on what you're measuring though — metre rulers are handy for large distances, while micrometers are used for measuring tiny things like the diameter of a wire.

2) The ruler should always be parallel to what you want to measure.

3) If you're dealing with something where it's tricky to measure just one accurately (e.g. water ripples, p.107), you can measure the length of some of them and then divide to find the length of one.

4) If you're taking multiple measurements of the same object (e.g. to measure changes in length) then make sure you always measure from the same point on the object. It can help to draw or stick small markers onto the object to line up your ruler against.

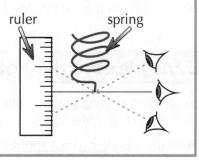

5) Make sure the ruler and the object are always at eye level when you take a reading. This stops parallax affecting your results.

> Parallax is where a measurement appears to change based on where you're looking from.
>
> The blue line is the measurement taken when the spring is at eye level. It shows the correct length of the spring.

Use a **Protractor** to Find **Angles**

1) First align the vertex (point) of the angle with the mark in the centre of the protractor.

2) Line up the base line of the protractor with one line that forms the angle and then measure the angle of the other line using the scale on the protractor.

3) If the lines creating the angle are very thick, align the protractor and measure the angle from the centre of the lines. Using a sharp pencil to draw diagrams helps to reduce errors when measuring angles.

4) If the lines are too short to measure easily, you may have to extend them. Again, make sure you use a sharp pencil to do this.

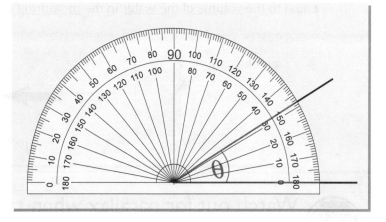

Measuring Volumes

Did you order some more measuring? Well, even if you didn't, here's some stuff about <u>measuring volumes</u>.

Measuring Cylinders and Pipettes Measure Liquid Volumes

1) <u>Measuring cylinders</u> are the most common way to measure a liquid.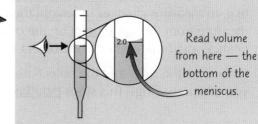

2) They come in all different <u>sizes</u>. Make sure you choose one that's the <u>right size</u> for the measurement you want to make. It's no good using a huge 1 dm³ cylinder to measure out 2 cm³ of a liquid — the graduations (markings for scale) will be <u>too big</u> and you'll end up with <u>massive</u> <u>errors</u>. It'd be much better to use one that measures up to 10 cm³.

3) You can also use a <u>pipette</u> to measure volume. <u>Pipettes</u> are used to suck up and <u>transfer</u> volumes of liquid between containers.

4) <u>Graduated pipettes</u> are used to transfer <u>accurate</u> volumes. A <u>pipette filler</u> is attached to the end of a graduated pipette to <u>control</u> the amount of liquid being drawn up.

5) Whichever method you use, always read the volume from the <u>bottom of the meniscus</u> (the curved upper surface of the liquid) when it's at <u>eye level</u>.

Read volume from here — the bottom of the meniscus.

Eureka Cans Measure the Volumes of Solids

1) <u>Eureka cans</u> are used in <u>combination</u> with <u>measuring cylinders</u> to find the volumes of <u>irregular solids</u> (p.57).

2) They're essentially a <u>beaker with a spout</u>. To use them, fill them with water so the water level is <u>above the spout</u>.

3) Let the water <u>drain</u> from the spout, leaving the water level <u>just below</u> the start of the spout (so <u>all</u> the water displaced by an object goes into the measuring cylinder and gives you the <u>correct volume</u>).

4) Place a <u>measuring cylinder</u> below the end of the spout. When you place a solid in the beaker, it causes the water level to <u>rise</u> and water to flow out of the spout.

5) Make sure you wait until the spout has <u>stopped dripping</u> before you measure the volume of the water in the measuring cylinder. The object's <u>volume</u> is equal to the <u>volume of the water</u> in the <u>measuring cylinder</u>.

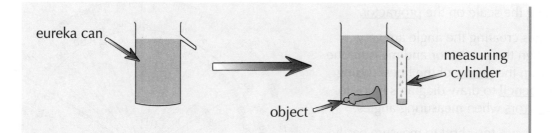

eureka can

object

measuring cylinder

Watch out for parallax when taking readings...

PRACTICAL TIP

Whether you're reading off a ruler, a pipette or a measuring cylinder, make sure you take all readings at <u>eye level</u>. And, if you're taking a reading for a volume, make sure you measure from the bottom of the <u>meniscus</u> (that's from the dip in the curved surface at the top of the liquid).

More on Measuring

Measure **Temperature** Accurately with a **Thermometer**

1) Make sure the <u>bulb</u> of your thermometer is <u>completely submerged</u> in any substance you're measuring the temperature of.

2) Wait for the temperature reading to <u>stabilise</u> before you take your initial reading.

3) Again, read your measurement off the <u>scale</u> on a thermometer at <u>eye level</u>.

bulb

When you're reading off a scale, use the value of the nearest mark on the scale (the nearest graduation).

You May Have to Measure the **Time Taken** for a Change

1) You should use a <u>stopwatch</u> to <u>time</u> most experiments — they're more <u>accurate</u> than regular watches.

2) Always make sure you <u>start</u> and <u>stop</u> the stopwatch at exactly the right time. Or alternatively, set an <u>alarm</u> on the stopwatch so you know exactly when to stop an experiment or take a reading.

3) You might be able to use a <u>light gate</u> instead (see below). This will <u>reduce the errors</u> in your experiment.

Mass Should Be Measured Using a **Balance**

1) For a <u>solid</u>, set the balance to <u>zero</u> and then place your object onto the scale and read off the mass.

2) If you're measuring the mass of a <u>liquid</u>, start by putting an empty <u>container</u> onto the <u>balance</u>. Next, <u>reset</u> the balance to zero.

3) Then just pour your <u>liquid</u> into the container and record the mass displayed. Easy peasy.

Light Gates Measure **Speed** and **Acceleration**

1) A <u>light gate</u> sends a <u>beam</u> of light from one side of the gate to a <u>detector</u> on the other side. When something passes through the gate, the beam of light is <u>interrupted</u>. The light gate then measures <u>how long</u> the beam was undetected for.

light gate

beam of light

card interrupts the beam

2) To find the <u>speed</u> of an object, connect the light gate to a <u>computer</u>. Measure the <u>length</u> of the object and <u>input</u> this using the software. It will then <u>automatically calculate</u> the speed of the object as it passes through the beam.

3) To measure <u>acceleration</u>, use an object that interrupts the signal <u>twice</u> in a <u>short</u> period of time, e.g. a piece of card with a gap cut into the middle.

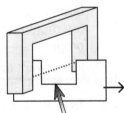

Have a look at page 113 for an example of a light gate being used.

4) The light gate measures the speed for each section of the object and uses this to calculate its <u>acceleration</u>. This can then be read from the <u>computer screen</u>.

Working With Electronics

Electrical devices are used in a bunch of experiments, so make sure you know how to use them.

You Have to Interpret Circuit Diagrams

Before you get cracking on an experiment involving any kind of electrical devices, you
have to plan and build your circuit using a circuit diagram. Make sure you know all
of the circuit symbols on page 40 so you're not stumped before you've even started.

You Can Measure Potential Difference and Current

Voltmeters Measure Potential Difference

1) If you're using an analogue voltmeter, choose the voltmeter
   with the most appropriate unit (e.g. V or mV).

2) If you're using a digital voltmeter, you'll most likely be able to switch between them.

3) Connect the voltmeter in parallel (p.46) across the component you want to test.

4) The wires that come with a voltmeter are usually red (positive) and black (negative).
   These go into the red and black coloured ports on the voltmeter. Funnily enough.

5) Then simply read the potential difference from the scale (or from the screen if it's digital).

Ammeters Measure Current

1) Just like with voltmeters, choose the ammeter with the most appropriate unit.

2) Connect the ammeter in series (p.44) with the component you want to
   test, making sure they're both on the same branch. Again, they usually
   have red and black ports to show you where to connect your wires.

3) Read off the current shown on the scale or by the screen.

*Turn your circuit off between
readings to prevent wires
overheating and affecting your
results (p.38).*

Multimeters Measure Both

1) Instead of having a separate ammeter and voltmeter, many circuits
   use multimeters. These are devices that measure a range of
   properties — usually potential difference, current and resistance.

2) If you want to find potential difference, make sure the
   red wire is plugged into the port that has a 'V' (for volts).

3) To find the current, use the port labelled 'A' or 'mA' (for amps).

4) The dial on the multimeter should then be turned to the
   relevant section, e.g. to 'A' to measure current in amps.
   The screen will display the value you're measuring.

Don't get your wires in a tangle when you're using circuits...

When you're dealing with voltmeters, ammeters and multimeters, you need to make sure that you
wire them into your circuit correctly, otherwise you could mess up your readings. Just remember,
the red wires should go into the red ports and the black wires should go into the black ports.

Safety and Experiments

There's <u>danger</u> all around, particularly in science experiments. But don't let this put you off.
Just be aware of the <u>hazards</u> and take <u>sensible precautions</u>. Read on to find out more...

Be **Careful** When You Do Experiments

1) There are always hazards in any experiment, so <u>before</u> you start an experiment you should read and follow any <u>safety precautions</u> to do with your method or the apparatus you're using.

2) Stop masses and equipment falling by using <u>clamp stands</u>.

3) Make sure any masses you're using in investigations are of a <u>sensible weight</u> so they don't break the equipment they're used with. Also, make sure strings used in <u>pulley systems</u> are of a sensible <u>length</u>. That way, any hanging masses won't <u>hit the floor</u> or the <u>table</u> during the experiment.

4) When <u>heating</u> materials, make sure to let them <u>cool</u> before moving them, or wear <u>insulated gloves</u> while handling them. If you're using an <u>immersion heater</u> to heat liquids, you should always let it <u>dry out</u> in air, just in case any liquid has leaked inside the heater.

5) If you're using a <u>laser</u>, there are a few safety rules you must follow. Always wear <u>laser safety goggles</u> and never <u>look directly into</u> the laser or shine it <u>towards another person</u>. Make sure you turn the laser <u>off</u> if it's not needed to avoid any accidents.

6) When working with electronics, make sure you use a <u>low</u> enough <u>voltage</u> and <u>current</u> to prevent wires <u>overheating</u> (and potentially melting) and also to avoid <u>damaging components</u>, e.g. blowing a filament bulb.

7) You also need to be aware of <u>general safety</u> in the lab — handle <u>glassware</u> carefully so it doesn't <u>break</u>, don't stick your fingers in sockets and avoid touching frayed wires. That kind of thing.

BEWARE — hazardous physics experiments about...

Before you carry out an experiment, it's important to consider all of the <u>hazards</u>. Hazards can be anything from <u>lasers</u> to <u>electrical currents</u>, or weights to heating equipment. Whatever the hazards, make sure you know all the <u>safety precautions</u> you should follow to keep yourself <u>safe</u>.

Practice Exam Paper
GCSE Combined Science

GCSE Combined Science

Physics Paper 1

Higher Tier

In addition to this paper you should have:
* A ruler.
* A calculator.
* The Physics Equations sheet
  (on the inside back cover).

Centre name				
Centre number				
Candidate number				

Time allowed:
* 1 hour 15 minutes

Surname	
Other names	
Candidate signature	

Instructions to candidates
* Write your name and other details in the spaces provided above.
* Answer **all** questions in the spaces provided.
* Do all rough work on the paper.
* Cross out any work you do not want to be marked.

Information for candidates
* The marks available are given in brackets at the end of each question.
* There are 70 marks available for this paper.
* You are allowed to use a calculator.
* You should use good English and present your answers in a
  clear and organised way.
* For Questions 1.6 and 5.5, ensure that your answers have a
  clear and logical structure, include the right scientific terms, spelt
  correctly and include detailed, relevant information.

Advice to candidates
* In calculations show clearly how you worked out your answers.

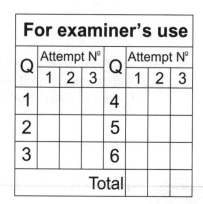

For examiner's use

Q	Attempt Nº			Q	Attempt Nº		
	1	2	3		1	2	3
1				4			
2				5			
3				6			
Total							

1   **Table 1** gives details of some isotopes.

Table 1

Isotope	Symbol	Type of decay
Radium-226	$^{226}_{88}\text{Ra}$	alpha
Radon-222	$^{222}_{86}\text{Rn}$	alpha
Radon-224	$^{224}_{86}\text{Rn}$	beta
Bismuth-210	$^{210}_{83}\text{Bi}$	alpha, beta
Bismuth-214	$^{214}_{83}\text{Bi}$	alpha, beta
Lead-210	$^{210}_{82}\text{Pb}$	beta

1.1   Calculate the number of neutrons in a bismuth-214 nucleus.

....
[1 mark]

1.2   Using data from **Table 1**, complete the equations in **Figure 1** to show how the following isotopes decay.

Figure 1

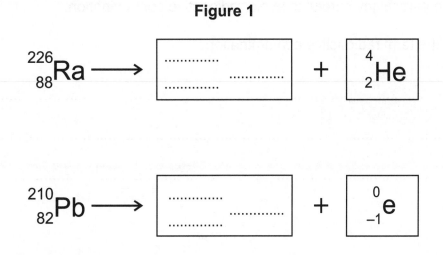

[2 marks]

Question 1 continues on the next page

Turn over ▶

138

Figure 2 shows the activity-time graph of a sample of polonium-210.

Figure 2

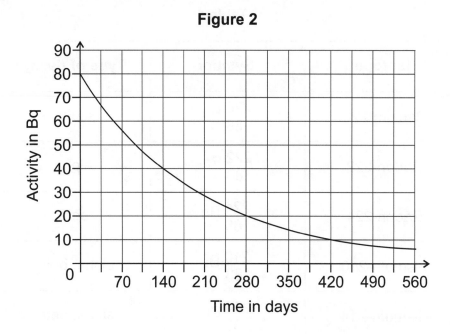

1.3 Using the graph in **Figure 2**, determine the time it takes for the activity of the sample to drop from 80 Bq to 10 Bq.

Time taken = ... days

[1 mark]

1.4 Determine the half-life of polonium-210.

Half-life = ... days

[1 mark]

Polonium-210 emits alpha radiation. Scientists who work with it must be particularly careful to avoid radioactive contamination.

1.5 Define the term radioactive contamination.

....

....

....

[1 mark]

1.6 Explain and compare the dangers of radioactive contamination with radioactive irradiation by an alpha source, such as polonium-210.

....

....

....

....

....

....

....

....

....

[4 marks]

Turn over for the next question

2   A student is investigating the two electrical circuits shown in **Figure 3**.
All the lamps and batteries used are identical.

Figure 3

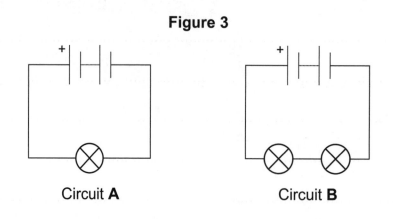

Circuit **A**   Circuit **B**

2.1   Compare the current and total resistance in circuits **A** and **B**.

....

....

....
[2 marks]

2.2   The student adds an ammeter and a voltmeter to circuit **A**.
They show readings of 0.30 A and 11 V respectively.
State the equation that links power, current and potential difference.

....
[1 mark]

2.3   Calculate the power of the lamp.

....

....

....

Power = ... W
[2 marks]

2.4   Compare the potential difference across the bulb in circuit **A** with the potential
difference across one of the bulbs in circuit **B**.
Explain your answer.

....

....

....

....
[2 marks]

The student considers adding one of the components in **Figure 4** to circuit **A**.

Figure 4

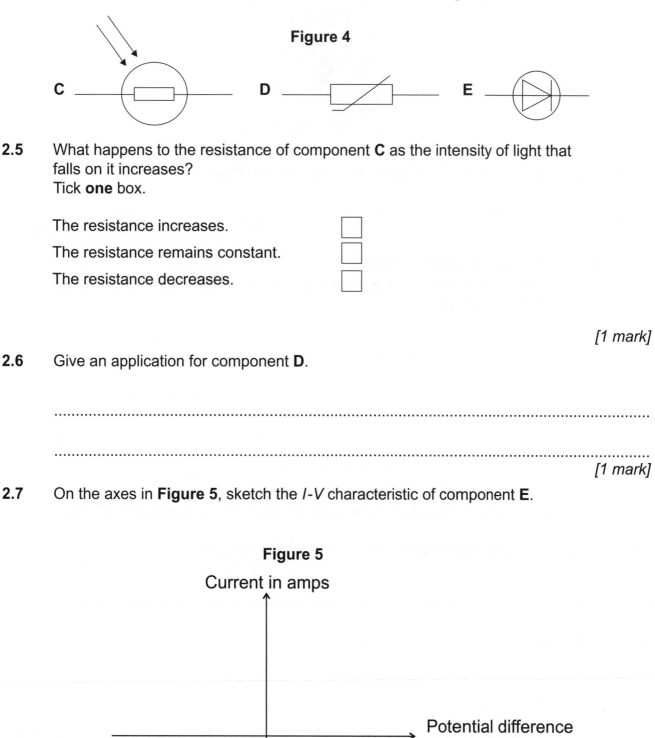

2.5 What happens to the resistance of component **C** as the intensity of light that falls on it increases?
Tick **one** box.

The resistance increases. ☐

The resistance remains constant. ☐

The resistance decreases. ☐

[1 mark]

2.6 Give an application for component **D**.

....

....

[1 mark]

2.7 On the axes in **Figure 5**, sketch the *I-V* characteristic of component **E**.

Figure 5

Current in amps

Potential difference
in volts

[2 marks]

Turn over for the next question

Turn over ▶

3   A representation of the particles of a substance is shown in **Figure 6**.

Figure 6

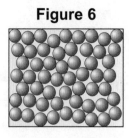

3.1   Name the state of matter of the substance shown in **Figure 6**.

......................................Liquid...

[1 mark]

3.2   The substance in **Figure 6** is heated.
Describe what happens to the internal energy of the substance when it is heated.
Explain why this occurs.

....

....

....

[2 marks]

The student wishes to find the density of the substance.
A sample of the substance has a mass of 0.36 kg, and a volume of 4×10^{-4} m^3.

3.3   Write down the equation that links mass, volume and density.

....

[1 mark]

3.4   Calculate the density of the substance.

....

....

Density = ... kg/m^3

[2 marks]

Figure 7 shows a graph of temperature against time for the substance as it is being continually heated.

Figure 7

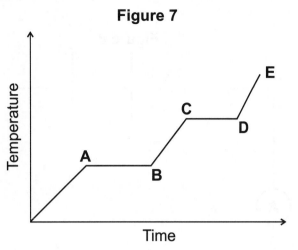

3.5 Which point represents the **boiling point**?
Tick **one** box.

☐ A

☐ B

☐ C

[1 mark]

3.6 Explain the shape of the line in **Figure 7** between points **A** and **B**.

....

....

....

....

[2 marks]

3.7 69 000 J of energy is transferred to a 1.5 kg solid sample of the substance to completely melt it without changing its temperature.
Calculate the specific latent heat of fusion of the substance.
Use the correct equation from the Physics Equation Sheet on the inside back cover.

....

....

....

Specific latent heat of fusion = ... J/kg
[3 marks]

Turn over for the next question

4   A student wanted to know how the current flowing through a filament lamp changes with the potential difference across it. She set up the circuit shown in **Figure 8**.

Figure 8

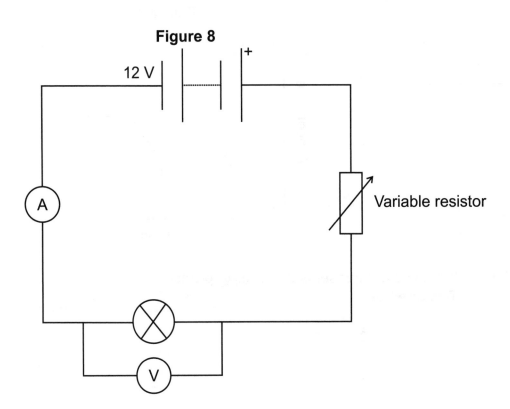

She used the variable resistor to change the potential difference across the lamp. For each setting of the variable resistor, the student recorded the readings of the voltmeter and the ammeter. Her results are plotted on the graph in **Figure 9**.

Figure 9

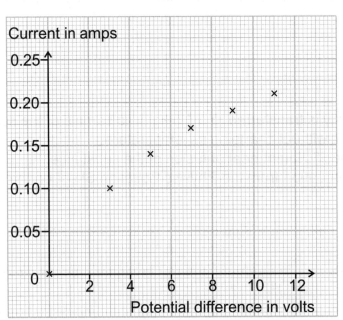

4.1   Draw a curve of best fit on the graph in **Figure 9**.

[1 mark]

Question 4 continues on the next page

4.2 The student took multiple readings of the current at each voltage.
Give **two** reasons as to why she did this.

....

....

....

....

[2 marks]

4.3 Explain, with reference to energy transfers, what happens to the resistance of the lamp as the current through it increases.

....

....

....

....

....

[4 marks]

4.4 The lamp is disconnected from the test circuit, and is connected to a 16 V power supply.
At this potential difference the lamp has a resistance of 64 Ω.
The lamp operates at this potential difference for 180 s.
Calculate the amount of charge which passes through the lamp in this time.

....

....

....

....

....

Charge = ... C

[5 marks]

Question 4 continues on the next page

Turn over ▶

Figure 10 shows the inside of the three-pin plug for an electric desk lamp.

Figure 10

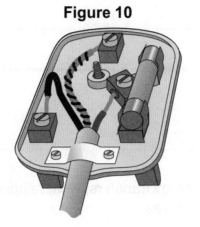

4.5   What colour is the live wire?
Tick **one** box.

blue ☐

brown ☐

yellow and green ☐

[1 mark]

4.6   The lamp's thee-core cable is frayed, so that the metal core of the live wire is exposed. Explain what would happen if someone touched the exposed live wire of the desk lamp when it is plugged in.

....

....

....

....

....

[3 marks]

5   **Figure 11** shows the amount of electricity generated by different renewable energy
     resources in the UK each season between 2012 and 2015.
     A kilowatt hour (kWh) is a unit of energy equal to 3.6×10^6 J.

Figure 11

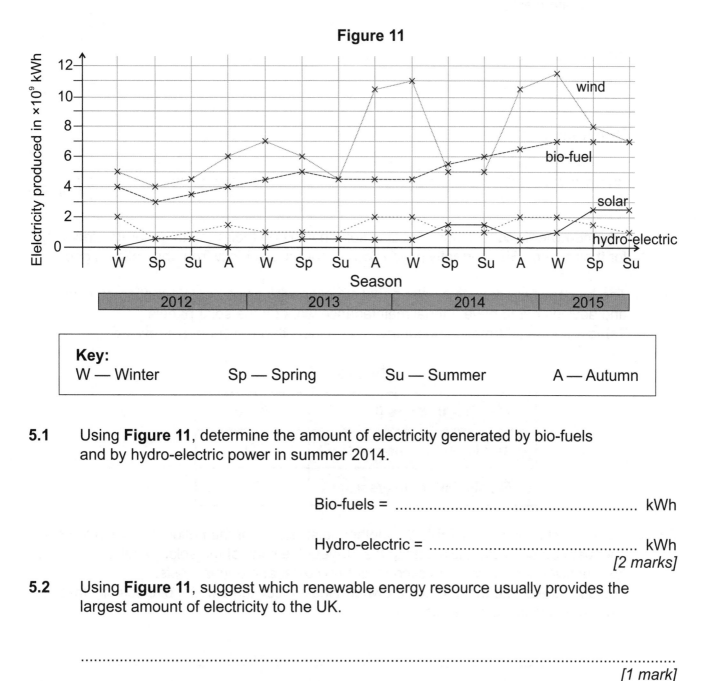

5.1   Using **Figure 11**, determine the amount of electricity generated by bio-fuels
      and by hydro-electric power in summer 2014.

                    Bio-fuels = ... kWh

                    Hydro-electric = ... kWh
                                                                    [2 marks]

5.2   Using **Figure 11**, suggest which renewable energy resource usually provides the
      largest amount of electricity to the UK.

      ....
                                                                    [1 mark]

5.3   **Figure 11** shows that the amount of electricity generated from solar power during
      summer is always larger than the amount generated during winter of the same year.
      Suggest a reason for this.

      ....

      ....
                                                                    [1 mark]

Question 5 continues on the next page

Turn over ▶

5.4 The majority of electricity in the UK is generated from non-renewable energy resources. Give **one** advantage and **one** disadvantage of using non-renewable energy resources to generate electricity.

Advantage = ...

....

Disadvantage = ...

....

[2 marks]

A homeowner is considering installing solar panels on their roof, to generate electricity for their home. She currently pays £650 a year for electricity from the national grid.

The homeowner contacts a solar panel supplier, who gives her information on costs, and advises her to have annual maintenance work on the solar panels.
Table 2 shows information about the solar panels that the supplier provided.

Table 2

Set-up costs (£)	8000
Annual maintenance cost (£)	250
Typical lifetime (years)	30

5.5 Explain, using data from **Table 2**, whether solar panels or the national grid would be a cheaper source of electricity during the 30-year life span of the solar panels.
Your answer should take into account set-up costs, and annual costs.
You should assume that the home owner uses exactly the amount of electricity that is generated by the solar panels.

....

....

....

....

....

....

....

....

[4 marks]

6   Two divers, **A** and **B**, are stood on diving boards, as shown in **Figure 12**.
Both divers have a mass of 65 kg.

Figure 12

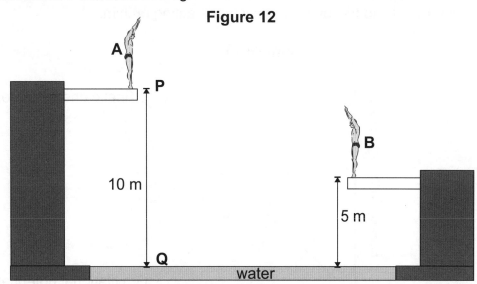

6.1   Which diver has more energy in their gravitational potential energy store?

....

[1 mark]

6.2   Diver **A** jumps off the diving board and falls into the water.
State the energy transfer which occurs during the fall.
You can ignore air resistance and friction.

....

....

[1 mark]

6.3   Write down the equation which links gravitational potential energy, mass, gravitational
field strength and height.

....

[1 mark]

6.4   Calculate the energy transferred from Diver **A**'s gravitational potential energy store
during the fall from point **P** to point **Q**.
The gravitational field strength is 9.8 N/kg.
Give your answer to 2 significant figures.

....

....

....

Energy transferred = ... J

[2 marks]

Question 6 continues on the next page

Turn over ▶

Figure 13 shows a graph of the energy in Diver **A**'s gravitational potential energy store and kinetic energy store as he falls from the diving board, **P**, to the pool surface, **Q**, assuming there is no friction or air resistance acting on him.

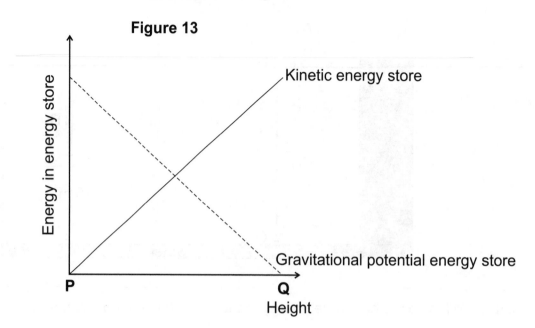

Figure 13

6.5 Explain the shape of the lines in **Figure 13** in terms of energy transfer and conservation of energy.

....

....

....

....

[2 marks]

6.6 Calculate the speed of Diver **A** as he enters the water,
assuming there is no friction or air resistance acting on him.
Use the correct equation from Physics Equation Sheet on the inside back cover.
Use your unrounded answer from **6.4**.

....

....

....

....

....

Speed of Diver **A** at point **Q** = ... m/s

[4 marks]

END OF QUESTIONS

GCSE Combined Science

Physics Paper 2

Higher Tier

In addition to this paper you should have:
*   A ruler.
*   A calculator.
*   The Physics Equations sheet
    (on the inside back cover)

Centre name				
Centre number				
Candidate number				

Time allowed:
*   1 hour 15 minutes

Surname	
Other names	
Candidate signature	

Instructions to candidates
*   Write your name and other details in the spaces provided above.
*   Answer **all** questions in the spaces provided.
*   Do all rough work on the paper.
*   Cross out any work you do not want to be marked.

Information for candidates
*   The marks available are given in brackets at the end of each question.
*   There are 70 marks available for this paper.
*   You are allowed to use a calculator.
*   You should use good English and present your answers in a
    clear and organised way.
*   For Question 3.2, ensure that your answers have a
    clear and logical structure, include the right scientific terms, spelt
    correctly and include detailed, relevant information.

Advice to candidates
*   In calculations show clearly how you worked out your answers.

For examiner's use

Q	Attempt Nº			Q	Attempt Nº		
	1	2	3		1	2	3
1				4			
2				5			
3				6			
	Total						

1 X-rays can be used in hospitals for medical treatments and diagnoses.
Figure 1 shows X-ray images used for diagnoses.
X-rays are directed at a body part being examined.
A detector is placed behind the body part to detect the X-rays that reach it.

Figure 1

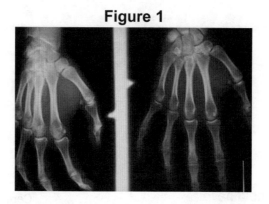

1.1 Explain how X-ray images, like those shown in **Figure 1**, are formed.

....

....

[2 marks]

1.2 Give **one** medical condition that X-rays can be used to either treat or diagnose.

....

....

[1 mark]

X-rays are part of the electromagnetic spectrum. Electromagnetic waves are a type of transverse wave. Transverse waves have a number of distinct properties. A trace of a transverse wave is displayed in **Figure 2**.

Figure 2

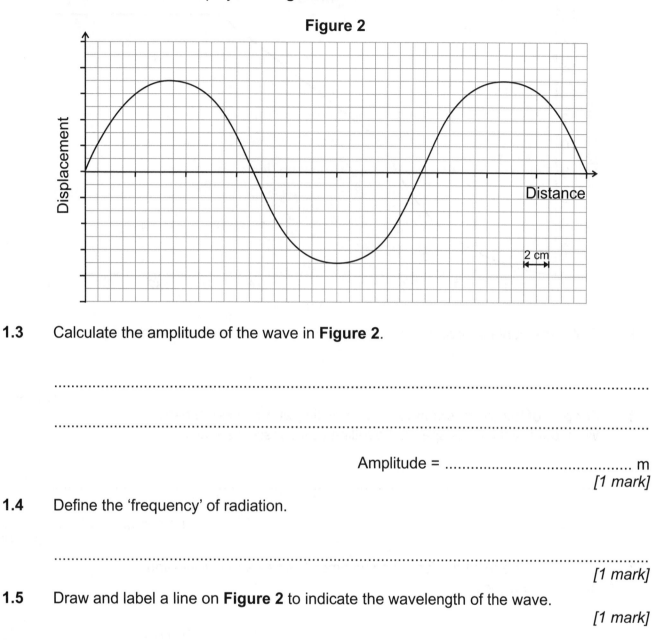

1.3 Calculate the amplitude of the wave in **Figure 2**.

....

....

Amplitude = ... m

[1 mark]

1.4 Define the 'frequency' of radiation.

....

[1 mark]

1.5 Draw and label a line on **Figure 2** to indicate the wavelength of the wave.

[1 mark]

Turn over for the next question

Turn over ▶

2   Two swimmers, **A** and **B**, are having a race. They each swim a length of a 20 m swimming pool. The distance-time graph in **Figure 3** shows swimmer **A**'s motion.

Figure 3

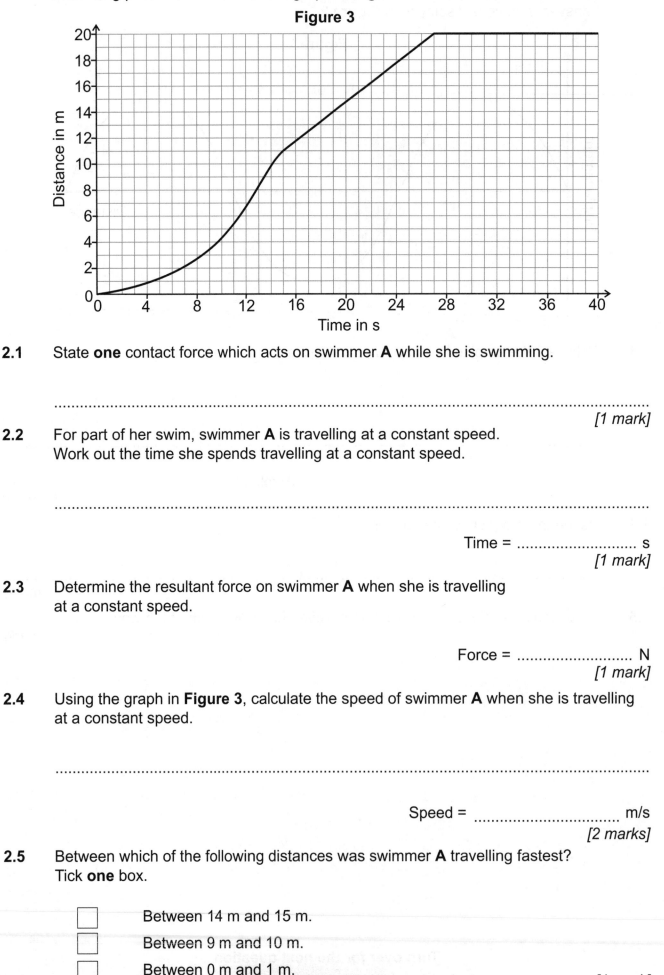

2.1   State **one** contact force which acts on swimmer **A** while she is swimming.

....
                                                                                                      [1 mark]

2.2   For part of her swim, swimmer **A** is travelling at a constant speed.
            Work out the time she spends travelling at a constant speed.

....

                                                               Time = ... s
                                                                                                      [1 mark]

2.3   Determine the resultant force on swimmer **A** when she is travelling
            at a constant speed.

                                                               Force = ... N
                                                                                                      [1 mark]

2.4   Using the graph in **Figure 3**, calculate the speed of swimmer **A** when she is travelling
            at a constant speed.

....

                                                               Speed = ... m/s
                                                                                                      [2 marks]

2.5   Between which of the following distances was swimmer **A** travelling fastest?
            Tick **one** box.

            ☐   Between 14 m and 15 m.

            ☐   Between 9 m and 10 m.

            ☐   Between 0 m and 1 m.
                                                                                                      [1 mark]

Figure 4 shows the distance-time graph of swimmer **B**'s motion.

Figure 4

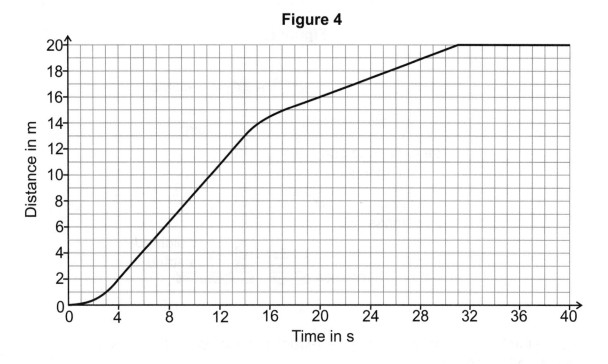

2.6 Using **Figure 4**, describe the motion of swimmer **B**.

....

....

....

....

....

....

....

....

....

....

[5 marks]

2.7 State whether swimmer **A** or swimmer **B** won the race.

....

[1 mark]

Turn over for the next question

Turn over ▶

156

3   A student is given a set of apparatus, set up as shown in **Figure 5**.

Figure 5

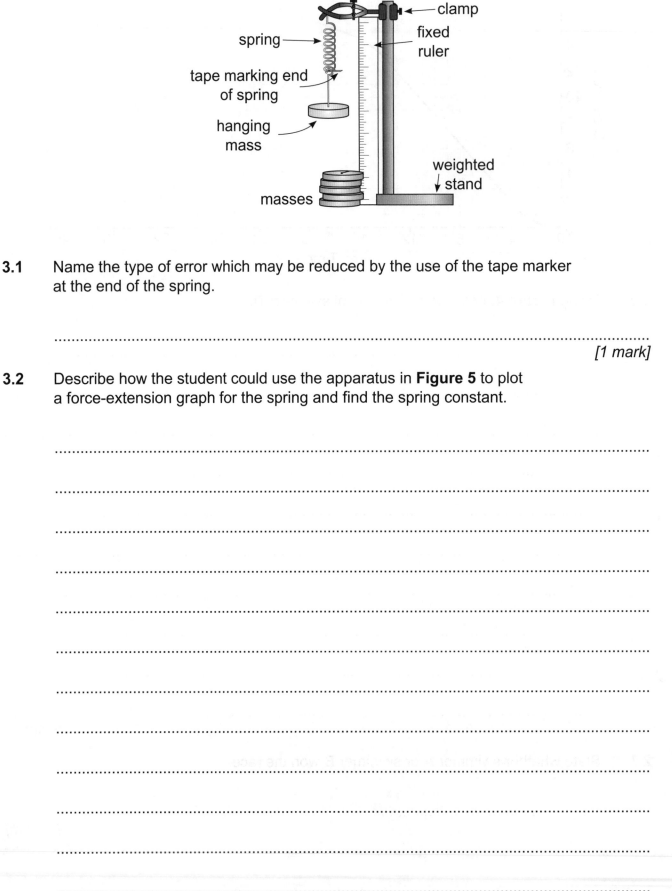

3.1   Name the type of error which may be reduced by the use of the tape marker
at the end of the spring.

....

[1 mark]

3.2   Describe how the student could use the apparatus in **Figure 5** to plot
a force-extension graph for the spring and find the spring constant.

....

....

....

....

....

....

....

....

....

....

....

[6 marks]

The student used the apparatus in **Figure 5** to produce the graph shown in **Figure 6**. She marked the limit of proportionality, and labelled it **A**.

Figure 6

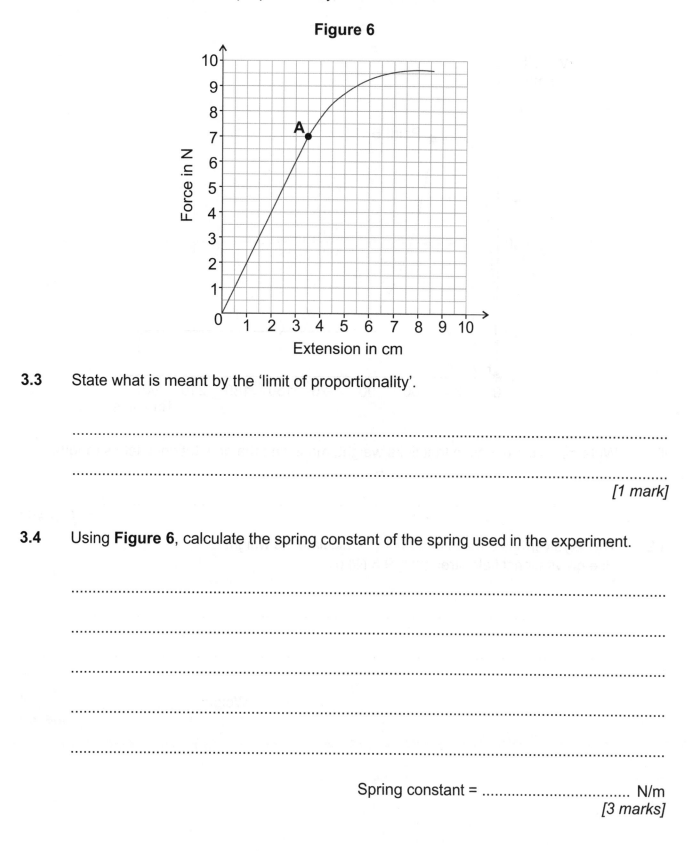

3.3   State what is meant by the 'limit of proportionality'.

....

....
[1 mark]

3.4   Using **Figure 6**, calculate the spring constant of the spring used in the experiment.

....

....

....

....

....

Spring constant = ... N/m
[3 marks]

Turn over for the next question

Turn over ▶

4 A skydiver jumps from an aeroplane and his motion is recorded.
Figure 7 shows the velocity-time graph of his fall.

Figure 7

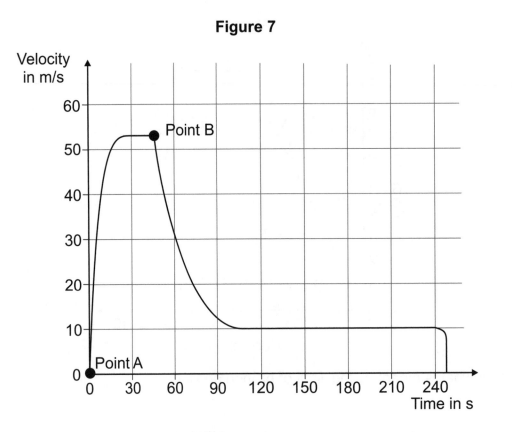

4.1 Write down the equation that links weight, mass and the gravitational field strength.

....

[1 mark]

4.2 The skydiver has a mass of 80.0 kg. Calculate his weight.
Use gravitational field strength = 9.8 N/kg.

....

....

Weight = ... N

[2 marks]

4.3 Using **Figure 7**, estimate the total distance travelled by the skydiver.

....

....

....

....

Distance = ... m

[4 marks]

4.4 When the skydiver jumps from the plane, the plane is travelling at a constant speed, at a constant height above the Earth.
Complete the free body diagram for the plane shown in **Figure 8**.
Label any arrows you draw with the name of the force they represent.

Figure 8

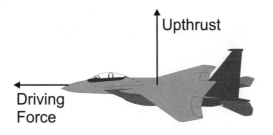

[4 marks]

4.5 Once the skydiver has jumped, the plane accelerates away.
Write down the equation which links force, mass and acceleration.

....

[1 mark]

4.6 The plane experiences a resultant driving force of 48 000 N as it accelerates.
The plane has a mass of 4000 kg.
Calculate the acceleration of the plane.

....

....

....

Acceleration = ... m/s²

[3 marks]

Turn over for the next question

Turn over ▶

5   A driving instructor is looking at the Highway Code. He finds the data shown in **Table 1** about stopping distances for a well-maintained car travelling on dry roads at various speeds.

Table 1

Speed (km/h)	Thinking distance (m)	Braking distance (m)	Stopping distance (m)
32	6	6	12
48	9	14	
64	12	24	
80	15	38	53
96	18	55	
112	21	75	96

5.1   Complete **Table 1** by calculating the remaining stopping distances

[1 mark]

5.2   The data in **Table 1** was obtained by observing a large number of drivers. Explain why it was sensible to use a large sample of people.

....

....

....

[2 marks]

5.3   Describe the thinking distance and braking distance of a car, and the different factors (other than speed) that can increase them.

....

....

....

....

....

....

....

....

[5 marks]

5.4   A 1000 kg car is travelling at 30.0 m/s.
Write down the equation that links momentum, mass and velocity.

....
[1 mark]

5.5   Calculate the momentum of the car.

....

....

....

Momentum = ... kg m/s
[2 marks]

5.6   The car makes an emergency stop to avoid hitting a hazard.
The driver applies the brakes when he is 100 m away from the hazard.
Calculate the minimum deceleration required for the car to stop before
hitting the hazard.
Use the correct equation from the Physics Equation Sheet on the inside back cover.

....

....

....

....

Deceleration = ... m/s²
[3 marks]

Turn over for the next question

Turn over ▶

6   **Figure 9** shows the magnetic field around a bar magnet.

Figure 9

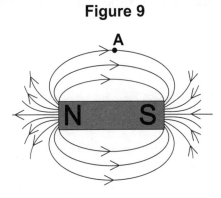

6.1   Identify the position of the compass needle if a compass was placed at point **A**.
Tick **one** box.

          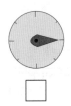

☐   ☐   ☐

[1 mark]

Figure 10 shows two bar magnets being brought together.

Figure 10

6.2   Draw field lines on **Figure 10** to show the magnetic field between the two magnets.
[2 marks]

Current-carrying wires also have a magnetic field around them.
A current-carrying wire can be used to make a solenoid, as shown in **Figure 11**.

Figure 11

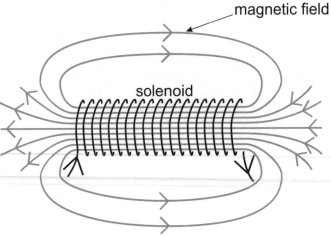

6.3 Explain how coiling a current-carrying wire into a solenoid affects the strength of the magnetic field around the wire.

....

....

....

....

....

[3 marks]

The apparatus shown in **Figure 12** can be used to show the force acting on a current-carrying bar in a magnetic field. When the switch is closed, current flows through the metal bar. The metal bar is free to move.

Figure 12

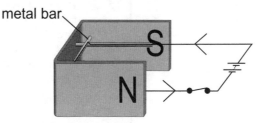

6.4 Suggest whether a force will act on the bar when the switch is closed.
Give a reason for your answer.

....

....

[2 marks]

6.5 Another magnet, with magnetic flux density of 1.5 T is set up. A current-carrying wire, carrying a 4.0 A current, is placed within the magnetic field, at right angles to the field. It experiences a force 0.45 N.
Calculate the length of wire inside the magnetic field.
Use the correct equation from the Physics Equation Sheet on the inside back cover.

....

....

....

Length of wire = ... cm

[4 marks]

END OF QUESTIONS

Answers

Topic 1 — Energy

Page 22
Warm-Up Questions
1) Any two from: e.g. mechanically (by a force doing work) / electrically (work done by when a current flows) / by heating / by radiation.
2) Energy is transferred from the chemical energy store of the person's arm to the kinetic energy stores of the arm and the ball (and the gravitational energy store of the ball). Once the ball is released, energy is transferred from the kinetic energy store of the ball to its gravitational potential energy store.
3) kinetic energy = ½ × mass × (speed)^2 / $E_k = \frac{1}{2}mv^2$
4) A lorry travelling at 60 miles per hour.

Exam Questions
1.1 gravitational potential energy = mass × gravitational field strength × height / $E_p = mgh$ *[1 mark]*
So, $h = E_p \div (m \times g)$ *[1 mark]*
$= 137.2 \div (20 \times 9.8)$ *[1 mark]*
$= \textbf{0.7 m}$ *[1 mark]*
1.2 Energy is transferred from the gravitational potential energy store *[1 mark]* to the kinetic energy store of the load *[1 mark]*.
1.3 Some of the energy would also be transferred to thermal energy store of the air (and the thermal energy store of the load) *[1 mark]*.
2.1 change in thermal energy = mass × specific heat capacity × temperature change / $\Delta E = mc\Delta\theta$
So, $c = \Delta E \div (m \times \Delta\theta)$ *[1 mark]*
$\Delta\theta = 100 - 20 = 80\ ^\circ C$ *[1 mark]*
$c = 36\ 000 \div (0.5 \times 80)$ *[1 mark]*
$= \textbf{900 J/kg}\ ^\circ\textbf{C}$ *[1 mark]*
2.2 Concrete has a higher specific heat capacity *[1 mark]* and so will be able to store a lot more energy in its thermal energy store *[1 mark]*.
Even if you got the answer to 2.1 wrong, if your conclusion is correct for your answer to 2.1, you'd get the marks for this question.
3.1 Reading values from the start and end of the linear point on the graph:
E.g. $\Delta E = 3 - 1 = 2\ kJ = 2000\ J$
$\Delta\theta = 2.4 - 0.4 = 2\ ^\circ C$
[1 mark for any values accurately calculated from a pair of points on the linear part of the graph]
change in thermal energy = mass × specific heat capacity × temperature change / $\Delta E = mc\Delta\theta$,
So, $c = \Delta E \div (m \times \Delta\theta)$ *[1 mark]*
$= 2000 \div (1 \times 2)$ *[1 mark]*
$= \textbf{1000 J/kg}\ ^\circ\textbf{C}$ *[1 mark]*
3.2 Lower *[1 mark]*. In the investigation, some of the energy transferred by the heater would have been transferred to the thermal energy stores of the surroundings rather than the block *[1 mark]*. For the same temperature change to have occurred for a smaller amount of energy transferred, the specific heat capacity must be smaller *[1 mark]*.
It's important to be able to spot reasons why the results of an investigation aren't perfectly accurate.

Pages 27
Warm-Up Questions
1) Energy can be transferred usefully, stored or dissipated, but can never be created or destroyed.
2) Power is the rate of doing work. The units are watts.
3) conduction, convection
4) E.g. lubrication
5) The higher the thermal conductivity, the greater the rate of the energy transfer (i.e. the faster energy is transferred) through it.
6) Some energy is always dissipated, so less than 100% of the input energy transfer is transferred usefully.

Exam Questions
1.1 power = work done ÷ time / $P = W \div t$ *[1 mark]*
$P = 1000 \div 20$ *[1 mark]*
$= \textbf{50 W}$ *[1 mark]*
1.2 Less energy is transferred to the thermal energy store of the motor's parts and the surroundings *[1 mark]*, so more is transferred to the scooter's kinetic energy store *[1 mark]*.
1.3 It will be faster / complete the course in less time *[1 mark]* because the motor transfers the same amount of energy, but over a shorter time *[1 mark]*.
2.1 efficiency = useful output energy transfer ÷ useful input energy transfer *[1 mark]*
2.2 efficiency = useful output energy transfer ÷ useful input energy transfer
$= 480 \div 1200$ *[1 mark]*
$= \textbf{0.4 (or 40\%)}$ *[1 mark]*
2.3 power = energy transferred ÷ time / $P = E \div t$
1 minute = 60 seconds
So, output power $= 600 \div 60$ *[1 mark]*
$= \textbf{10 W}$ *[1 mark]*
2.4 efficiency = useful output power ÷ total output power
So, total input power = useful output power ÷ efficiency *[1 mark]*
total input power $= 10 \div 0.55$ *[1 mark]*
$= 18.181... = \textbf{18 W (to 2 s.f.)}$ *[1 mark]*
2.5 Disagree *[1 mark]*. Torch B has a lower input energy transfer than torch A, i.e. it transfers less energy per minute than torch A (as $18 \times 60 = 1080$, and $1080 < 1200$) *[1 mark]*.
Even if you got the answer to 2.4 wrong, if your conclusion is correct for your answer to 2.5, you'd get the marks for this question. You could also answer this question by comparing the input powers of the torches.

Page 35
Warm-Up Questions
1) Any three from: coal / oil / natural gas / nuclear fuel (plutonium or uranium).
2) Advantage: E.g. they'll never run out.
Disadvantage: Any one from: e.g. energy output often depends on outside factors which cannot be controlled / they can't respond to immediate increases in energy demands.
3) Any one from: e.g. Bio-fuels can be used to run vehicles / electricity generated using renewable resources can be used to power vehicles.
4) Any two from: e.g. it releases greenhouse gases and contributes to global warming / it causes acid rain / coal mining damages the landscape.
5) Any two from: e.g. renewable resources don't currently provide enough energy / energy from renewables cannot be relied upon currently / it's expensive to build new renewable power plants / it's expensive to switch to cars running on renewable energy.

Exam Questions
1.1 Any two from: e.g. wave / tidal / geothermal / bio-fuels *[1 mark for each correct renewable energy resource]*.
1.2 Any one from: e.g. flooding a valley for a dam destroys animal habitats / carbon dioxide is released by rotting vegetation in flooded valley *[1 mark]*.
2.1 From the gravitational potential energy store of the water *[1 mark]* to its kinetic energy store *[1 mark]*.
2.2 E.g. they cause no pollution / they use a renewable energy source *[1 mark for each correct advantage, up to a maximum of two]*.

3.1   power = energy transferred ÷ time / $P = E \div t$

So, $E = P \times t$ *[1 mark]*

seconds in 5 hours = $5 \times 60 \times 60 = 18\ 000$ s

Energy provided by 1 m² solar panel

               in 5 hours = $200 \times 18\ 000$ *[1 mark]*

                       = $3\ 600\ 000$ J *[1 mark]*

Number of panels needed = energy needed ÷ energy provided

= $32\ 500\ 000 \div 3\ 600\ 000$ *[1 mark]*

= $9.027... =$ **10 panels (to next whole number)** *[1 mark]*

Remember, because you have to have a set number of whole panels, if you get a decimal answer, you need to round up to the next whole number to be able to provide the right amount of energy.

3.2   Ten 1 m² solar panels are needed, and they have 10 m² of space on their roof (10×1 m² = 10 m²), so the family can install sufficient solar panels *[1 mark]*.

3.3   E.g. Solar panels are less reliable than coal-fired power stations *[1 mark]*. The energy output of the solar panels will vary based on the number of hours of good sunlight, and may not be able to provide enough energy on a given day *[1 mark]*. The energy output of coal-fired power stations is not influenced by environmental factors like weather, and energy output can be increased to meet demand *[1 mark]*.

Topic 2 — Electricity

Page 41
Warm-Up Questions
1)   Ohms / Ω
2)   The greater the resistance, the smaller the current / the smaller the resistance, the greater the current.
3)

4)   Any one from: e.g. a wire / a fixed resistor
5)   In parallel.
6)   A graph that shows how the current flowing through a component changes as the potential difference across it varies.

Exam Questions
1.1   potential difference = current × resistance / $V = IR$

So, $R = V \div I$ *[1 mark]*

= $1.5 \div 0.30$ *[1 mark]*

= **5.0 Ω** *[1 mark]*

1.2   charge = current × time / $Q = It$

= 0.30×35 *[1 mark]*

= **10.5 C** *[1 mark]*

1.3   The amount of current flowing through the circuit will decrease *[1 mark]*.

1.4

[1 mark]

1.5   The resistance of the filament lamp increases as the temperature increases *[1 mark]*.

2.1   Potential difference (across the component) *[1 mark]*.

2.2   Diodes only allow current to flow in one direction *[1 mark]*.

2.3   At point A, $V = 6$ V, $I = 3$ A *[1 mark]*

potential difference = current × resistance / $V = IR$

$R = V \div I$ *[1 mark]*

= $6 \div 3$ *[1 mark]*

= **2 Ω** *[1 mark]*

Page 48
Warm-Up Questions
1)   Any one from: e.g. in automatic night lights / outdoor lighting / burglar detectors.
2)   The resistance decreases.
3)   E.g.

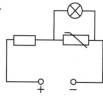

4)   Any one from: e.g. if you remove or disconnect one component, then the whole circuit is broken / you can't switch components on or off independently.
5)   The total resistance is the sum of all the resistances.
6)   Two resistors connected in series.
7)   E.g.

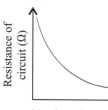

Exam Questions
1.1   total resistance = $R_1 + R_2 + R_3$

= $2 + 3 + 5$ *[1 mark]*

= **10 Ω** *[1 mark]*

1.2   The current will be 0.4 A *[1 mark]* because in a series circuit, the same current flows through all parts of the circuit *[1 mark]*.

1.3 V = source pd

$V_3 = V - V_1 - V_2$

= $4 - 0.8 - 1.2$ *[1 mark]*

= **2 V** *[1 mark]*

2.1   15 V *[1 mark]*

Potential difference is the same across each branch in a parallel circuit.

2.2   potential difference = current × resistance / $V = IR$

$I = V \div R$ *[1 mark]*

= $15 \div 3$ *[1 mark]*

= **5 A** *[1 mark]*

2.3 $I_2 = 5 + 3.75$ *[1 mark]*

= **8.75 A** *[1 mark]*

Even if you got the answer to 2.2 wrong, award yourself the marks for 2.3 if you did the sum above correctly.

Page 54
Warm-Up Questions
1)   The live wire, neutral wire, and earth wire.
2)   Energy is transferred electrically to the thermal energy store of the heating element.
3)   power = (current)² × resistance / $P = I^2R$
4)   The network of cables and transformers that distributes electricity across the country.

Exam Questions
1.1   Alternating current is produced by an alternating potential difference in which the positive and negative ends keep alternating / which is constantly changing direction *[1 mark]*.

1.2   The live wire is at a potential difference of around 230 V *[1 mark]*. Touching the wire forms a low-resistance path from the wire to the earth through your body *[1 mark]*, causing a large current to flow through you, which is an electric shock *[1 mark]*.

2   Step-up transformers increase the potential difference
[1 mark] of the electricity supply, allowing the electricity
to be transmitted at a high potential difference, and
so a low current *[1 mark]*. This reduces the energy
lost through heating in the cables *[1 mark]*.

3.1   power = potential difference × current / $P = V × I$ *[1 mark]*

3.2 $I = P ÷ V$ *[1 mark]*
    $= (2.8 × 1000) ÷ 230$ *[1 mark]*
    $= 12.17... $ A $= $ **12** *[1 mark]* **A** *[1 mark, allow 'amps']*

3.3   She should choose kettle B because it has the higher
power rating *[1 mark]*. This means that it transfers
more energy usefully / to heat the water per unit
time, so it will boil the water faster *[1 mark]*.

4.1   power = potential difference × current / $P = IV$
    $P = 0.5 × 3.0$ *[1 mark]*
    $= $ **1.5 W** *[1 mark]*
    energy transferred = power × time / $E = Pt$
    $t = 0.5$ hours $= (30 × 60)$ s $= 1800$ s
    $E = 1.5 × 1800$ *[1 mark]*
    $= $ **2700 J** *[1 mark]*

4.2   energy transferred = charge flow × potential difference /
    $E = QV$
    So, $Q = E ÷ V$ *[1 mark]*
    $Q = 2700 ÷ 3.0$ *[1 mark]*
    $= $ **900 C** *[1 mark]*

*In the exam, you'd probably get all the marks for 4.2 if you did the sum
above correctly, even if you got the answer to 4.1 wrong.*

Topic 3 — Particle Model of Matter

Pages 61-62
Warm-Up Questions

1)   In a liquid, the particles are held close together, but can
move past each other. They form irregular arrangements.
The particles move in random directions at low speeds.

2)   Density is a measure of the amount of mass
in a given volume / compactness.

3)   Cooling a system decreases its internal energy.

4)   The specific latent heat of vaporisation of a
substance is the amount of energy needed to change
1 kg of that substance from a liquid to a gas.

5)   J/kg

Exam Questions

1.1   Particles are held close together in a fixed, regular pattern
[1 mark]. They vibrate about fixed positions *[1 mark]*.

1.2   melting *[1 mark]*

1.3   evaporation *[1 mark]*

2.1   The densities of each of the toy soldiers are the
same, but their masses may vary *[1 mark]*.

2.2   The volume of the toy soldier / the volume of
water displaced by the toy soldier *[1 mark]*.
The mass of the toy soldier *[1 mark]*.

2.3   How to grade your answer:
    Level 0:   There is no relevant information. *[No marks]*
    Level 1:   There is a brief explanation of an experiment to
            measure the density of the toy soldier.
            The answer lacks coherency. *[1 to 2 marks]*
    Level 2:   There is an explanation of an experiment to
            measure the density of the toy soldier, with
            reference to the equipment needed. The answer
            has some structure. *[3 to 4 marks]*
    Level 3:   There is a clear and detailed explanation of an
            experiment to measure the density of the toy
            soldier. The method includes details of the
            equipment needed and how to process the results
            to work out the density of the toy soldier. The
            answer is well structured. *[5 to 6 marks]*

Here are some points your answer may include:
Measure and record the mass of the toy soldier using the
mass balance.
Fill a eureka can with water.
Place an empty measuring cylinder beneath the spout of the
eureka can.
Submerge the toy soldier in the eureka can.
Measure the volume of water displaced from the eureka can
using the measuring cylinder.
The volume of water displaced is equal to the volume of the
soldier.
Use the equation 'density = mass ÷ volume / $ρ = m ÷ V$'
to calculate the density of the toy soldier.

*With questions where you have to describe a method, make sure your
description is clear and detailed.*

3.1   specific latent heat of fusion *[1 mark]*

3.2   thermal energy for a change of state =
                mass × specific latent heat / $E = mL$
    So, $L = E ÷ m$ *[1 mark]*
    40.8 g $= (40.8 ÷ 1000)$ kg $= 0.0408$ kg
    $L = 47.7 ÷ 0.0408$ *[1 mark]*
    $= $ **1170 J/kg (to 3 s.f.)** *[1 mark]*

3.3   The internal energy of the system increases as it's
heated *[1 mark]*. This is because heating a system
transfers energy from thermal energy stores to the
kinetic stores of the particles in the system *[1 mark]*.

3.4   When a system is heated, energy is transferred to the
particles in the system, causing them to gain energy
in their kinetic stores/move faster *[1 mark]*. If the
substance is heated enough, the particles will have
enough energy in their kinetic stores to break the bonds
holding them together, so they change state *[1 mark]*.

4.1   The particles in a gas have high energies *[1 mark]*, move
in random directions at high speeds *[1 mark]* and are not
arranged in any pattern *[1 mark]*.

4.2   In a sealed container, the gas particles collide with the
container walls *[1 mark]* and exert a force on the walls,
(creating an outward pressure) *[1 mark]*.

4.3   density = mass ÷ volume / $ρ = m ÷ V$ *[1 mark]*

4.4 $ρ = 8.2 ÷ 6.69$ *[1 mark]*
    $= $ **1.2 g/cm³** *[3 marks for correct answer,
    including units. Deduct 1 mark if reported to
    an incorrect number of significant figures and
    deduct 1 mark if incorrect units given]*

4.5   The pressure of the gas within the container increases
as the container is heated *[1 mark]*. This is because the
increase in temperature causes the particles to move faster
/ increases the energy in the kinetic energy stores of the
particles, meaning more force is exerted on the walls of the
container when the particles collide with it *[1 mark]*. The
increased speed / average energy in kinetic stores of the
particles also means there are more collisions, which also
increases the total force exerted on the container *[1 mark]*.

5   density = mass ÷ volume / $ρ = m ÷ V$
    So, $m = ρ × V$ *[1 mark]*
    volume of cube $= 1.5 × 1.5 × 1.5 = 3.375$ cm³ *[1 mark]*
    The cube's density is 3500 kg/m³.
    1 g/cm³ $= 1000$ kg/m³, so this is
    $3500 ÷ 1000 = 3.5$ g/cm³ *[1 mark]*
    $m = 3.5 × 3.375$ *[1 mark]*
    $= 11.8125 = $ **12 g (to 2 s.f.)** *[1 mark]*

Topic 4 — Atomic Structure

Pages 73-74

Warm-Up Questions

1) The nuclear model of the atom contains a tiny nucleus which contains protons and neutrons. The rest of the atom is mostly empty space. Electrons exist in fixed energy levels round the outside of the nucleus.
2) Isotopes of an element are atoms with the same number of protons / the same atomic number but a different number of neutrons / a different mass number.
3) alpha particles
4) Beta emitters are not immediately absorbed, like alpha radiation, and do not penetrate as far as gamma rays. Therefore variations in the thickness of the sheet significantly affect the amount of radiation passing through.
5) beta radiation
6) gamma rays
7) Substances with a short half-life decay very quickly so emit high amounts of radiation initially.

Exam Questions

1.1 Beta (particles) *[1 mark]*, because the radiation passes through the paper, but not the aluminium, so it is moderately penetrating in comparison to the other two *[1 mark]*.
1.2 E.g. a Geiger-Muller tube/counter *[1 mark]*
2.1 The time taken for the number of radioactive nuclei in a sample to halve / the time taken for the count-rate or activity to fall to half of its initial level *[1 mark]*.
2.2 4 minutes is equivalent to $4 \div 2 = 2$ half-lives *[1 mark]*. After 1 half-life, there will be ½ of the unstable nuclei left. So, after 2 half-lives, there will be $\frac{1}{2} \div 2 = \frac{1}{4}$ / **one quarter** of the unstable nuclei left *[1 mark]*.
3.1 $2 \times 60 = 120$ seconds
$120 \div 40 = 3$ half-lives *[1 mark]*
$8000 \div 2 = 4000$, $4000 \div 2 = 2000$,
$2000 \div 2 = \textbf{1000 Bq}$ *[1 mark]*
3.2 $8000 \div 2 = 4000$, $4000 \div 2 = 2000$, $2000 \div 2 = 1000$, $1000 \div 2 = 500$, $500 \div 2 = 250$.
So it takes **5 half-lives** to drop to 250 Bq *[2 marks for correct answer, otherwise 1 mark for attempting to halve values to find number of half-lives]*.
3.3 $(100 \div 8000) \times 100$ *[1 mark]* = **1.25%** *[1 mark]*
4.1 Protons *[1 mark]* and neutrons *[1 mark]*.
4.2 The total number of protons and neutrons in the nucleus/atom *[1 mark]*.
4.3 Atom A and atom B *[1 mark]* because isotopes of the same element have the same atomic number, but different mass numbers *[1 mark]*.
5.1 E.g. $_{-1}^{0}\text{e}$ / $_{-1}^{0}\beta$ *[1 mark]*
5.2 The atomic number increases by 1 *[1 mark]* and the mass number stays the same *[1 mark]*.
5.3 The atomic number doesn't change *[1 mark]* and neither does the mass number *[1 mark]*.
5.4 $$_{84}^{209}\text{Po} \rightarrow \,_{82}^{205}\text{Pb} + \,_{2}^{4}\text{He}$$
[1 mark for both the mass number and atomic number of He, 1 mark for the atomic number of Po, 1 mark for the mass number of Pb]

Topic 5 — Forces

Page 81

Warm-Up Questions

1) Contact force: e.g. air resistance
Non-contact force: e.g. gravitational attraction
2) Vector quantity: e.g. velocity / momentum / force
Scalar quantity: e.g. mass / speed / volume
3) a) N/kg
b) kg
c) N
4) If all force arrows placed tip-to-tail form a closed loop, the forces are balanced.

Exam Questions

1.1 Total force to the right = $1700 + 300 = 2000$ N
Total force to the left = 2000 N
Total horizontal force = $2000 - 2000 = 0$ N *[1 mark]*
Resultant force = downwards force – upwards force
$= 800 - 300$
$= \textbf{500 N}$ *[1 mark]* **downwards** *[1 mark]*
1.2 Total vertical force = 0 N
so, $y = \textbf{400 N}$ *[1 mark]*
Total horizontal force = 0 N
so, $x + 500$ N = 2000 N
$x = 2000 - 500 = \textbf{1500 N}$ *[1 mark]*
2.1 work done = force × distance moved along the line of action of the force / $W = Fs$
$W = 42\,000 \times 700$ *[1 mark]*
$= 29\,400\,000$ J *[1 mark]*
$= \textbf{29 400 kJ}$ *[1 mark]*
2.2

[1 mark for four arrows in directions shown, 1 mark for upwards arrow same length as downwards arrow, 1 mark for driving force arrow bigger than resistive force arrow, 1 mark for all arrows labelled correctly]

You'd still get the marks if you've drawn the driving force to the right, and the resistive force to the left, as the direction that the train was travelling in was not specified in the question.

3.1 The spring would stretch less on Mars because the gravitational field strength on Mars is less than that on Earth *[1 mark]*, so the ball would weigh less *[1 mark]* and the force on the spring would be lower *[1 mark]*.
3.2 weight = mass × gravitational field strength / $W = mg$
so $g = W \div m$ *[1 mark]*
$= 0.37 \div 0.10$ *[1 mark]*
$= \textbf{3.7 N/kg}$ *[1 mark]*

168

Page 86
Warm-Up Questions
1) false
2) Force = spring constant × extension / $F = ke$
3) The limit of proportionality is the point at which the spring stops behaving according to $F = ke$ / F is no longer proportional to e.
4) E.g. to check that the masses to be used in the experiment are appropriate.

Exam Questions
1 shape / length / size *[1 mark]*, proportional *[1 mark]*, elastic *[1 mark]*.
There are quite a few things you could write for the first word — as long as your answer seems sensible give yourself the mark.
2.1 The mass on the bottom of the spring / the force applied to the bottom of the spring *[1 mark]*.
2.2 Any one from: e.g. the spring used throughout the experiment / the temperature the experiment is carried out at *[1 mark]*.
2.3 extension = 2.5 cm = 0.025 m *[1 mark]*
force = spring constant × extension / $F = ke$
so $k = F \div e$ *[1 mark]*
= 4 ÷ 0.025 *[1 mark]*
= **160 N/m** *[1 mark]*
Remember to convert the measurement of extension from cm into m before you do your calculation.
2.4 The spring has been inelastically deformed *[1 mark]*.

Page 93
Warm-Up Questions
1) Speed is scalar, velocity is a vector / velocity has a direction, speed does not.
2) a) E.g. 3 m/s
b) E.g. 55 m/s
c) E.g. 250 m/s
Your answers may be slightly different to these, but as long as they're about the same size, you should be fine to use them in the exam.
3) An upwards curved line / a curve with increasing gradient.
4) A straight, horizontal line.
5) As the speed of the car increases, air resistance on the car increases.

Exam Questions
1.1 The cyclist travels at a constant speed (of 3 m/s) between 5 s and 8 s *[1 mark]*, then decelerates between 8 s and 10 s *[1 mark]*.
1.2 Area of triangle = 0.5 × width × height
Width = 5 − 2 = 3 s
Height = 3 m/s
Distance = 0.5 × 3 × 3 = **4.5 m**
[2 marks, otherwise 1 mark for an attempt to calculate the area under the graph between 2 and 5 seconds]
1.3 Acceleration is given by the gradient of a velocity-time graph.
change in y = 3 − 0 = 3 m/s
change in x = 5 − 2 = 3 s
acceleration = 3 ÷ 3 = **1 m/s²**
[2 marks, otherwise 1 mark for an attempt to calculate the gradient of the line between 2 and 5 seconds]
You could also have used $a = \Delta v \div \Delta t$ here.
1.4 average acceleration = change in velocity ÷ change in time / $a = \Delta v \div \Delta t$
velocity at 8 s = 3 m/s; velocity at 10 s = 2 m/s
so Δv = 2 − 3 = −1 m/s *[1 mark]*
So, a = −1 ÷ 2 *[1 mark]*
= −0.5 m/s²
= **0.5 m/s²** *[1 mark]*
Your answer should be positive since the question asks for deceleration, rather than acceleration.

2.1 (final velocity)² − (initial velocity)² = 2 × acceleration × distance / $v^2 - u^2 = 2as$
So, $a = (v^2 - u^2) \div 2s$ *[1 mark]*
$a = (15^2 - 9^2) \div (2 \times 15)$ *[1 mark]*
= **4.8 m/s²** *[1 mark]*
2.2 upwards / in the opposite direction to the direction of motion *[1 mark]*
2.3 distance travelled = average speed × time / $s = vt$
So, $v = s \div t$ *[1 mark]*
v = 102 ÷ 5.00 *[1 mark]*
= **20.4 m/s** *[1 mark]*
2.4 Its (average) speed will be higher *[1 mark]* as the air resistance acting on the bird will be lower *[1 mark]*.

Page 98
Warm-Up Questions
1) 0 N
2) boulder B
Boulder B needs a greater force to accelerate it by the same amount as boulder A.
3) true
This is Newton's Third Law.
4) Masses should be added to the trolley.

Exam Questions
1.1 The ball exerts a force of −500 N on the bat *[1 mark]*, because, due to Newton's Third Law, if the bat exerts a force on the ball, the ball exerts an equal force on the bat in the opposite direction *[1 mark]*.
1.2 The acceleration of the ball is greater *[1 mark]* because it has a smaller mass, but is acted on by the same size force (and $F = ma$) *[1 mark]*.
2.1 force = mass × acceleration / $F = ma$
So, $a = F \div m$ *[1 mark]*
Set direction of van's motion to be positive, so $F = -200$ N
$a = -200 \div 2500$ *[1 mark]*
= −0.08 m/s²
So, deceleration = **0.08 m/s²** *[1 mark]*
The question asked for deceleration, so you should really quote your answer without the minus sign. However, you should get the marks either way.
2.2 force = mass × acceleration / $F = ma$
$F = 10.0 \times 29.0$ *[1 mark]*
= **290 N** *[1 mark]*
2.3 By Newton's Third Law, force on van in collision is −290 N *[1 mark]*.
force = mass × acceleration / $F = ma$
So, $a = F \div m$
$a = -290 \div 2500$ *[1 mark]*
= −0.116 m/s²
So deceleration = **0.116 m/s²** *[1 mark]*
You'd still get the marks here, even if you got 2.2 wrong, as long as your method's correct.
3* How to grade your answer:
Level 0: There is no relevant information. *[No marks]*
Level 1: A simple experiment to investigate force and acceleration which can be performed with the given equipment is partly outlined. How to process the results is not explained or is explained poorly. The answer lacks coherency. *[1 to 2 marks]*
Level 2: An experiment to investigate force and acceleration which can be performed with the given equipment is outlined in detail. How to process the results to find the spring constant is described clearly and in detail. The answer is well structured. *[3 to 4 marks]*

Here are some points your answer may include:
Place all of the masses in the trolley.
Calculate and record the weight of the trolley.
Place the trolley on the starting line.
Release the trolley, so that it moves through the light gate, and record the acceleration measured.
Take one of the masses from the trolley, and attach it to the hook.
Calculate and record the new total weight of the hook and the new total weight of the trolley.
Reset the position of the trolley on the starting line.
Release the trolley again so that it moves through the light gate, and record the acceleration measured.
Repeat these steps until all the masses from the trolley have been moved to the hook.
Plot your results on a graph of acceleration against weight, and draw a line of best fit.

Page 103
Warm-Up Questions
1) The thinking distance is the distance travelled during your reaction time (the time between seeing a hazard, and applying the brakes).
2) The braking distance.
3) Any one from: e.g. poor grip on the roads increases braking distance / poor visibility delays when you see the hazard / distraction by the weather delays when you see the hazard.
4) Get the individual to sit with their arm resting on the edge of a table. Hold a ruler end-down so that the 0 cm mark hangs between their thumb and forefinger. Drop the ruler without warning. The individual must grab the ruler between their thumb and forefinger as quickly as possible. Measure the distance at which they have caught the ruler.
Use $v^2 - u^2 = 2as$, $a = 9.8$ m/s^2 and $a = \Delta v \div t$ to calculate the time taken for the ruler to fall that distance. This is their reaction time.
5) Energy is transferred from the kinetic energy stores of the wheels to the thermal energy stores of the brakes.
6) $p = mv = 2.5 \times 10 = $ **25 kg m/s**
7) In a closed system, the total momentum before an interaction must equal the total momentum after the interaction.
8) The momentum is zero.

Exam Question
1.1 stopping distance = braking distance + thinking distance,
So, thinking distance = stopping distance
– braking distance *[1 mark]*
thinking distance = 58 – 41
= **17 m** *[1 mark]*
1.2 Their braking distance may increase *[1 mark]*, because the frost on the road will decrease the friction between the tyres and the road, causing them to decelerate at a lower rate and travel further whilst braking *[1 mark]*.
1.3 thinking distance = unchanged *[1 mark]*
braking distance = decreases *[1 mark]*
2.1 momentum = mass × velocity / $p = mv$ *[1 mark]*
2.2 $p = mv$
$p = 650 \times 15.0$ *[1 mark]*
= **9750 kg m/s** *[1 mark]*
2.3 9750 kg m/s *[1 mark]*
Due to conservation of momentum, the total momentum after the collision is equal to the total momentum before the collision.
2.4 The two cars will move away at a speed lower than that of the initially moving car *[1 mark]* as the momentum is the same as before the collision, but the mass has increased (so the velocity must decrease) *[1 mark]*.

Topic 6 — Waves

Pages 111
Warm-Up Questions
1) In a longitudinal wave, the vibrations are parallel to the direction of travel/energy transfer.
2) wave speed = frequency × wavelength / $v = f\lambda$
3) E.g. Set up and turn on a ripple tank. Then, dim the lights and turn on the strobe light. Alter the frequency of the strobe light until the wave pattern on the screen below the ripple rank appears to freeze and stop moving. From the screen, measure the distance between the shadow lines that are a certain number of wavelengths apart, e.g. ten wavelengths. Divide the distance by this number of wavelengths to find the average wavelength. Use the equation wave speed = frequency × wavelength / $v = f\lambda$ to find the speed of the waves.
4) true

Exam Questions
1.1 transverse *[1 mark]*
1.2 5 cm *[1 mark]*
1.3 2 m *[1 mark]*
1.4 It will halve *[1 mark]*.
$v = f\lambda$, so if f doubles, then λ must halve, so that v stays the same.
2.1 The distance he measures is 1 wavelength *[1 mark]*. This can be used, together with the frequency of the signal, in the formula for wave speed, wave speed = frequency × wavelength / $v = f\lambda$ *[1 mark]*.
2.2 wave speed = frequency × wavelength / $v = f\lambda$
So $v = 50 \times 6.8$ *[1 mark]*
= **340** *[1 mark]* **m/s** *[1 mark]*

Page 119-120
Warm-Up Questions
1) gamma rays
2) Alternating current is made up of oscillating charges, which produce oscillating electric and magnetic fields in the form of radio waves.
3) The microwaves penetrate a few centimetres into the food before being absorbed by water molecules. The energy from the absorbed microwaves causes the food to heat up.
4) E.g. to carry data over long distances.
5) It has enough energy to knock electrons off atoms — this can cause gene mutations, cell destruction and cancer.
6) It emits more IR radiation than it absorbs.
7) Leslie cube

Exam Questions
1.1 Any one from: e.g. fluorescent light bulbs / tanning lamps *[1 mark]*.
1.2 Any one from: e.g. sunburn / premature ageing of skin / blindness / increased risk of skin cancer *[1 mark]*.
1.3 A gamma ray emitter is injected into/swallowed by the patient *[1 mark]* and the gamma rays emitted are detected by an external detector *[1 mark]*. By seeing where the gamma rays come from, they can track the progress of the tracer around the body and check it is functioning correctly *[1 mark]*.
1.4 Gamma rays can pass out of the body without being absorbed *[1 mark]*.

2.1 Radio waves can bend around / pass through objects so the signal can reach the inside of the house *[1 mark]*. Light waves would be blocked by the mountain / walls, and so would not be able to reach the receiver inside the house *[1 mark]*.

2.2 Microwave radiation *[1 mark]*. It passes through Earth's watery atmosphere without being absorbed, so can reach the satellites *[1 mark]*.

2.3 They are transmitted through the atmosphere into space, where they are picked up by a satellite receiver orbiting Earth *[1 mark]*. The satellite transmits the signal back to Earth in a different direction, where it is received by a satellite dish connected to the house *[1 mark]*.

3.1 Any one from: e.g. place the thermometers at equal distances away from the cube / place the thermometers at the same height as each other / make sure no thermometers are in direct sunlight/a draught *[1 mark]*.

3.2 Matt surfaces are better infrared radiation emitters then shiny surfaces *[1 mark]*.

3.3 Black surfaces are better infrared radiation emitters than white surfaces *[1 mark]*.

3.4 The times recorded would be longer *[1 mark]*. Cooler objects emit infrared radiation at a lower rate *[1 mark]*.

3.5 E.g. the resolution of the digital thermometer is higher, so there will be less uncertainty in the results (the results will be more accurate) / the student is less likely to misread the temperature (human error is less likely) *[1 mark for each correct reason, up to a maximum of 2]*.

Topic 7 — Magnetism and Electromagnetism

Page 125
Warm-Up Questions

1)

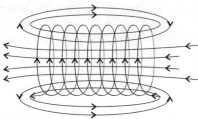

2) It's made up of concentric circles around the wire (with the wire at the centre).

3) A coil of current-carrying wire, often used to make electromagnets.

Exam Questions

1.1 E.g. Put the magnets on a piece of paper and place many compasses in different places between the magnets to show the magnetic field at those points *[1 mark]*. The compass needles will line up with the magnetic field lines *[1 mark]*.

They could also use iron filings to show the pattern.

1.2 The field lines point straight across from the north pole towards the south pole *[1 mark]*.

1.3 Attraction *[1 mark]*, as opposite poles are facing each other and opposite poles attract *[1 mark]*.

2.1

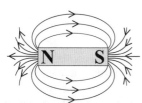

[1 mark for correct field shape, 1 mark for direction]

2.2 E.g. iron *[1 mark]*

2.3 The paperclips will fall *[1 mark]*, because an electromagnetic only has a magnetic field if a current is flowing *[1 mark]*.

Page 129
Warm-Up Questions

1) When a current-carrying wire in a magnetic field experiences a force.

2) First finger — magnetic field
Second finger — current
Thumb — force (motion)

3) Swapping the polarity of the dc supply (reversing the current), or swapping the magnetic poles over (reversing the field).

Exam Questions

1.1

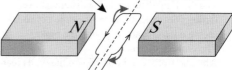

[1 mark]

1.2 The direction of the force would be reversed too *[1 mark]*.

1.3 The force would be lower *[1 mark]*.

1.4 There would be no force on the wire *[1 mark]*.

2.1 E.g.

direction of rotation   axis of rotation

[1 mark for any indication that the current goes anticlockwise]

2.2 force = magnetic flux density × current × length of conductor inside field / $F = BIl$
$F = 0.2 \times 15 \times 0.1$ *[1 mark]*
= **0.3 N** *[1 mark]*

2.3 By swapping the direction of the current/contacts every half turn (using a split-ring commutator) *[1 mark]* so the forces on the loop always act in a way that keeps the loop rotating *[1 mark]*.

Practice Paper 1

1.1 $214 - 83 =$ **131 neutrons** *[1 mark]*

1.2

$^{222}_{86}$ Rn   *[1 mark]*

$^{210}_{83}$ Bi   *[1 mark]*

1.3 420 days *[1 mark]*

1.4 Half-life when activity drops to half original total.
Activity after 1 half-life = 80 ÷ 2 = 40 Bq
Using **Figure 2**, when activity = 40 Bq, time = 140 days.
Therefore, half-life = **140 days** *[1 mark]*

1.5 Contamination is when unwanted radioactive atoms are on or inside an object *[1 mark]*.

1.6 How to grade your answer:
Level 0: There is no relevant information. *[No marks]*
Level 1: There is a brief explanation on the dangers of alpha contamination and irradiation, but little to no comparison between them. The answer has little or no clear structure. *[1 to 2 marks]*
Level 2: There is a clear explanation and comparison of the dangers of contamination and irradiation by alpha sources. The answer is well structured. *[3 to 4 marks]*

Here are some points your answer may include:

Alpha radiation is strongly ionising.

If alpha radiation enters living cells, it can kill or damage them and cause cancer.

Contamination on the outside of the body by an alpha source could result in the ingestion of the alpha source.

If an alpha source is ingested, inside the body it is almost certain to be absorbed by living cells and cause damage.

The alpha radiation will do a lot of damage to a very localised area.

Irradiation by an alpha source is less dangerous than contamination by an alpha source.

Alpha radiation is easily absorbed by thin barriers (e.g. skin) or the air, so is unlikely to reach the body's delicate organs if the source is outside the body.

2.1 E.g. the current is higher in circuit A *[1 mark]*. The total resistance is higher in circuit B *[1 mark]*.

2.2 power = potential difference × current / $P = VI$ *[1 mark]*

2.3 $P = 11 × 0.30$ *[1 mark]* = **3.3 W** *[1 mark]*

2.4 The bulb in circuit A has a greater potential difference across it *[1 mark]* because in a series circuit, the potential difference from the power supply is shared between components *[1 mark]*.

2.5 The resistance decreases *[1 mark]*.

2.6 E.g. a car engine temperature sensor *[1 mark]*.

2.7

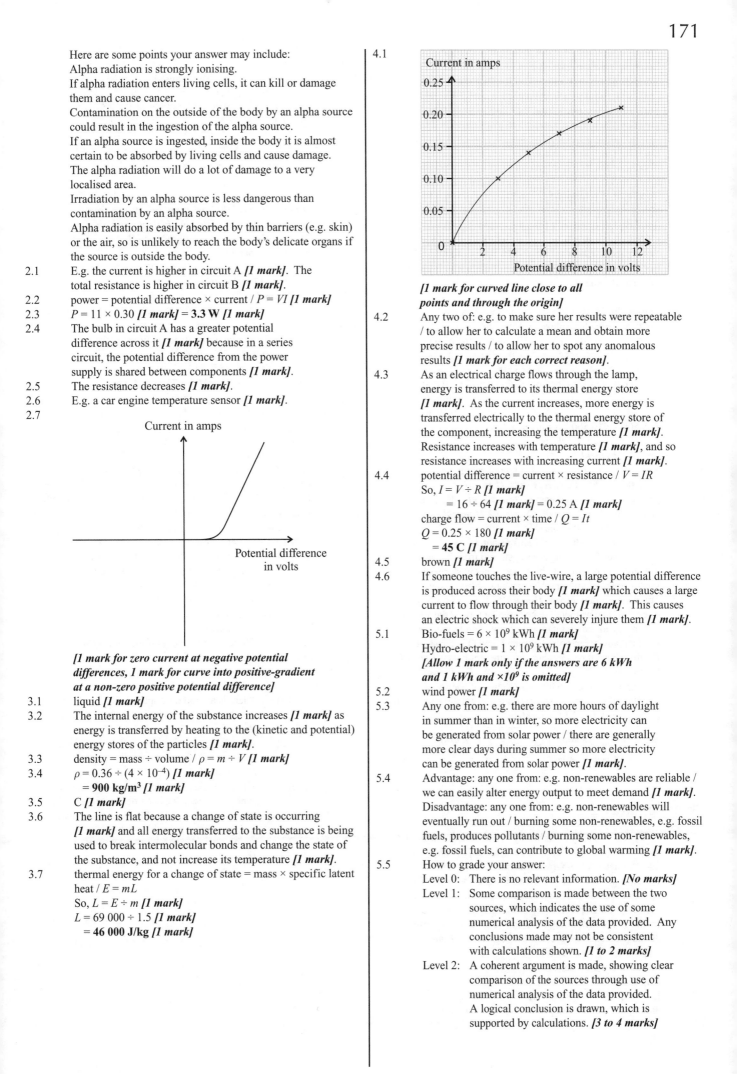

Current in amps

Potential difference in volts

[1 mark for zero current at negative potential differences, 1 mark for curve into positive-gradient at a non-zero positive potential difference]

3.1 liquid *[1 mark]*

3.2 The internal energy of the substance increases *[1 mark]* as energy is transferred by heating to the (kinetic and potential) energy stores of the particles *[1 mark]*.

3.3 density = mass ÷ volume / $\rho = m ÷ V$ *[1 mark]*

3.4 $\rho = 0.36 ÷ (4 × 10^{-4})$ *[1 mark]*
   = **900 kg/m³** *[1 mark]*

3.5 C *[1 mark]*

3.6 The line is flat because a change of state is occurring *[1 mark]* and all energy transferred to the substance is being used to break intermolecular bonds and change the state of the substance, and not increase its temperature *[1 mark]*.

3.7 thermal energy for a change of state = mass × specific latent heat / $E = mL$
   So, $L = E ÷ m$ *[1 mark]*
   $L = 69\,000 ÷ 1.5$ *[1 mark]*
   = **46 000 J/kg** *[1 mark]*

4.1

Current in amps

Potential difference in volts

[1 mark for curved line close to all points and through the origin]

4.2 Any two of: e.g. to make sure her results were repeatable / to allow her to calculate a mean and obtain more precise results / to allow her to spot any anomalous results *[1 mark for each correct reason]*.

4.3 As an electrical charge flows through the lamp, energy is transferred to its thermal energy store *[1 mark]*. As the current increases, more energy is transferred electrically to the thermal energy store of the component, increasing the temperature *[1 mark]*. Resistance increases with temperature *[1 mark]*, and so resistance increases with increasing current *[1 mark]*.

4.4 potential difference = current × resistance / $V = IR$
   So, $I = V ÷ R$ *[1 mark]*
   = $16 ÷ 64$ *[1 mark]* = 0.25 A *[1 mark]*
   charge flow = current × time / $Q = It$
   $Q = 0.25 × 180$ *[1 mark]*
   = **45 C** *[1 mark]*

4.5 brown *[1 mark]*

4.6 If someone touches the live-wire, a large potential difference is produced across their body *[1 mark]* which causes a large current to flow through their body *[1 mark]*. This causes an electric shock which can severely injure them *[1 mark]*.

5.1 Bio-fuels = $6 × 10^9$ kWh *[1 mark]*
   Hydro-electric = $1 × 10^9$ kWh *[1 mark]*
   [Allow 1 mark only if the answers are 6 kWh and 1 kWh and ×10⁹ is omitted]

5.2 wind power *[1 mark]*

5.3 Any one from: e.g. there are more hours of daylight in summer than in winter, so more electricity can be generated from solar power / there are generally more clear days during summer so more electricity can be generated from solar power *[1 mark]*.

5.4 Advantage: any one from: e.g. non-renewables are reliable / we can easily alter energy output to meet demand *[1 mark]*.
   Disadvantage: any one from: e.g. non-renewables will eventually run out / burning some non-renewables, e.g. fossil fuels, produces pollutants / burning some non-renewables, e.g. fossil fuels, can contribute to global warming *[1 mark]*.

5.5 How to grade your answer:
   Level 0: There is no relevant information. *[No marks]*
   Level 1: Some comparison is made between the two sources, which indicates the use of some numerical analysis of the data provided. Any conclusions made may not be consistent with calculations shown. *[1 to 2 marks]*
   Level 2: A coherent argument is made, showing clear comparison of the sources through use of numerical analysis of the data provided. A logical conclusion is drawn, which is supported by calculations. *[3 to 4 marks]*

Here are some points your answer may include:

Solar panels have a set up cost of £8000, while the national grid has no set-up cost.

Each year, solar panels maintenance costs £400 less than purchasing electricity from the national grid (£650).

After 20 years, the amount saved by using solar panels instead of buying electricity from the national grid will equal the solar panel's set-up cost.

Total maintenance cost over 30 years of solar panels
= 30 × 250 = £7500

Total cost of solar panels over 30 years = 7500 + 8000
= £15 500

Total cost of electricity from the national grid over 30 years
= 30 × 650 = £19 500

Solar panels will save 19 500 – 15 500 = £4000 in 30 years.

Solar panels are a cheaper source of electricity over the 30 year lifetime

OR

During the 30-year life span of the solar panels:

Total cost of solar panels = set-up cost +
(30 × annual maintenance cost)
= 8000 + (30 × 250)
= £15 500

Total cost of electricity from national grid = 30 × annual cost
= 30 × 650
= £19 500

£15 500 < £19 500, so solar panels are a cheaper source of electricity.

6.1   diver A *[1 mark]*

6.2   From diver A's gravitational potential energy store to their kinetic energy store *[1 mark]*.

6.3   gravitational potential energy = mass × gravitational field strength (g) × height / $E_p = mgh$ *[1 mark]*

6.4 $E_p = 65 × 9.8 × 10$ *[1 mark]*
= 6370 J = **6400 J (to 2 s.f.)** *[1 mark]*

6.5   As the diver falls, energy is transferred from his gravitational potential energy store to his kinetic energy store, so the kinetic energy store graph slopes upwards as the g.p.e store graph slopes downwards *[1 mark]*. Due to conservation of energy, and as there are no resistive forces, the sum of the energy in the gravitational potential and kinetic energy stores at any given point between P and Q is constant (so the lines have the same, but opposite, gradient) *[1 mark]*.

6.6   kinetic energy = 0.5 × mass × (speed)^2 / $E_k = \frac{1}{2}mv^2$
No resistive forces, so by conservation of energy, all energy transferred from g.p.e. store goes to the kinetic energy store.
So, $E_p = E_k = 6370$ J *[1 mark]*
So, $v = \sqrt{\dfrac{2E_k}{m}}$ *[1 mark]* $= \sqrt{\dfrac{2 × 6370}{65}}$ *[1 mark]*
= **14 m/s** *[1 mark]*

Practice Paper 2

1.1   X-rays aren't easily absorbed by tissues, but are absorbed by denser materials like bones and metal *[1 mark]*. The detector detects the X-rays transmitted at each point and creates a picture showing areas of tissue and bone *[1 mark]*.

1.2   Any one from, e.g. X-rays can be used to treat cancers / X-ray photographs can be used to diagnose bone fractures / X-ray photographs can be used to diagnose dental problems (problems with your teeth) *[1 mark]*.

1.3   amplitude = 7 squares tall
one square = 1 cm tall
amplitude = 7 × 1 = **7 cm** *[1 mark]*

1.4   E.g. frequency is the number of complete waves passing a certain point per second / the number of waves produced by a source each second *[1 mark]*.

1.5   E.g.

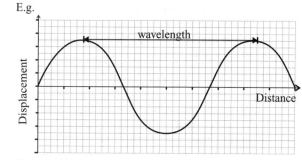

[1 mark for straight horizontal line drawn from a point on the wave to an equivalent point on the wave, labelled 'wavelength' or 'λ']

2.1   E.g. drag *[1 mark]*

2.2   Graph is linear between 15 s and 27 s.
27 – 15 = **12 s** *[1 mark]*

2.3   0 N *[1 mark]*
When an object is travelling at a constant speed in a fixed direction, all the forces are balanced and so the resultant force will be zero.

2.4   Speed is the gradient of a distance time graph.
change in y = 20 – 11 = 9 m
change in x = 27 – 15 = 12 s
speed = 9 ÷ 12 *[1 mark]* = **0.75 m/s** *[1 mark]*

2.5   Between 9 m and 10 m *[1 mark]*.
The swimmer is travelling fastest when the gradient of the graph is steepest. Of the options given, the graph is steepest between 9 m and 10 m. You can draw a tangent to see this more clearly.

2.6   Swimmer B accelerates during the first 2 m / between 0 m and 2 m / for the first 4 seconds *[1 mark]*.
They swim at a constant speed for the next 11 m / between 2 and 13 m / for the next 10 seconds *[1 mark]* and then undergo a period of deceleration for the next 2 m / between 13 m and 15 m / for the next 3 seconds *[1 mark]*.
They then swim at a slower constant speed than before for the next 5 m / between 15 m and 20 m / for the next 14 seconds *[1 mark]*. They then remain stationary, having reached the end of the pool (in 31 s) *[1 mark]*.

2.7   Swimmer A won the race *[1 mark]*.

3.1   Random errors *[1 mark]*

3.2   How to grade your answer:
Level 0:   There is no relevant information. *[No marks]*
Level 1:   There is a brief description of an experiment using the equipment shown. The answer lacks coherency. *[1 to 2 marks]*
Level 2:   There is a good description of an experiment which can be performed with the equipment shown, and some description of how the results should be processed to calculate the spring constant. The answer has some structure. *[3 to 4 marks]*
Level 3:   There is a clear and detailed description of an experiment which can be performed using the equipment show, and of how the to calculate the spring constant from the resulting force-extension graph. The answer is well structured. *[5 to 6 marks]*

Here are some points your answer may include:

Measure the mass of each of the masses using a mass balance.

Calculate the weight of each of the masses using weight = mass × gravitational field strength / $W = mg$.

Using the ruler, measure the length of the spring when it has no masses hanging from it (the unstretched length).

Hang a mass from the spring.

Record the force applied by the mass (the weight of the mass) and the new length of the spring.

Calculate the extension of the spring by subtracting the unstretched length from the new length.

Repeat these steps, increasing the mass hanging from the spring, recording the new weight and calculating the extension each time.

After you have a suitable number of points, plot your results on a force-extension graph, with force on the y-axis, and tension on the x-axis.

Draw a line of best fit on your results.

Identify the linear part of your graph.

Since force applied to spring = spring constant × extension / $F = ke$, $k = F ÷ e$, so the gradient of the linear part of the graph is equal to the spring constant.

Calculate the spring constant by calculating the gradient of the linear part of the graph.

3.3 The point beyond which the spring no longer obeys the relation force applied to spring = spring constant × extension / $F = ke$ **[1 mark]**.

3.4 Below the limit of proportionality (where the graph is linear) the spring obeys:

force applied to spring = spring constant × extension / $F = ke$

So, k = gradient = change in y ÷ change in x

change in y = 7.0 − 0 = 7.0 N

change in x = 3.5 − 0 = 3.5 cm = 0.035 m **[1 mark for an attempt to work out a change in x and y between points on the linear part of the graph]**

k = 7.0 ÷ 0.035 **[1 mark]** = **200 N/m [1 mark]**

You'd get the marks here for using any values for the change in y and x, as long as they're from the linear part of the graph.

4.1 Weight = mass × gravitational field strength / $W = mg$ **[1 mark]**

4.2 W = 80.0 × 9.8 **[1 mark]** = **784 N [1 mark]**

4.3 Area under the graph = ~16 squares (Allow between 15 and 17) **[1 mark]**

Each square = 30 × 10 = 300 m **[1 mark]**

Distance fallen = 16 × 300 **[1 mark]**

= **4800 m**

[1 mark, allow between 4500 m and 5100 m]

4.4

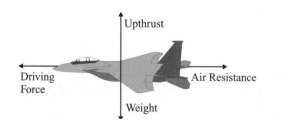

Upthrust

Driving Force

Air Resistance

Weight

[1 mark for arrow pointing to the right, from the right side of the plane, the same length as the Driving Force arrow, 1 mark for labelling the right-pointing arrow 'Air Resistance', 1 mark for arrow pointing downwards from the middle of the plane, the same length as the Upthrust arrow, 1 mark for the downwards arrow labelled as 'Weight']

4.5 force = mass × acceleration / $F = ma$ **[1 mark]**

4.6 $F = ma$

so, $a = F ÷ m$ **[1 mark]**

= 48 000 ÷ 4000 **[1 mark]** = **12 m/s² [1 mark]**

5.1 23
36
73 **[1 mark for all three correct]**

5.2 Reaction times vary from person to person **[1 mark]**. A sample needs to be large to be representative of the population **[1 mark]**.

To get a single representative value, it's a good idea to take an average from a large number of results.

5.3 The thinking distance is the distance the vehicle travels during the driver's reaction time **[1 mark]**.

The braking distance is the distance the car travels under the braking force **[1 mark]**.

Any three from: e.g. the thinking distance is increased if the driver is tired / the thinking distance is increased if the driver is under the influence of drugs or alcohol / the braking distance is increased in poor weather conditions / the braking distance is increased if the surface of the road has reduced friction (due to rain, snow, ice, etc) / the braking distance is increased by having worn or faulty brakes / the braking distance is increased by having worn or faulty tyres **[1 mark for each correct factor]**.

5.4 momentum = mass × velocity / $p = mv$ **[1 mark]**

5.5 p = 1000 × 30.0 **[1 mark]**
= **30 000 kgm/s² [1 mark]**

5.6 (final velocity)² − (initial velocity)² = 2 × acceleration × distance / $v^2 - u^2 = 2as$

So, $a = (v^2 - u^2) ÷ 2s$ **[1 mark]**
= (0 − 30²) ÷ (2 × 100) **[1 mark]**
= −4.5 m/s²

so deceleration = **4.5 m/s² [1 mark]**

Since the question asked for deceleration, you should ignore the minus sign when you give your answer.

6.1

[1 mark]

6.2

N   N

[1 mark for correct shape of field lines, 1 mark for at least 2 field lines, all correctly labelled with arrows, and no field lines crossing each other]

6.3 Coiling the wire into a solenoid brings the magnetic field lines around the wire close together, so that they all line up and are pointing in the same direction **[1 mark]**.

The closer the magnetic field lines are, the stronger the magnetic field **[1 mark]** so the strength of the magnetic field around the wire is increased **[1 mark]**.

6.4 The metal bar won't feel any force **[1 mark]** because the current through it is parallel to the magnetic field **[1 mark]**.

6.5 force = magnetic flux density × current × length of conductor inside field / $F = BIl$

So, $l = F ÷ (BI)$ **[1 mark]**
= 0.45 ÷ (1.5 × 4.0) **[1 mark]**
= 0.075 m = (0.075 × 100) cm **[1 mark]**
= **7.5 cm [1 mark]**

Index

A

absorption 109, 117
  of infrared 117
acceleration 88, 94
  due to gravity
        18, 92, 96, 100
  measuring 96, 133
  on distance-time graphs
        89
  on velocity-time graphs
        90
  uniform 88
accuracy 6
activity (radioactivity)
        69, 70
air resistance 91, 92
alpha radiation 67, 68
alpha scattering experiment
        64
alternating currents (ac)
        49, 112
ammeters 39, 134
amplitude 105
angle of incidence 110
angle of refraction 110
anomalous results 7
area under a graph 85, 90
atomic models
  development of 64, 65
  nuclear 65
  plum pudding 64
atomic number 66, 68
atoms 64-68
averages 8

B

bar charts 9
beta radiation 67, 68
bias 2
bio-fuels 32
boiling 58, 59
brakes 99, 101
braking distances 99, 101

C

cancer 115, 116
carbon neutral 32
categoric data 9
cavity wall insulation 25
centre of mass 77
changes of state 58, 59
charge
  electric 37, 51
  ions 65
  of a nucleus 64-66, 68
  relative charges of
        particles 65
circuit diagrams 37
circuits 37, 39, 40, 43-47
circuit symbols 37
closed systems 17
coal 28, 33
compasses 122, 123
components (electrical)
        37, 40
components (of a force) 80
compression (of springs)
        82, 83
compressions (in waves)
        106
conclusions 13
condensing 58, 59
conduction 24
conservation of energy 23
conservation of mass 58
conservation of momentum
        102
contact forces 76
contamination 71, 72
continuous data 9
control variables 5
convection 24
converting units 12
correlations 10, 14
count-rate 69
current 37-40, 45, 46
  alternating 49, 112
  direct 49
  in parallel 46
  in series 45
  I-V characteristics 40
  magnetism 123, 126-128
  measuring 134
current-carrying wires
        123, 126, 128

D

dangers of ionising radiation
        72, 115, 116
deceleration 88, 101
  on distance-time graphs
        89
  on velocity-time graphs
        90
density 57
dependent variables 5
designing investigations 5-7
diodes 38, 40
direct currents (dc) 49
discrete data 9
displacement (distance) 87
displacement (waves) 105
dissipated energy 23, 25
distance 87
distance-time graphs 89
double-glazing 25
drag 91, 92
draught excluders 25

E

earth wires 49
efficiency 26
elastic deformation 82, 85
elastic objects 82
elastic potential energy
        stores 19, 82, 85
electric cars 34
electric heaters 26, 114
electricity 37-40,
        42-47, 49-53
  supply and demand 52
  usage 33
electric motors 128
electric shocks 49
electromagnetic spectrum
        112
electromagnetic waves 112
  dangers 116
  gamma rays
        67, 68, 115, 116
  infrared 114, 117
  microwaves 113
  uses 112-115
  UV 115, 116
  visible light 115
  X-rays 115, 116

electromagnetism 124
electrons 64, 65, 67
elements 66, 68
emission (infrared)
        117, 118
energy 17-21, 23-26,
        28-34
  conservation 23
  internal 58
  stores 17
  transfers 17, 18, 24, 25
energy resources 28-34
  non-renewables 28, 33
  renewables 28-32
  transport 28, 34
  trends in use 34
energy stores 17
  elastic potential
        19, 82, 85
  gravitational potential
        18, 19
  kinetic 19
  thermal 17, 20, 24, 114
energy transfers 17-19,
        24, 26, 79
  by heating
        24, 25, 58, 60
  by waves 105
  efficiency 26
  electrical 50, 51
  rate of 23
  reducing 25
  work done 79
environmental impact (of
        energy resources)
        29-34
equilibrium (forces) 80, 95
estimating 88, 94, 101
ethics 3
eureka cans 57, 132
evaluations 16
evaporation 58, 59
experimental safety 135
extension (of springs) 82-85

Index

F

fair tests 5
falling objects 92
field lines 122
field strength
  gravitational 19, 77
  magnetic 122, 124, 127
fields
  gravitational 19, 77
  magnetic 122-124,
      126-128
filament lamps 38, 40
Fleming's left-hand rule
      127, 128
force-extension graphs
      83, 85
forces 76-80, 82-85,
      87-92, 94-97, 101
  contact 76
  free-body diagrams 78
  frictional
      25, 91, 92, 101
  gravitational 18, 77
  interaction pairs 76, 95
  magnetic 122-124,
      126-128
  Newton's laws 94, 95
  non-contact 76, 122
  normal contact
      18, 76, 95
  resolving 80
  resultant 78, 79, 94
  weight 77
fossil fuels 28, 33
free-body diagrams 78
freezing 58, 59
frequency 105
  of EM waves 112
  of mains supply 49
friction 25, 91, 92, 101

G

gamma radiation
      67, 68, 72, 112
  dangers of 116
  uses 115
gases
  gas pressure 60
  particle motion 56, 60
  state of matter 56
Geiger-Muller tube 69
geothermal power 30
global warming 33
government targets 34
gradients 10
graphs 9, 10
  distance-time 89
  force-extension 83, 85
  heating and cooling 59
  radioactive decay 70
  velocity-time 90
gravitational fields 19, 77
gravitational field strength
      77
gravitational force 18, 77
gravitational potential
      energy stores 18, 19

H

half-life 69, 70
hazards 7, 135
heating 17, 20, 58
helium nucleus 67, 68
hybrid cars 34
hydro-electric power 30
hypotheses 1

I

independent variables 5
induced magnets 123
inelastic deformation 82
inertia 95
inertial mass 95
infrared cameras 114
infrared radiation
      114, 117, 118
  investigating 117, 118
insulation 25
interaction pairs 76, 95
internal energy 58

investigating
  IR absorption 117
  IR emission 117, 118
  I-V characteristics 40
  motion 96, 97
  resistance 39, 47
  specific heat capacity 21
  springs 84, 85
  wave speed 107, 108
ionisation 65-67, 72, 116
ionising power 66, 72
ionising radiation 67, 72
  alpha 67, 68, 72
  beta 67, 68, 72
  dangers of 71, 72,
      115, 116
  gamma 67, 68, 72
  uses of 115
ions 65, 66
irradiation 71, 72
isotopes 66, 69
I-V characteristics 40

K

kinetic energy stores 19

L

lasers 135
laws of motion 94, 95
lengths
  measuring 131
Leslie cubes 118
light-dependent resistor
      (LDR) 42, 43
light gates 96, 133
limit of proportionality
      83, 85
linear components 40
liquids 56
  density of 57
live wires 49
loft insulation 25
longitudinal waves 106
lubricants 25, 26

M

magnetic fields 122-124,
      126-128
  field lines 122
  field strength
      122, 124, 127
  flux density 127
  of the Earth 122
magnetic forces 122-124,
      126-128
magnetic materials 122
mass 77
  inertial mass 95
  measuring 133
mass number 66, 68
matter
  particle model
      56, 58, 60
mean (average) 8
measuring cylinders 132
mechanical energy transfers
      17
median 8
medical imaging 115
medical tracers 115
melting 58, 59
micrometers 131
microwave ovens 114
microwaves 113, 114
mode 8
models 2
momentum 102
motor effect 126, 127
motors 128
multimeters 134

N

national grid 52, 53
neutral wires 49
neutrons 65, 66, 68
Newton's First Law 94
Newton's Second Law
      94, 96, 97
Newton's Third Law 95
non-contact forces 76
non-linear components 40
non-renewables 28, 33
north poles 122
nuclear equations 68
nuclear fuels 28, 33
nuclear model 65
nuclear power 33
nuclear waste 33
nuclei 65, 66, 68, 69

Index

O

ohmic conductors 38
oil (energy resource)
    28, 33
optical density 109
optical fibres 115

P

parallax 131
parallel circuits 46, 47
particle model of matter
    56, 58, 60
period 105
permanent magnets 123
physical changes 58
pilot experiments 84
plum pudding model 64
plutonium 28
potential difference 37, 38
  energy transferred 51
  in parallel 46
  in series 44
  I-V characteristics 40
  measuring 134
  national grid 53
power 23
  electrical 50, 51
power ratings 50
precision 6
pressure
  gas 60
protons 65, 66, 68
protractors 131

R

radiation 66-72
  alpha 67, 68, 72
  beta 67, 68, 72
  gamma 67, 68, 72, 112
radiation dose 116
radio waves 112, 113
radioactive decay 66-72
radiotherapy 115
radius (of an atom) 65
random errors 7, 15
rarefactions 106
ray diagrams 110
reaction times 99, 100
reducing energy transfers
  25
reflection 109
refraction 109, 110
reliability (of energy
    resources) 29-34

renewables 28-32
repeatability 5, 6
reproducibility 5, 6
resistance (air) 91, 92
resistance (electrical)
    37, 38
  in parallel 46, 47
  in series 45, 47
resistors 42, 43
  in parallel 46
  in series 45
resolving (a force) 80
resultant forces 78, 79, 94
right-hand thumb rule 123
ripple tanks 107
risks 4, 7, 135
  of using radiation
    72, 115, 116
rounding 8
ruler drop test 100

S

safety 7
  during experiments 135
  handling radioactive
    sources 71, 72
sample size 6
satellites 113
scalar quantities 76
scale drawings 79
scaling prefixes 12
scientific method 1
sensing circuits 43
series circuits 44, 45, 47
significant figures 8
S.I. units 11
skin cancer 116
smoke detectors 67
solar cells 29
solar power 29, 34
solenoids 124
solids 56
  density of 57
sound waves 107
source potential 44
south poles 122
specific heat capacity
    20, 21
specific latent heat 59
speed 19, 87-90
  braking distances 99
  of sound in air 107
  typical speeds 87
  waves 106-110
spring constant 83
springs 82-85

states of matter 56, 58, 59
step-down transformers 53
step-up transformers 53
stopping distances 99
stopwatches 133
streamlining 26, 91
sublimation 58
sunburn 116
systematic errors 7
systems 17

T

taking measurements
    131-134
tangents 10
temperature
  internal energy 60
  measuring 133
  specific heat capacity
    20, 21
  specific latent heat 59
temperature detectors 42
terminal velocity 92
thermal conductivity 24
thermal energy stores
    17, 20, 24, 114
thermal insulation
    21, 25, 26
thermistors 42, 43
thermometers 133
thermostats 42
thinking distance 99
three-core cables 49
tidal barrages 31
timing 133
tracers 115
transformers 53
transmission 109
transverse waves 106
trends in electricity use 52
trends in energy resources
    34
TV signals 113
typical speeds 87

U

UK mains supply 49
ultraviolet (UV) 115, 116
uncertainties 15
uniform acceleration 88
uniform fields 124
units 11, 12
uranium 28, 33

V

validity 5
variables 5
vectors 76
velocity 87, 88, 90
  momentum 102
  terminal 92
velocity-time graphs 90
voltmeters 39, 134
volume
  measuring 132
  of a gas 60

W

wasted energy 23, 26
wave equation 106
wave front diagrams
    109, 110
wave power 31
wave speed 106-110
wavelength 105, 112
waves 105-110, 112-118
  electromagnetic 112-116
  longitudinal 106
  refraction 109, 110
  speed 106, 109, 110
  transverse 106
  investigating 107, 108
weight 77
wind power 29
wind turbines 29
work 18, 23, 50,
    79, 82

X

X-rays 115, 116

Z

zero errors 7

SCPAS41, SCPS41